TEACHER GUIDE

D1636145

GLOBAL SCIENCE

ENERGY, RESOURCES, ENVIRONMENT

Sixth Edition

JOHN W. CHRISTENSEN
TERI L. CHRISTENSEN

KENDALL/HUNT PUBLISHING COMPANY
4050 Westmark Drive   Dubuque, Iowa 52002

CONTENTS

GUIDE TO CHAPTERS AND ACTIVITIES

APPENDICES 371

GLOBAL SCIENCE

ENERGY, RESOURCES, ENVIRONMENT

GLOBAL SCIENCE

ENERGY, RESOURCES, ENVIRONMENT

NEW 6th EDITION

Global Science: Energy, Resources, Environment focuses on environmental issues through an integrated science approach.

Throughout the program, this curriculum covers each of these sciences: Life, Earth, Physical Science, Chemistry, and Physics.

Global Science correlates to:

— National Science Education Content Standards (NRC)

— Standards of the North American Association of Environmental Educators (NAAEE).

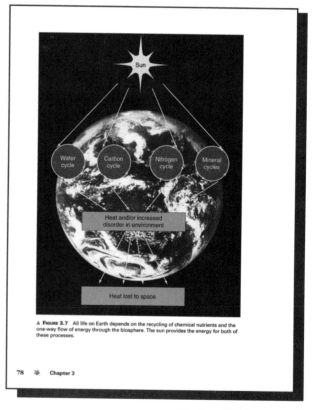

▲ **FIGURE 3.7** All life on Earth depends on the recycling of chemical nutrients and the one-way flow of energy through the biosphere. The sun provides the energy for both of these processes.

78 ☙ Chapter 3

Student Edition page 78

Beautifully laid out full-color interior pages and updated illustrations add to the visual appeal of *Global Science* 6th Edition.

NSTA SciLinks®

Global Science 6th Edition now includes **NSTA SciLinks®**. These **integrated web resources** are printed in the Student Edition margins.

SciLinks® allow students, teachers, and parents to learn more about a specific topic by going online to www.scilinks.org and entering the code found on the specific page.

Try it for yourself! Go to www.scilinks.org and enter "GloSci77" into the code bar to see the numerous educational web sites listed. These sites are monitored and maintained by NSTA to be safe, updated, and accurate.

SCI LINKS®
NSTA
Topic: matter and energy
Go to: www.scilinks.org
Code: GloSci77

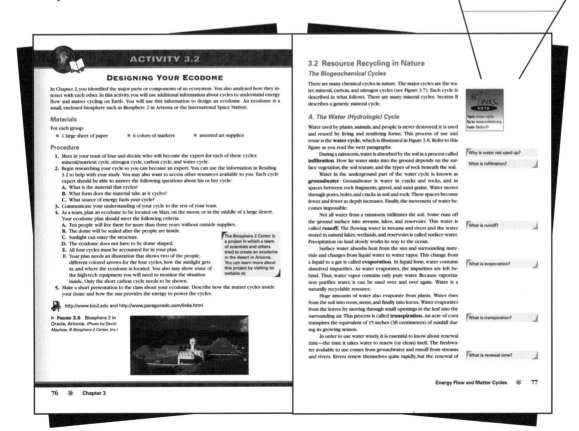

Global Science Curriculum
The Teacher Guide

The *Global Science* program has been more than 35 years in the making. This **complete curriculum** develops ecosystem concepts and basic laws that govern energy-resource use. It examines traditional energy sources and the situation of supply and demand. *Global Science* also examines alternatives for the future.

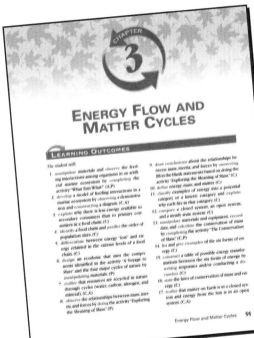

The Teacher Guide provides information necessary for introducing the curriculum.

- Sample schedules
  (semester / one-year/two-year)

- Answers to questions and key topics

- Video list

- Complete instructions for setting up and facilitating labatory investigations

Teacher Resource CD-ROM

Understanding the time constraints of educators today, the Teacher Resource CD-ROM (TRCD) contains many useful teaching components organized clearly into sections all at the click of your mouse:

- **Assessments** (One per chapter)

- **Activities** (All 134 activities from the textbook are on the TRCD.)

- **Blackline Masters** (Contains both the essential Blackline Masters [BLMs] that are in the Teacher Guide and the supplemental BLMs that are only on the TRCD.)

- **Study Guides** (One per chapter. These can be used as chapter reviews, make-up assignments, student organizers, or quarter/semester reviews.)

- **Transparencies** (Four-color transparencies available in PDF format.)

ExamView® Testbank CD-ROM NEW!

ExamView® Test Generator is a tool that lets you create paper, LAN-based, and Internet tests. Using the online testing features, you can access numerous reports that will help you focus on your students' learning needs.

- **Internet Tests and Study Guides** - Create a test/study guide and then save it as an Internet test.

- **Test-Hosting** - Publish tests directly to the Internet using the innovative test-hosting service.

- **Question Selection Methods** - Use any (or all) of five question selection options.

ExamView® supports 13 question formats including the new bimodal type!

Use undo, cut, copy, paste, find, replace, fonts, styles, tables, borders and shading, and a spell checker.

Global Science Technology

Teacher Technology Resource Package

To help teachers manage technology in the classroom, the Teacher Technology Resource Package was created. The CDs included in this teacher component are: Teacher Resource CD-ROM, Global Science Explorer CD-ROM, and the Testbank CD-ROM.

Global Science Explorer CD-ROM

The Global Science Explorer CD-ROM integrates core textbook concepts with those not covered in-depth in the textbook.

Teachers are notified in the 36-week schedule in the front of the Teacher Guide (with a CD icon) of when to use the *Global Science* Explorer CD-ROM during a lesson.

This CD-ROM is a perfect supplement to the core content of *Global Science*, adding further study in areas such as:

Astronomy, Oceanography, Meteorology, and Weather Forecasting

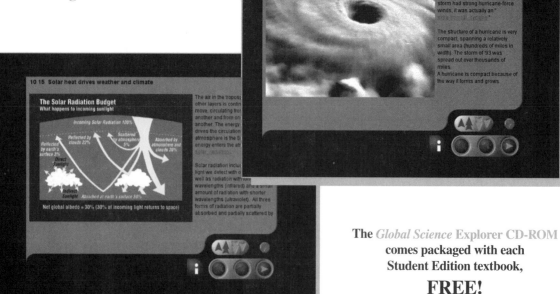

The *Global Science* Explorer CD-ROM
comes packaged with each
Student Edition textbook,
FREE!

The Biosphere 2 Center is a project in which a team of scientists and others tried to create an ecodome in the desert in Arizona. You can learn more about this project by visiting its website at:

Mass.

SCIENCE AT WORK

SCI LINKS NSTA

Topic: food chain/ food web
Go to: www.scilinks.org
Code: GloSci75

Margin notes provide further information and/or explanation on a topic discussed in the text.

The key icon directs students' attention to key concepts in the text.

The Science at Work icon directs students to Appendix 1 for the supplementary Science at Work readings. Students learn more about various science-related careers.

The SciLinks® icon directs students to web-based resources printed in the Student Edition. Teachers can also monitor students web access.

The Student Edition

Every chapter of *Global Science* begins with an illustration and a quotation chosen to engage students in the main ideas of the chapter.

Students' skills are assessed with questions throughout the chapter.

The *Global Science* Student Edition comes packaged with the Student Edition CD-ROM (backpack friendly) and the Global Science Explorer CD-ROM.

Backpack Friendly!

The Student Edition CD-ROM comes packaged with the Student Edition textbook, **FREE!**

Students are able to take home the portable CD-ROM and enjoy all the features of the Global Science textbook.

? QUESTIONS

Think about these questions and be ready to contribute to a discussion based on them:
1. Explain why vegetarians use food energy more efficiently than non-vegetarians.
2. Why don't lions hunt mice?
3. Elephants and blue whales are the largest of all animals on Earth. Both are vegetarians. Why do meat-eaters not get as large as elephants and blue whales?
4. Why are there more rabbits than coyotes?

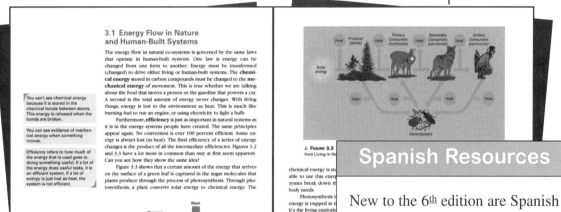

3.1 Energy Flow in Nature and Human-Built Systems

The energy flow in natural ecosystems is governed by the same laws that operate in human-built systems. One law is energy can be changed from one form to another. Energy must be transformed (changed) to drive either living or human-built systems. The **chemical energy** stored in carbon compounds must be changed to the **mechanical energy** of movement. This is true whether we are talking about the food that moves a person or the gasoline that powers a car. A second is the total amount of energy never changes. With living things, energy is lost to the environment as heat. This is much like burning fuel to run an engine, or using electricity to light a bulb.

Furthermore, **efficiency** is just as important in natural systems as it is in the energy systems people have created. The same principles appear again. No conversion is ever 100 percent efficient. Some energy is always lost (as heat). The final efficiency of a series of energy changes is the product of all the intermediate efficiencies. Figures 3.2 and 3.3 have a lot more in common than may at first seem apparent. Can you see how they show the same idea?

Figure 3.3 shows that a certain amount of the energy that arrives on the surface of a green leaf is captured in the sugar molecules that plants produce through the process of photosynthesis. Through photosynthesis, a plant converts solar energy to chemical energy. The

You can't see chemical energy because it is stored in the chemical bonds between atoms. This energy is released when the bonds are broken.

You can see evidence of mechanical energy when something moves.

Efficiency refers to how much of the energy that is used goes to doing something useful. If a lot of the energy does useful tasks, it is an efficient system. If a lot of energy is just lost as heat, the system is not efficient.

▲ **FIGURE 3.2** Diagram of an electric power plant sh... through from coal to alternating current. (National Coal A...

72 ❧ Chapter 3

▲ **FIGURE 3.3** from Living in ...

chemical energy is sto... able to use this ener... zymes break down th... body needs.

Photosynthesis i... energy is trapped in t... It's the living equivale... stantly refilled by the ... would 'run out of gas...

When a **primar** and transformed. The ... rials is changed to ki... heat energy is release... ergy is stored in the b...

If the animal is ... **ondary consumer** (... transfer. Hence, the to... sumers is always less ... Likewise, the total am... is always less than wh... trapped through phot...

A **food chain** is ... other. Producers,gree... ...ivores o... ...major por...

Spanish Resources

New to the 6th edition are Spanish Resources for students. A Spanish Glossary and all Appendices are added to every *Global Science* Student Edition to help English language learners comprehend science terms easily.

NEW!

Spanish Resources

lobal Science is a secondary-level science curriculum that emphasizes those aspects of science that are both relevant and vitally important to everyone. Science has an important message that must be brought to and understood by all. Science cannot tell us the full meaning of life, but it can tell us how to live life more meaningfully. This is the central theme of *Global Science*. It is the story of life on a wonderful, but finite, planet. It is the story of ecosystems, limiting laws, and our quest for the good life.

Global Science carefully analyzes the various interactions that are taking place between modern humans and their environment. It places special emphasis on our need for and use of energy and mineral resources. The course develops the ecosystem concept and the basic laws that govern energy/resource use. It examines our traditional energy sources and consumption patterns and then analyzes our current supply/demand situation. Finally, it considers our alternatives for the future. In addition, *Global Science* examines the environmental and socioeconomic impacts of large-scale energy development and mineral use. It considers the role played by government, industry, international politics, and the individual in the energy/resource/environmental system.

Global Science emphasizes direct student involvement in specially designed and classroom-tested laboratory-type activities. The text clarifies and expands on those activities. In addition, it provides questions, problems, and reference materials to help students master the course content.

The Teacher Guide provides information necessary for introducing the curriculum. It includes sample schedules for teaching the key topics, complete answers to questions and problems, a video list, and complete instructions for setting up and running the labs. Laboratory equipment that is unique to the *Global Science* program is available by calling your Kendall/Hunt representative.

The *Global Science* program is a complete curriculum. The course can be taught selectively as a semester option or as a yearlong lab science. We teach physical science, life science, and earth science; this is a course in global science. *Global Science* is the study of how individuals and societies use resources, and influence the environment, in their attempts to satisfy human wants. Some teachers infuse *Global Science* materials into their existing courses. Others feel that these materials are so important that they should serve as the basic science course in a sequence. Students who are committed to science, and those who are not, should all take *Global Science*. The committed can then go on to study more specialized areas.

The *Global Science* program has been more than 35 years in development. The major contribution is by a single high school science teacher—*in the classroom*. However, hundreds of people contribute to the course in countless ways. The materials are continually revised and improved. Many teachers examine, use, and give feedback on various components of the course. More than 25 schools pilot tested the materials. The schools represented urban, suburban, and rural settings.

The most important themes of the course are:

Fact 1: Earth and its resources are finite. Human imagination seems limitless.

Fact 2: Humans are partners with nature, *not* masters of nature.

Goal: The goal of individuals and society should be to achieve the highest standard of living that is compatible with our environment.

In summary, *Global Science* is a fundamental laboratory curriculum. Students who take this course will be confronted with the scientific and social challenges of our age—the challenge to design homes and buildings that are cool in the summer and warm in the winter and yet don't require large amounts of energy to operate; the challenge to develop transportation systems that conserve energy, mineral, and economic resources; the challenge to extract and use our energy and mineral resources in an environmentally acceptable manner; and the challenge to achieve population levels and build economic systems that are stable and functional. Finally, we have the challenge to live in harmony with our environment and also live with freedom and dignity. These are the challenges of our age. These are the concepts to emphasize. These are the messages of life, of cooperation, of hope.

We seem to struggle to define our national purpose, to provide meaning in what we do in school, and to find challenges to take on ourselves and to inspire our youth. The *Global Science* program is a beginning. Students who choose to study it will be confronted with something of value.

THE CONSTRUCTIVIST THEORY OF LEARNING

Constructivism summarizes a set of ideas about learning and teaching. In science education this word is typically used to encompass ideas related to both constructivist learning theories and instructional approaches that support these theories. The key idea behind constructivism is that all learners put together new information by connecting it to other ideas with which they are already familiar.

Classrooms in which understanding is constructed feature these characteristics:

* Opportunities for students to identify their prior knowledge about new concepts or topics
* Student dialogue in which students have ample time to identify their understandings (or lack) of key concepts
* Curricula organized around broad scientific concepts
* Opportunities for students to apply their understanding to new situations
* A focus on depth of understanding in lieu of breadth of coverage of topics

Using teaching strategies that are consistent with constructivist theories of learning also provides natural opportunities for students to conduct their own scientific inquiries. In view of the *National Science Education Standards'* emphasis on students' developing the abilities to conduct scientific inquiries, this consistency is helpful to teachers.

Several features in *Global Science* assist you in developing a constructivist approach in your classroom. Every chapter begins with a photograph and a quotation chosen to engage the students in the main ideas of the chapter. The chapters also have hands-on activities integrated throughout. The early activities are written to encourage the identification of prior knowledge and to help the students build a preliminary understanding of key concepts. Later activities introduce new ideas that build on the early concepts or provide opportunities to apply those early ideas.

If you are interested in learning more about constructivist theories of learning and the implications for teaching science, consider these resources:

Bereiter, C., and M. Scardamalia. 1989. Intentional learning as a goal of instruction. In *Knowing, Learning, and Instruction: Essays in Honor of Robert Glaser,* L.B. Resnick, ed.: 361–392. Hillsdale, NJ: Lawrence Erlbaum and Associates.

Brown, A.L., and J.C. Campione. 1994. Guided discovery in a community of learners. In *Classroom Lessons: Integrating Cognitive Theory and Classroom Practice,* K. McGilly, ed.: 229–270. Cambridge, MA: MIT Press.

Bruer, J.T. 1993. *Schools for Thought: A Science of Learning in the Classroom.* Cambridge, MA: MIT Press.

Carey, S. 1985. *Conceptual Change in Childhood.* Cambridge, MA: IT Press.

Cohen, D.K., M.W. McLaughlin, and J.E. Talbert, eds. 1993. *Teaching for Understanding: Challenges for Policy and Practice.* San Francisco: Jossey-Bass.

Darling-Hammond, L. 1992. *Standards of Practice for Learner Centered Schools.* New York: National Center for Restructuring Schools and Learning.

Driver, R. et al. 1994. *Making Sense of Secondary Science.* London and New York: Routledge.

Harlen, W. 1992. *The Teaching of Science.* London: David Fulton Publishers.

McGilly, K., ed. 1994. *Classroom Lessons: Integrating Cognitive Theory and Classroom Practice.* Cambridge, MA: MIT Press.

NRC (National Research Council). 1994. *Learning, Remembering, Believing: Enhancing Human Performance,* D. Druckman and R.A. Bjork, eds. Washington, DC: National Academy Press.

Shapiro, B. 1994. *What Children Bring to Light: A Constructivist Perspective on Children's Learning in Science.* New York: Teachers College Press.

An Essay on Values

> No civilized society—especially a self-governing one—can be neutral regarding human character and personal responsibility.
>
> —William J. Bennett
> Former U.S. Secretary of Education

Throughout history, good people have desired to live in a world where their life could have meaning and the environment was clean. Camelot was such a place. Unfortunately, Camelot was a dream, and many think it is unattainable. Still others think about tomorrow and seek ways to build the sustainable world.

The sustainable world requires much from the people who live in it. It requires an examination of the human condition and what makes societies function well. The people must work at meaningful occupations, contribute both time and money to various institutions (schools, roads, protection, etc.), and care about the welfare of all citizens.

Why do people commit themselves to such behaviors? They do so because of the values they hold. Values are the principles and beliefs that individuals and societies regard as desirable. They are the emotional rules, by which a society governs itself. Values help bring order and meaning to our personal lives and to the society in which we live.

All values are not the same. Some are better than others. As one studies history and analyzes why some societies prosper and others fall apart and disappear, it is possible to discover those values that can enable us to build a sustainable world. These stabilizing values include:

Ethical Behavior (Honesty/Integrity) A society cannot long endure if people cannot trust the individuals they deal with on a daily basis. The honor code is simple: I will not lie, cheat, steal, or tolerate those who do. We must be honest in all aspects of our lives.

Productive Effort (Hard Work) People earn their right to consume by doing work, either physically or mentally. Without rewarded work, societies soon crumble. Delayed gratification teaches the values of the reward that is earned. Individuals must learn to work, to care for themselves and their families.

Equity (Fairness/Justice) All people should have opportunities to better themselves and live meaningful lives. A most efficient society practices the politics of inclusion.

Family Mothers, fathers, and children, as a family, go through trusting, personal experiences that build both confidence and character to shield them from the influences of an often cold and heartless world. In families, we learn what is right and wrong and how to apply that knowledge in the world outside. Many children today don't grow up in a traditional family. In these cases, it is the responsibility of adults (single mothers, single fathers, foster parents, stepmothers, stepfathers, or whoever is responsible) to provide love, guidance, and a positive role model for the children they raise.

Diversity Strong societies respect those of different classes, races, nationalities, and religions. The strength of diversity comes from the power of tolerance. Families, communities, and nations that tolerate and examine a broad range of differing ideas are stronger than those that are narrow and rigid. A society that values diversity can allow its members to feel proud of their heritage and feel good about themselves. Tolerance is a virtue. Diversity adds richness.

Truth/Lifelong Education Truth and meaning are something all free humans seek. A major path to finding truth and meaning is through formal and informal education. This occurs in homes, schools, churches, and communities. Truth comes through searching and not by authoritarian edict.

Personal Responsibility Individuals must be taught to be responsible for themselves and for their actions, no matter who they are or their social condition.

Individual Potential One rises or falls because of personal goals and commitments. You earn your rewards, and society is not responsible for your failures. Learn to take pride in your work. If something is worth doing, it is worth doing well—even if it is hard or unpleasant.

Respect for Nature (Kindness/Caring) Life is a wonderful and fragile thing. It must be held in highest regard and not carelessly snuffed out. We must be kind to others and expect kindness in return. All individuals can contribute something if allowed to be their best. Respect should extend beyond individuals to the Earth and all things on it. We must also value our own mental and physical health.

Thrift The resources at our disposal are valuable and limited. Time, money, and natural resources must be handled with care. We must be stewards of our planet if we are to receive the maximum benefit from what we have been given.

Conflict Resolution To be civilized is to settle conflict without violence. Unfortunately, all individuals and societies are not civilized. Therefore, we must continually search for methods to resolve conflict that minimize violence and maintain the dignity of the parties in dispute.

Individual Liberty (Freedom) All individuals desire to make choices for themselves regarding their future direction. Sustainable societies allow this because freedom maximizes happiness and efficiency, provided it is coupled with responsibility. For example, every personal choice is tied to a personal responsibility. The objects you purchase require responsible use and disposal.

Shared Responsibility (Community) No person is an island. We are all part of a community of individuals and nations. From the community we get support and a sense of worth. We all should return something to that community, including our loyalty. We all must assume some responsibility for the less fortunate—but for fate, many of us would be in the same situation.

> *We make a living by what we get. We make a life by what we give.*
>
> Winston Churchill

Values are a reflection of our beliefs about who we are and how we fit into the world around us. They are the internal compass that determines what we do and how we behave. We learn values in our homes, in our churches, in our communities, from our friends, and from the media that writes about us and entertains us. It is important that these institutions instill good values and commitments in all of us. Our political leaders and sports heroes should represent and exemplify what is best about us. We are only as great and stable as the values we commit to and live by.

Stable societies teach their values and penalize noncompliance. The penalty must fit the infraction, and it must be certain. The purpose of punishment is to exact a price for violating the rights of others. On occasion, punishment can also serve to rehabilitate, but that is not its primary function. We teach right from wrong by rewarding right behavior and penalizing wrong behavior.

The values just described transcend the various religions of the world and all our national divisions. They are a part of all societies that are regarded as civilized and humane. They are the glue that binds a pluralistic society together. What we believe determines how we behave. How we behave determines whether or not we will survive in the future.

—*John W. Christensen*

ASSUMPTIONS ABOUT SECONDARY-LEVEL SCIENCE EDUCATION

Global Science makes four assumptions about secondary-level science education:

1. The study of science should be a meaningful endeavor for *all* students in a modern society.
2. Science is best learned by experimenting and analyzing data—not just by reading and doing problems. This is how basic science skills are gained.
3. Society is best served, and student interest held, when relevant material is emphasized.
4. The required portion of the high school science curriculum should emphasize the ecosystem concept and resource management. Public understanding of these topics is vital to both our physical survival and our economic strength.

OBJECTIVES OF THE GLOBAL SCIENCE PROGRAM

- To build a firm understanding of the ecosystem concept—the basic components of an ecosystem, how the living and the nonliving interact, and the cyclic activities that take place. In essence, to appreciate the earth and our place on it.
- To build an understanding of the concepts and laws that govern our use of water, air, land, energy and mineral resources.
- To examine our present energy sources and consumption patterns. To use this knowledge as a component for future planning.
- To build an understanding of the fundamentals of exponential growth (the phenomenon, growth rates, doubling times, graphical representation, applications in resource depletion) and relate this understanding to

population, food, and resource situations at national and global levels.

- To model the depletion of a resource and use this model to understand historical resource depletion data. To use that data in an attempt to foresee and forestall.
- To explore the many energy sources not extensively used today. To realize the complexity of developing useful, new resources by examining problems related to their wide-scale use. To begin sorting our energy/resource options as one attempts to satisfy future goals.
- To examine how humans relate to their economic environment. To learn the basic principles of economics and how they relate to resource/environmental problems. To appreciate the role economics plays in making social/scientific decisions.
- To develop an awareness of the "Spaceship Earth" ethic and the interrelatedness of resources, economics, environment, food production, and population growth. To examine some global scenarios and relate them to humans in general and ourselves in particular.
- To develop basic scientific skills and attitudes as useful tools for problem solving. *Global Science* is a solid *lab science*.
- To develop the skills and attitudes needed to clarify and modify personal values and goals continuously as we react to a changing world.
- To enable students to observe, analyze, and draw conclusions from situations related to resources and the environment and to use this information to take effective action as responsible citizens.
- To acquaint students with careers and challenges in our resource industries and industries that will depend crucially on our resource decisions.

Global Science contains the following components:

1. Student Textbook
    - A *Global Science Explorer CD* and *Student Edition CD-ROM* accompany each student textbook.
2. Teacher Guide with *Global Science Explorer CD*
3. Teacher Technolgy Resource Package
    - *Testbank CD-ROM*
    - A *Teacher Resource CD-ROM*, which contains the Blackline Masters, Assessments, Extensions, Transparencies, student activities, and study guides for all 16 chapters.
4. Color Transparencies

The curriculum is used most effectively when all four components are integrated. This Teacher Guide is designed to help you with the integration. Also, a set of symbols or icons help correlate various features both within and between the four components.

The icons are as follows:

STUDENT TEXT

 A key indicates major questions/ ideas. It is placed with the appropriate marginal notes.

 A globe, notebook, and pencil indicate an activity, simulation, research project, or laboratory investigation. It may also be placed by text that focuses on one of those items. The number of the activity will also appear on the symbol.

 A question mark emphasizes questions to be answered.

 Books indicate key reference material.

 This symbol indicates websites that tie to a topic of interest.

 SciLinks icon provides additional information on a topic.

TEACHER GUIDE

 An arrow at the subheading "Learning Outcomes" for visual recognition in each chapter subsection.

 A key at the subhead "Key Terms" for visual recognition in each chapter subsection.

 An icon at the subheading "Recommended Blackline Masters" for visual recognition in each chapter subsection.

 A globe, notebook, and pencil at the heading "Teaching Strategies and Answers for Activities" to create a visual link with the activities in the student text.

 A laboratory icon at the subheading "Safety in the Lab."

 A pencil at the heading for each chapter assessment for visual recognition in each chapter subsection.

 A pencil with an "A" to indicate answers to blackline masters, extensions, and the chapter assessment in each chapter subsection.

 An icon highlighting the Flow Chart for the chapter.

The following pages briefly describe the components of *Global Science* and some of the other features of this Teacher Guide.

Following the overview of the full curriculum, the Teacher Guide organizes instructional aids by chapter.

An issue concerning textbooks in the past several decades has been the readability level of the materials. Controlling the difficulty of printed material has been a vexing problem for writers and publishers alike. During this time, educators looked for an appropriate and easy way to determine the reading difficulty of the textbooks they were considering for adoption. As a result of this demand, several decades of research were invested in developing easy-to-use methods. These efforts resulted in a number of "readability formulas."

All of the formulas looked at two of the most common aspects of written language: (1) the length of sentences and (2) the complexity of words. Two readability formulas that pay attention to these concerns are Raygor's Readability Estimate and Fry's Readability Estimate. Both are easy to apply. For this reason, many schools have come to depend on readability formulas to help them appraise the reading difficulty of books under consideration.

Recently, reading experts have begun to question the excessive attention paid to this aspect of printed material. They have raised the issue of whether this trend has resulted in "watered down" materials that actually do a disservice to the reader. As a collective body, these experts encourage writers and publishers to concentrate not only on readability levels, but equally as important, on issues such as (1) clarity, (2) coherence, (3) organization, (4) interest, (5) literary quality, and (6) subject matter. To this end, we have made a conscious effort to include features in this course that encompass the concerns put forth by reading educators.

In the student textbook *Global Science*, 6th edition, we have concentrated on factors that make the material "reader friendly." These include (1) placing key content words in bold print to help the readers focus on the words they encounter; (2) using marginal notes/questions to aid the reader in determining the key ideas/points; (3) summarizing the chapters; (4) using application questions/problems to assist students in making connections between theory and practice; (5) providing marginal notes in question format for immediate review; (6) providing photos and illustrations that directly tie to and enhance the text, the quality and clarity of which should both add interest and increase understanding; (7) referencing sources of information right where the information is given, which helps emphasize the importance of knowing where information comes from. All textbooks should follow this practice. The source of a fact is as important as the fact itself! In addition, we have tried to keep the readability level keyed to the ninth-grade level of difficulty.

An axiom of education states:

> *I hear, and I forget.*
> *I see, and I remember.*
> *I do, and I understand.*

Because of a belief in this philosophy, *activities* are the heart of the *Global Science* curriculum. For this reason, the activities are placed in the textbook where they best fit the content. Every major theme in the course is addressed with an activity. The entire program can be taught by doing the activities. To emphasize that fact, a flow chart of activities is featured at the beginning of the section for each chapter in this Teacher Guide.

The extensive use of hands-on activities is the *key to readability.* Reading becomes easier and comprehension is greater if the student has had experience with the concept(s) being taught.

The simple format of the textbook and the care with which we have taken to write the materials in a readable fashion should enable your students to use the book to its fullest potential.

THE READABILITY FACTOR: TEXT ANALYSIS

Tamra A. Keller, Ed.D.

In the past, text analysis consisted of the concept of readability measures of text. These measures were based upon average sentence length, number of multi-syllabic words in a sample, and number of words used that appeared on a master list of frequently used words. Using a formula, the readability level of a portion of text was determined. As theorists and practitioners looked more closely at text, however, certain other elements were noted as being "reader friendly"—that is, enhancing comprehension. These elements vary somewhat from genre to genre.

Readability ease is also determined by the distribution of sentence subjects—although this is not computed by formulas. Generally, placing the subject at the head of a sentence is the most straightforward writing style; it is what most readers expect and, therefore, is easier to comprehend than a sentence with an embedded subject. Along this same line, topic sentences are helpful to a reader; text without clear topic sentences is difficult for many readers to "order."

Other elements of analysis include article ratios, use of discipline-based jargon, and meta-discoursal features such as connectives, sequencers, and hedges. These are typically not considered when a readability level is requested for textbooks.

Readability Formulas. Several basic readability analysis formulas for middle and upper grades include those of Dale-Chall, Gunning's Fog Index, Raygor, Fry, and Flesch Reading Ease/Flesch-Kincaid. Because the Dale-Chall formula relies on a familiar/unfamiliar word list, it is appropriate for middle grade *general*—not content area—reading. (Most words in grades 1–4 material would appear on the familiar word list; beyond grade 8, content reading material consists of many "unfamiliar," or content-specific, words.) A factor of the Gunning's Fog Index is the number of words consisting of three or more syllables in a passage. This alone qualifies it as an instrument more appropriate for upper grades. However, since much of content area reading consists of "long" words, the

levels of this instrument fairly consistently compute two or more grades higher than other instruments. The Raygor and Fry formulas are fairly consistent with each other; the computed levels are also within close range of the Flesch Reading Ease/Flesch-Kincaid levels. The following chart summarizes the range of appropriate applicability of various readability instruments.

RECOMMENDED GRADE LEVELS										
Method	1	2	3	4	5	6	7	8	9	10
Dale-Chall	–	–	–	–	5	+	+	8	–	–
Raygor	–	–	–	4	+	+	+	+	+	Prof.
Fry	1	+	+	+	+	+	+	+	+	Coll.
Flesch	–	–	–	–	+	+	+	8	+	Coll.
Gunning's Fog	–	–	–	–	–	–	–	8	+	Coll.

These formulas deal with two common factors: (1) the length of sentences and (2) the complexity of words. They differ in the identification of difficult words and the ranking of such factors as letters per word, syllables per word, and/or number of unfamiliar words.

A common assumption of several of these formulas is that the longer the sentence, the more complex and difficult it is to comprehend. The opposite is more often true: longer sentences can make text clear by eliminating the need for the reader to draw inferences to make connections between/among sentences and within the texts. Thus, comprehension often is easier and more accurate with longer sentences. It follows, then, that the reading ease of a passage might actually be at a lower level than what readability computations would indicate.

Conversely, too many concepts (T-units) within a single sentence are confusing, as many readers try unsuccessfully to break down the sentence into manageable T-units. T-units are standard subject/predicate/complete idea groupings of words. A sentence may consist of one complete idea. A sentence may consist of more than one complete idea, using a comma and a conjunction or using a semi-colon rather than a period to separate ideas. In such a case, the sentence consists of two (or more) T-units. Most readability level computations count sentences at the point at which end punctuation occurs; they do not consider T-units. Formulas that rely on the number of sentences rather than the number of T-units within the word count less accurately estimate readability levels of text.

Another problem with writing to formula is deciding which formula to use. Although various instruments have been suggested for specific grades, there is an overlap. Does an author choose Gunning's Fog Index or another instrument for determining the readability level of a high school content text? Is there really a difference? The following passage and its readability computations from Chapter 6 of the *Global Science* text demonstrate the dilemma:

> *There are several different kinds of cells, but generally they can be grouped into two main categories. The first group is the most simple type of cells. These cells are called prokaryotes. Prokaryotes do not have a nucleus, and they have very few cell organelles (parts that help the cell function). Examples of this type of cell are bacteria and viruses. The second group of cells is more complex than the prokaryotes. This group of cells is called eukaryotes. All eukaryotes have a true nucleus and many cell organelles to carry out the cell's functions.*

Instrument	Flesch	Flesch-Kincaid	Gunning's Fog Index	Fry	Raygor
Grade Level	8.3	6.9	10.2	7	7

Finally, over-reliance on readability formulas has caused many publishers to try to "beat the system." Books are reworked to get the readability level down to the reading level of the intended audience. To do that, sentences are shortened and the majority of difficult (polysyllabic) words removed. Simpler synonyms are substituted, which result in books that are "dumbed-down"—books that many students and teachers consider dull. The sentences are choppy; the language is repetitive. The text lacks the feeling for the subject matter. Science texts, in particular, are stripped of the vocabulary students are required to know to discuss scientific concepts intelligently.

***Global Science:* A Readable Text.** The authors of *Global Science* are cognizant of the need for readable text that remains true to its subject matter. How does the author team address the question of writing at an appropriate level for the intended audience of *Global Science: Energy, Resources, Environment*? During the writing of this revision, in addition to testing the text against several readability formulas, multiple aspects of text writing have been given attention.

Readability Level Computations. The following material appeared in the new copy of Chapter 15 of the *Global Science* text:

> *Sand dunes and parched landscapes, like those in the Namib Desert in southern Africa (see Figure 15.21) are the impressions that many people have of deserts, but these aren't necessarily accurate images. The hottest desert in North America is the Sonoran Desert (see Figure 15.22). It has the most complex, and perhaps most varied, desert vegetation on Earth.*
>
> *Arid and extremely arid lands provide the areas we call deserts. Deserts cover nearly one third of the Earth's surface and exist on every continent except Europe, which does have several semiarid (desert-like) regions.*
>
> *Sand covers only about 20 percent of the world's deserts. Nearly half of desert surfaces are plains where the sands have been removed by the wind and erosion.*

An edit to increase reading ease resulted in the following:

> *The impressions that many people have of deserts include sand dunes and parched landscapes, like those in the Namib Desert in southern Africa (see Figure 15.21). These are not necessarily accurate images. For example, the hottest desert in North America is the Sonoran Desert (see Figure 15.22). It has the most complex, and perhaps most varied, desert vegetation on Earth.*
>
> *Arid and extremely arid lands provide the areas we call deserts. Deserts cover nearly one third of the Earth's surface; they exist on every continent except Europe, which does have several semiarid (desert-like) regions.*
>
> *Sand covers only about 20 percent of the world's deserts. Nearly half of desert*

surfaces are plains where the sands have been removed by the wind and erosion.

The text edit readability computations did not change appreciably for Flesch tests and the Gunning's Fog Index. However, the edits resulted in the Fry leveling moving from grade 16 to grade 10; the Raygor leveling moved from college/professional level to grade 10.

The *Global Science* text has been tested against various formulas to maintain its readability for the targeted audience.

Vocabulary. A major factor of readability formulas is vocabulary difficulty. Content-specific vocabulary (in this case, scientific terms) typically does not show up on the word lists used by some readability formulae. This content–specific vocabulary also tends to be polysyllabic, thus increasing grade level "scores."

One way to lower readability scores is to use simpler vocabulary. However, avoiding scientific/content-specific terms is not desirable. Information and simplicity fall by the wayside when text is made up of only frequently used terms. Often, the result is awkward text that makes little sense to the reader.

In this text, when a term is first introduced, it is presented in bold-faced type. The term is either defined within that sentence or immediately before or after the term appears. Sometimes a paragraph is devoted to the explanation of a term. Terms are often broken down into more specific aspects of the term through margin notes. Another way this text handles vocabulary is through an activity that helps students come to a complete understanding of the term/concept.

Sentence Length. Sentence length is another factor the authors considered when writing this text. Sentences average 15 words in length—a comfortable length for most readers at the target level. This length determines the number of concepts a reader must hold in mind while attempting to comprehend a sentence. Reading *extremely* long sentences interferes with concept attainment. However, reading short, choppy sentences also interferes with comprehension; short sentences necessitate that the reader make more inferences while reading, which could lead to miscommunication of concepts. *Global Science*

typically includes one T-unit (defined earlier) per "sentence." If more than one appears in a sentence, the concepts are clearly stated through the use of signal words.

Sentence Subject. Textual ease at the sentence level revolves around the placement of the sentence subject. The authors took great care to move subjects to the front of sentences, rather than bury them in the middle of sentences. An exception to this is when sentences begin with an introductory phrase that would, otherwise-placed, result in confusing, misplaced modifiers. A second exception is to avoid boring reading by using leading articles (the) to begin each sentence.

Paragraph Structure. The paragraphs within this text are concise, cohesive units. They are well-structured with one unit of thought leading to the next. Where appropriate, a list format is used, rather than strings of terms or ideas in a long sentence or a lengthy paragraph. This helps the reader deal with text information in "chunks," which is easier to visualize and, thus, understand.

Cohesion. Paragraph cohesion is also apparent within this text. The authors took care to use connectives within paragraphs and within subsections of chapters. Such attention to text writing improves the readability/comprehension of the text. In addition, the number of new ideas in a paragraph are kept to a minimum.

Text Structure. Predictable organization of the text was also considered by the authors when revising *Global Science.*

- *Chapter organization* is consistent throughout the text.
- *New terms* appear in bold-faced type with definitions either appearing within that same sentence or immediately before or following the sentence containing the term. These words are also defined in the glossary.
- *Signal words* help to indicate the pattern of organization of the subsections of chapters. For example, Chapter 6 Section 6.6 offers an explanation to the question "Why So Much Diversity?" Clues to the organization of the section include: *Several reasons explain these questions; Over time…; Therefore…; Another reason. . .; can result; A third reason. . .; For example…; This is because…*

This organized writing allows the reader to take notes or annotate text easily. The use of signal words helps guide the reader through the paragraph. Careful use of pronouns and their antecedents and repetitions of words also maintain clarity of text. Likewise, the authors have been careful to include topic sentences. These are especially important when introducing concepts.

- A *summary* appears at the end of each chapter, tying together chapter topics.
- *Activities* appear throughout each chapter as concepts are discussed, rather than included as separate pieces, which allows for immediate involvement with the concepts.
- *Questions* appear throughout the chapters, as well, following concept discussions and/or concept development activities. Such placement better ensures the understanding of concepts prior to continuing with further development of those concepts. Additional questions appear within the margins, to help the reader question/react/confirm comprehension while reading.
- *Marginal notes* also are included throughout this text. These comments give further examples of concepts and keep readers focused on key points.

Graphic Aids. Graphic aids such as charts, graphs, illustrations, and photos are used extensively to help students grasp important concepts by offering a visual connection. Students do not have to rely on their ability to visualize while reading to comprehend the material. (See Chapter 3: text and diagram of the carbon cycle.)

The writing of a textbook is a never-ending process. Texts can always be improved to better meet the needs of the audiences they serve. Meeting those needs includes more than writing to satisfy a readability formula. It includes writing text that is considerate of the reader—which is done, in part, by responding to feedback from teachers and students. The authors and publisher of *Global Science* have used such feedback to develop an even more effective edition. Working together—as authors, publishers, and readers—we can continue to develop texts that best achieve our ultimate goal: an understanding of the content that strives to develop a well-informed, caring public.

Tamra A. Keller is the reading/language arts consultant for Kendall/Hunt Publishing Company. Most recently, she authored the new Kendall/Hunt spelling program for grades 2–6: Words for Writing, *and has edited the Kendall/Hunt Pegasus reading/language arts program for grades K–6. Dr. Keller has taught remedial and regular classes in both elementary and high schools; she also has taught content-area reading, composition, speech, and analytical thinking/study skills courses at the college/university level and for teacher certification. Dr. Keller has worked closely on* Global Science *with senior author John W. Christensen to help ensure the general readability of this text.*

This Teacher Guide contains all the information necessary for organizing a semester, yearlong, or two-year-long program using *Global Science.*

The guide begins by explaining the philosophical basis of the curriculum. The major components of the program are described so that you can use them to their full advantage.

The Getting Organized section should help you plan a schedule to meet your needs be it 18, 36, or 72 weeks. The rough schedule can be firmed up after the core activities, sources of videos, and supplemental materials have been chosen.

The laboratory preparations section is placed just before the guide to chapters and activities in this guide. It is the key to organizing your laboratory program. First examine the issues of student safety. Then determine what equipment you need, what you have, and what you must order.

Most science teachers and departments find *Global Science* to be their most cost-effective science offering. They can offer a full year of meaningful laboratory investigations for less cost per pupil than any of their traditional science offerings. This is because the *Global Science* laboratory investigations can be done without a lot of specialized, high-tech equipment. Those schools that have the luxury of having many computers and other more expensive equipment, such as electronic balances, microscopes, and timing devices, can include these features. This, however, is an option—not a requirement.

Each chapter guide begins with a set of learning outcomes. Schools and school districts can use these learning outcomes (an accountability tool) to outline course content and what is expected from students. A learning outcome is a specification of desired learner performance. Most learning outcomes focus on (1) specifying a desired academic change on the part of the student and (2) how the change will be measured.

In their purest form, learning outcomes have six elements:

1. The human variable (student).
2. The academic variable (cognitive, affective, and psychomotor behaviors).
3. The instructional variable (content variable that describes knowledge presented).
4. The method of measurement.
5. The time or prerequisites required.
6. The proficiency level.

All learning outcomes for *Global Science* contain elements 1-3. Element 4 is included for those items that relate to experiments and activities. In all other cases, the method of *measurement* is an item left to individual teachers. This is also the reason that *time on task, prerequisites,* and *proficiency level* are not specified. There is such wide variability in schools, school districts, teacher curricular expectations, and individual student situations that these matters must be determined at the local level.

The booklet "Developing and Writing Performance Objectives" (Educational Innovators Press, 1971) was used in the construction of these learning outcomes. To help you with the use of the outcomes, the terms *cognitive, affective,* and *psychomotor* are defined below.

Cognitive: (C) Outcomes that place primary emphasis on the mental or intellectual processes of the learner. The levels are *knowledge, comprehension, application, analysis, synthesis,* and *evaluation.*

Affective: (A) Outcomes that primarily emphasize attitudes, emotions, and values of the learner and are usually reflected by interests, appreciations, and adjustments. This is a more nebulous area than the cognitive variable, but equally important. The levels are *receive, respond, value, organize,* and *characterize.*

Psychomotor: (P) Outcomes that place primary emphasis on neuromuscular or physical skills involving various degrees of physical dexterity. The levels are *imitate, manipulate, precision, articulate,* and *naturalize.*

NOTE

Each of the above outcomes (C, A, P) is indicated in the Learning Outcomes section for each chapter in the chapter resources section of this guide.

More learning outcomes are provided per chapter than you will use. Choose those that apply to what you decide to emphasize.

The key terms for the chapter are listed next for your reference and can be used as you see fit. In the text, key terms are printed in bold type when they first appear, which is when the student is most ready to learn their meaning. The definitions can be found quickly in the glossary.

The key terms are followed by a list of recommended Blackline Masters. These Blackline Masters are supplemental to the activity/reading and can be found on the *Teacher Resource CD.* A flow chart appears next to emphasize the importance of the activities. A teacher guide to chapters and activities is included for each chapter. Complete instructions for doing each activity are provided. No special workshop training is necessary. Careful planning and organization should produce the desired result.

Finally, a sample chapter exam with answers is included. The chapter assessments are provided as a teacher resource intended to determine quickly and easily if the key ideas in a chapter have been covered adequately and if a majority of students understand the material. Modify and adjust each assessment to your local situation.

Being able to assess student learning and understanding is an essential part of any teacher's job. It is similar to the process of doing science in that both the scientist and the teacher must collect adequate data to answer the current question. For scientists, their questions focus on understanding and explaining the natural world. They use tools to help them collect data that will yield information to answer their questions. Teachers on the other hand, are asking questions about their students. Often these questions have to do with what students know, understand, and can do.

When you are teaching a program that integrates different areas of science and the methods of scientific inquiry in a constructivist manner, such as *Global Science,* traditional forms of assessment, such as tests that emphasize the recall of specific facts, will not provide enough data to answer the question, How well do my students understand the key ideas? Instead the forms of assessment must be varied, just like your instructional strategies. When you match your assessment strategies to your instructional strategies, you are making your assessment *authentic.*

To accomplish this match between instruction and assessment, you will need to use some forms of nontraditional, or *alternative,* forms of assessment. You can use strategies such as individual student projects, lab activities, oral or written reports, or group projects as forms of assessment that will provide the varied types of information you will need to assess student progress in this program. For some of these projects, you will find that scoring rubrics will make them much easier to assess and assign grades fairly.

If you are interested in authentic or alternative assessment, consider these resources:

Baxter, G.P., R.J. Shavelson, and J. Pine. 1992. Evaluation of procedure-based scoring for hands-on science assessment. *Journal of Educational Measurement,* 29 (1): 1–17.

Champagne, A.B., and S.T. Newell. 1992. Directions for research and development: Alternative methods of assessing scientific literacy. *Journal of Research in Science Teaching,* 29 (8): 41–860.

Glaser, R. 1992. *Cognitive Theory as the Basis for Design of Innovative Assessment: Design Characteristics of Science Assessments.* Los Angeles, CA: National Center for Research on Evaluation, Standards, and Student Testing.

Kulm, G., and S.M. Malcom (eds.). 1991. *Science Assessment in the Service of Reform.* Washington, DC: AAAS.

Shavelson, R.J. 1991. Performance assessment in science. *Applied Measurement in Education,* 4 (4): 347–62.

Shavelson, R.J., G. Baxter, and J. Pine. 1992. Performance assessments: Political rhetoric and measurement reality. *Educational Researcher,* 21 (4): 22–27.

To assist you with planning, a sample 36-week schedule is provided (pages 381–384). Choose what fits your situation. Make adjustments using materials you already have and other resources suggested in this section.

If you have only one semester to address the important concepts in *Global Science,* the 36-week schedule can serve as a guide in scheduling the topics you choose to emphasize.

If you have two years to teach *Global Science,* there are more activities in the textbook and videos on the recommended list than can fit in the 36-week schedule. You may supplement with additional materials to meet all of the National Science Content Standards in 72 weeks. To assist you, a sample 72-week schedule is provided (pages 385–392). Adjust it to meet your needs.

Schools using bloc scheduling will need to make adjustments to their situation.

Some schools offer *Global Science* as a two-semester course as follows:

Semester I: Human Ecology (mostly life science)
Chapter 1
Chapter 2
Chapter 3 Activities 3.1 and 3.2 and Readings 3.1 and 3.2
Chapter 5
Chapter 6
Chapter 7
Chapter 15
Chapter 16
Emphasis: Building the Sustainable World
Semester II: Energy and Resource (mostly physical science)

Chapter 3 From Reading 3.3 to the end of the chapter
Chapter 4
Chapters 8–14.
Emphasis: Wise Use of Our Natural Resources

GLOBAL SCIENCE CONCEPT FLOW

SCIENCE AS A WAY OF KNOWING
Chapter 1 The Nature of Science

THE ECOSYSTEM CONCEPT
Chapter 2 A Grand Oasis in Space (the needs of living things)
Chapter 3 Energy Flow and Matter Cycles
Chapter 4 Mineral Resources

POPULATION/NUTRITION
Chapter 5 Growth and Population
Chapter 6 Seeds of Life
Chapter 7 Agriculture and Nutrition

PROVIDING ENERGY FOR SOCIETIES
Chapter 8 Energy Today
Chapter 9 Nonrenewable Resource Depletion
Chapter 10 Nuclear Energy
Chapter 11 Energy Alternatives
Chapter 12 Strategies for Using Energy

MANAGING NATURAL RESOURCES
Chapter 13 Water: Quantity and Quality
Chapter 14 Resource Management: Air
Chapter 15 Resource Management: Land

BUILDING A SUSTAINABLE PLANET
Chapter 16 Options for the Future

NOTE
Global Science is not a spiraled curriculum.

SAFETY IN THE LAB

Safety in school laboratories is critical. All precautions must be taken to protect the health and safety of our students. It is imperative to protect them by following well-established safety procedures. In the process, you also protect yourself from injury and lawsuit. With two-thirds of the world's lawyers living in the United States, it is unlikely you will receive much sympathy—especially if you didn't plan ahead.

A few general rules follow. You are asked to follow them and then to write to be placed on Flinn Scientific's mailing list.

SAFETY RULES

1. Never, ever, do a demonstration in front of your students or an experiment with your students without trying it ahead of time.
2. Never leave your classroom while students are working with laboratory equipment. It is best not to be gone when students are in the room, period.
3. Safety goggles must be worn any time chemicals, glassware, or heat are used in the lab. No exceptions.
4. Have a fire-blanket in your lab/classroom. It should be mounted near the floor and be easily seen. *Note:* A camping utility blanket (100% wool) works well.
5. Eye-washing capability must be available in your lab/classroom that meets these requirements:
   a. washes both eyes simultaneously,
   b. uses a clean water source, and
   c. provides a continuous wash for 20 minutes.
   Note: If your school can't afford a commercial eye wash and a body shower/drench, go to the local hardware or housewares store. Purchase a hose with a funnel-shaped end that can be affixed to your existing water faucet. This type of hose is commonly used to fill portable clothes or dishwashers. It should be about 6 feet long. Next, acquire a plastic showerhead that will accept the other end of your hose. Hang this contraption on the wall by your sink. Label it "Eye Wash." Instruct students on how to use it. It may look strange, but you'll be glad it's there if an emergency should arise.
6. Know how to handle chemical spills. See the Flinn catalog for various options on spill control.
7. Inventory, safely store, and properly dispose of your chemicals.
   It is important you know what chemicals you have in your laboratory and what their properties are. It is important that chemicals are stored by compatible chemical families and not alphabetically. Finally, it is important that all chemical materials are disposed of in a safe and environmentally acceptable manner. The Flinn catalog explains all this in detail.

To learn what you need to know about chemicals and laboratory safety, get on the Flinn Scientific mailing list.

BENEFITS

* Get a copy of the Flinn Chemical Catalog/Reference Manual each year.
* Receive their safety and technical mailings regularly.
* Receive invitations to useful workshops and seminars.
* Get updates on the latest rules and regulations that apply to safety on school premises.

TO GET ON THE LIST

Write: Flinn Scientific, Inc.
P.O. Box 219
Batavia, IL 60510
Phone: (800) 452-1261
Provide: Your name and your school name and address.

Carefully read the catalog sections on school laboratory safety. You may also wish to purchase additional reference materials and necessary equipment to upgrade your facilities. These decisions can all be made as you process this information. Also see the September, 1999 issue of *The Science Teacher* magazine.

MATERIALS LIST

It is recommended that *Global Science* teachers select the lab activities they plan to do and then list the equipment necessary to do them. Then examine the Materials List that follows (pages xxiv–xxx). Also see the equipment list by activity in the Appendix (pages 404–405). Make a list of the items you need to purchase that you cannot purchase locally. Call your Kendall/Hunt representative at 1-800-228-0810 to order items from the Materials List.

Item Description	Class Qty.	Activity Number
Consumable Items		
Bag, Self-Sealing, 2 × 3″, Each	100	6.3, 6.5
Balloon, Round 9″, Pkg/35	1	14.6
Battery, Alkaline, Size D, 1.5 V, Shelf Life 7 Yrs	12	8.7
Bubble Wrap, 6″ × 12″, Perforated	12	10.8
Bulb, Incandescent, 90W, Clear	6	Frequent Use
Candle, Paraffin, 10 cm L × 2 cm, Pkg/12	1	8.3
Colored Pencils, Set/12 Assorted	6	Frequent Use
Cotton Balls, Pkg/300	6	10.8
Detergent, Household 12.6 oz (dish detergent)	1	14.3
Food Coloring, 8 mL each, Set/4 Colors	1	1.2, 8.5, 11.1
Forks, Plastic Pkg/24	1	6.6
Gauze Pad 3×3 Inch	1	4.8
Glue, School White 4 oz	6	10.7
Graph Paper, 22 × 28 cm, 10 sq. per Inch Pkg/100	2	Frequent Use
Incandescent Lamp, 2.47 V, Screw Base #14, Mini	6	8.7
Jiffy Pots (Peat Pots), 6 cm × 6 cm, Pkg/12	3	3.7
Knives, Plastic Pkg/24	1	6.6
Lemon Juice, 500 mL	1	14.3
Lids, Plastic for 300 ml Cup Pkg/50	1	2.1
Light Stick, Red, Shelf Life 18 Months	1	3.6
Marker, Black, Permanent	1	10.6
Markers, Asst. Color, Broad Tip Pkg/10, Washable	6	Frequent Use
Medium, Vermiculite Planting Medium, 9 kg	1	14.5
Milk of Magnesia 12 oz	1	14.3
Oil, Vegetable, 16 oz	2	4.8
Pan, Aluminum Foil 22.5 cm Diam (pie pan)	6	4.9
Paper Clips, Jumbo, Box/100	1	8.7, 15.8
Paper Towel Roll	2	Frequent Use
Paper, Construction, White, Pkg/50, 12 × 18″	1	4.13, 7.6, 15.3
Paper, Filter, Medium Flow, 15 cm dia, Pkg/100	1	4.10
Parafilm M, 10 cm × 38 m Roll (4 in × 125 ft)	1	2.3
Peanuts, Foam Pkg/200	6	10.8
Pencil, Marking, Black Wax	6	2.3
pH Paper, Wide Range, 1/4″ × 2″, Vial/100	6	6.7, 13.4, 14.3
Pipet, Thin Stem, Disposable, Pkg/100	1	6.7, 7.4
Plastic Wrap, 100 sq ft Roll	1	14.7
Safety Matches (pkg/10 boxes)	1	8.3
Sand, Fine, 2.5 kg (5.5lbs) Double Bagged	7	Frequent Use
Seeds, Assorted, 6 Types (30 g Pkg Oriental Mung, Brown Bean, Corn, Grass, Lima Beans, Sunflower Seeds)	1	3.7, 6.3, 6.4, 7.4

Item Description	Class Qty.	Activity Number
Consumable Items Continued		
Seeds, Tomato 4.5 g	1	6.5
Seeds, Tomato Earliana Pkt	1	6.5
Seeds, Tomato Florandel Pkt	1	6.5
Seeds, Tomato New Yorker Pkt	1	6.5
Seeds, Tomato Yellow Jubilee Pkt	1	6.5
Seeds, Tomato, Beefsteak Pkg/300	1	6.5
Seeds, Tomato, Cherry Variety	1	6.5
Seeds, Tomato, Roma Pkg/300	1	6.5
Soil, Clay, 2.5 kg, (12-1/2 cups)	1	7.1
Soil, Loam, 2.5 kg, (12-1/2 cups)	1	7.1
Soil, Potting 8 lbs	3	Frequent Use
Soil, Sandy 2.5 kg	1	7.1
Soil, Vacant Lot, 1 kg (4-1/2 cups)	1	7.1
Spoon, Plastic, Pkg/24	2	6.6, 15.7
Stick, Stirrer, Pkg/50	1	Frequent Use
Straw, Plastic, Pkg/200	1	2.3, 14.4
String, Cotton 200 ft	2	3.3, 10.8
Sugar, Granulated, 454 g (Approx. 2-1/2 cups)	3	Frequent Use
Tagboard, 24" × 36"	54	Frequent Use
Tagboard, 9 × 12" Pkg/25	2	11.2
Tape, Duct, 2" Wide, 60 Yard Roll, Silver	1	10.8
Tape, Masking, 3/4" × 60 yards	6	4.8, 14.6
Tape, Transparent Dispenser Roll, 27.1 ft	6	2.1, 4.6
Vinegar, 473 mL, White	7	Frequent Use
Water, 3.785 L, Distilled	6	Frequent Use
Live Materials *When ordering live material please indicate the delivery date.*		
Live - Elodea anacharis, Pkg/12 Plants	2	2.3, 6.3
Live - Plant, Begonia	2	14.5
Live - Plant, Coleus, White Variegated	2	14.5
Live - Pond Snails, Pkg/12	2	2.3
Chemicals		
Acetic Acid, 500 mL, 36% Sol	1	14.4
Alka Seltzer Tablets, Pkg/24	1	1.3
Ammonia, Household, 500 mL, 4% by mass	1	Frequent Use
Benedict's Solution, Qualitative, 1 L	1	7.4
Biuret Reagent, 500 mL, Sol in Sodium Hydroxide	1	7.4
Bleach, 100 mL, (Sodium Hypochlorite)	2	6.4, 14.3
Bromothymol Blue Sodium Salt, 500 mL, 0.04%	1	2.3, 14.4
Calcium Acetate Monohydrate, 500 g, Powder	1	3.4
Calcium Hydroxide, Lime Water, 1 L, 0.14%	1	14.4
Copper(II) Sulfate Pentahydrate, 500 g, Crystals	1	4.8, 4.10, 10.1
Crystal Violet, Staining Sol., 100 mL	1	6.2
Epsom Salt, 500 g, Crystals	1	4.8
Hydrochloric Acid, 500mL, 3M	4	4.3, 4.4, 4.10
Iodine Tincture, Lugol's Sol. (Starch Test), 100 mL	1	6.2, 7.4
Isopropyl Alcohol, 2-Propanol, 3.785 L, Anhydrous	1	2.1
Methyl Alcohol, 1L, Methanol	1	10.3
Nitric Acid, ACS Grade, 500 mL, 15.8 M	1	14.3, 14.5
Potassium Permanganate, 100 g, Crystals	1	4.8, 11.1
Sodium Bicarbonate, 500 g, Powder (Baking Soda)	1	6.4, 14.3
Sodium Carbonate, 500 g, Granular, Anhydrous	1	3.4
Sodium Chloride, 737 g, 26 oz, Iodized Table Salt	2	Frequent Use

Item Description	Class Qty.	Activity Number
Chemicals Continued		
Sodium Nitrate, Lab Grade, 500 g	1	13.5
Sodium Phosphate Dodecahydrate, 500 g, Powder	1	13.5
Sudan III, Lipid Test, 100 mL	1	7.4
Non-Consumable Items		
Air Core Solenoid	6	8.7
Bead, Plastic, Multifaceted, 3/8", Pkg/144	2	10.6
Bolt, 1/2-13 × 3", Carriage Bolt, Zinc Plated	1	10.8
Book, CRC Handbook of Chemistry & Physics	1	1.9
Bowl!, Plastic, Large, 40 oz	6	5.1, 10.6
Bowl, White, 2 Liters, 6 1/4" D × 4 1/4" H	6	11.5
Calculator, Solar Powered, Scientific, TI-30XIIS	6	Frequent Use
Chip, Red, Game, 3/4", Pkg/100	3	16.5
Comb, Plastic, 15 cm	6	14.6
Compass w/ Pencil, 12" diameter, Safety, Plastic	6	2.1, 4.5
Copper Shot, 4oz. Pkg	1	4.9
Cover Glass, 1 oz, 22 mm	1	6.2
Cup, Polypropylene Measuring, 8 oz	6	14.2
Cup, Foam, 14 oz, Pkg/25	1	3.11
Cup, Paper, 100 ml, Pkg/100	1	2.1
Cup, Plastic, 300 ml, Pkg/50	4	Frequent Use
Dice, Game Size, Pkg/12	125	5.1, 10.6
Fan, 10"	1	11.8
Flashlight, Plastic, Economy	6	3.6, 10.3, (11.7)
Forceps, Medium Point, Straight, Nickel Plated	6	4.9, 4.10, 14.3
Friction Pad, Animal Fur	6	14.6
Friction Rod, Black, Hard Nylon	6	14.6
Globe, Physiographic Relief, 30 cm D	1	2.1
Globe, Raised Relief, Semi-Meridian, 30 cm Dia.	6	Frequent Use
Jar, Wide Mouth Specimen, 118 mL, Screw Cap Type	24	14.4
Jar Screw Cap, 58 mm	24	14.4
Lid, Plastic for 40 oz. Bowl	6	5.1, 10.6
Light Socket, Clamp On (Sun Simulator)	6	4.2, 11.3, 14.7
Light Sockets, Pkg. 6, Mini w/ Fahnstock Clips	1	8.7
Magnet, Alnico Bar, 150 mm × 19 mm × 7 mm	6	4.10, 8.7
Magnifier,Dual, 3 × & 6 × (hand lens)	6	Freuquent Use
Marble, 5/8", Pkg/300	3	10.6
Meter Stick, Basswood, Metric & English Scales	6	6.7, 7.2, 11.5
Mineral Collection 1 ((Includes calcite, talc, gypsum, pyrite, quartz, fluorite, apatite, feldspar/microcline, magnetite, graphite), Pkg/6 Each	1	4.3
Mineral, Biotite Specimen Pak (6 pieces)	1	4.3
Mineral, Galena Specimen Pak (6 pieces)	1	4.3
Mineral, Halite Specimen Pak (6 pieces)	1	4.3
Mineral, Hematite Specimen Pak (6 pieces)	1	4.3
Mineral, Hornblende Each	6	4.3
Mineral, Limonite, Tenpack	1	4.3
Mineral, Muscovite (Mica) Specimen Pak (6 pieces)	1	4.3, 4.10
Nails, 5 cm 6D, Pkg/50	1	4.3. 4.8, 10.1
Pad, Steel Wool, Pkg/6	1	10.1
Pail, Utility, Polyethylene, w/Lid, 19 L (5 Gal)	1	4.9
Protractor, Plastic, 180 deg, 10 cm; 6" Ruler	6	8.1
Radiometer, Crooker's	1	3.6

Item Description	Class Qty.	Activity Number
Non-Consumable Items Continued		
Rock Collection (Includes breccia, conglomerate, gabbro, gneiss, granite, marble, limestone, sandstone, slate) Pkg/ 6 Each	1	4.4
Rock, Basalt Specimen Pak (6 pieces 2-3 cm)	1	4.4
Rock, Obsidian Specimen Pak (6 pieces 2-3 cm)	1	4.4
Rock, Rhyolite Specimen Pak (6 pieces 2-3 cm)	1	4.4
Rock, Schist Specimen Pak (6 pieces 2-3 cm)	1	4.4
Rock, Shale(Gray) Specimen Pak (6)	1	4.4
Ruler, Plastic, Clear, 15 cm, 6", Pkg/10	1	6.3
Ruler, Plastic, 30 cm; 12", Assorted Colors	30	Frequent Use
Scale, Bathroom, 130 kg (286 lbs) Capacity	1	7.2
Scalpel, Student, Carbon Steel, 150 mm	6	7.4
Scissors, General Purpose, Nickel Plated (6")	6	Frequent Use
Screen Sieve, 15 cm W, 5 cm Deep, Set/4	1	4.10
Slides, Microscope, Pkg/12	2	6.2
Spoon, Measuring, Set/6	6	4.2
Stirring Rod, 5 × 150 mm	6	7.4, 4.10
Stopwatch, Electronic LED, 1/100 Second	6	Frequent Use
Streak Plate, Low Cost, Glass, Pkg/10	1	4.3
Streak Plate, Ceramic, 50 × 50 × 3 mm, Pkg/8	1	4.3
Test Tube, Plastic w/Cap, 16 × 150 mm Polystyrene	6	1.2, 4.8
Thermometer, Digital Oral, 35 C to 42 C	1	3.6
Tray, Plastic, Blue, 10" × 14"	6	3.10
Tube, Acrylic, 34 cm L × 2.5cm OD × 1/16" Wall	1	4.8
UV Pocket Lantern	1	6.4
Vial, Flint Glass, 28 mL, Pkg/12	2	11.1
Vial, Plastic w/ Snap-On Cap, 18 mL, Pkg/12	3	4.9. 4.10
Wire Leads, Black, w/ Alligator Clips	6	8.7, 11.7
Wire Leads, Red w/ Alligator Clips	6	8.7, 11.7
Kit and Specialty Items		
Generator, Genecon Hand Operated	6	8.7
Generator, Wind Power (optional demonstration)	1	11.8
Graph Paper, 2-Cycle Semi-log, Pkg/100 Sheets	6	5.1, 10.5
Immersion Heater	6	3.11
Kit, Aluminum Mass Set	6	1.9
Kit, Cloud Chamber Set	6	10.3
Kit, Coal Types	6	8.6
Kit, Electrostatic Materials Class Set	1	14.6
Kit, Friction Rod	1	14.6
Kit, Fuel Cell, Solar Hydrogen	1	12.3
Kit, Milling Lab Samples	1	4.10
Kit, Population Sample Survey, TD-CT	5	5.1
Kit, Radioactive Source, Set/3, Alpha/Beta/Gamma	1	Reading 10.2
Kit, Solar Cell	6	3.6, 11.7
Kit, Solar Heating (Collector)	6	11.5
Kit, Solar Hydrogen Fuel Cell	1	12.3
Kit, Solar Oven, Hubbard Scientific	1	11.4
Kit, Sunpower House, Hubbard Scientific	6	11.3
Mineral collection, Importance Of Minerals Kit	1	4.11
Pendulum Bob, Inertial Mass	1	3.3
Plant Stand with Light	1	2.2, 3.7, 14.5
Slide Set, Intro Plant and Animal, Set of 5	1	6.2

Item Description	Class Qty.	Activity Number
Kit and Specialty Items Continued		
Test Kit, Green Water Monitoring, 100 Tests	1	13.4
Test Kit, Soil, Rapitest	1	7.1
Kit, Copper Plating Set * *Purchase the items directly under this listing for this activity*		
9v, Battery connector	8	15.7, 15.8
Battery, 9V, Alkaline	8	15.7, 15.8
Alligator clip with wire, pkg 10	2	15.7, 15.8
Copper Chloride, 100g	1	15.7, 15.8
Copper Strips, 2 × 3/4″	8	15.7, 15.8
Cup, Graduated, 10 oz	8	15.7, 15.8
Lamp, Mini	8	15.7, 15.8
Paper Clips, package	1	15.7, 15.8
Stir Sticks, glass	8	15.7, 15.8
Kit, Exponential Growth * *Purchase the items directly under this listing for this activity*		
Bin, C-Thru, 13″ × 7-1/4″ × 4-1/2″ w/Lid	6	5.1
Dice, Game Size, Pkg/12	125	5.1
Graph Paper, 2-Cycle Semi-log, Pkg/100 Sheet	6	5.1
Graph Paper, 22 × 28 cm, 10 sq. per Inch Pkg/100	2	5.1
Kit, Radioactive Decay Chain * *Purchase the items directly under this listing for this activity*		
Marbles, 5/8″, Pkg/300	3	10.6
Beads, Plastic, Multifaceted, 3/8″, Pkg/144	1	10.6
Bin, C-Thru, 13″ × 7-1/4″ × 4-1/2″ w/Lid	6	10.6
Dice, Game Size, Pkg/12	78	10.6
Marker, Permanent	6	10.6
Kit, Resource Depletion * *Purchase the items directly under this listing for this activity*		
Bead, Plastic, Multifaceted, 3/8″, Pkg/144	10	9.1
Bin, C-Thru, 13″ × 7-1/4″ × 4-1/2″ w/Lid	6	9.1
Seed, Field Corn, Pkg/450 g	24	9.1
Cup, Plastic, 300 ml, Pkg/50	4	9.1
LabWare Items		
Beaker, Pyrex Low Form, 30 mL, Single Scale	3	13.1
Beaker, Pyrex Student Grade 50 mL, Low Form	30	Frequent Use
Beaker, Pyrex Student Grade, 100 mL Low Form	30	3.4, 4.10, 13.4
Beaker, Pyrex Student Grade, 150 mL Low Form	3	4.8
Beaker, Pyrex Student Grade, 250 mL Low Form	18	Frequent Use
Beaker, Pyrex Student Grade, 400 mL Low Form	6	8.5
Beaker, Pyrex Student Grade, 600 mL Low Form	6	Frequent Use
Beaker, Pyrex Student Grade, 1000 mL Low Form	6	6.7, 11.1, 13.1
Beaker, Pyrex Student Grade, 2000 mL Low Form	6	11.5
Bottle, Dropping, Barnes, Glass, 30 mL	30	2.3, 7.4, 14.4
Clamp, Buret, w/Symmetrical Round Coated Jaws	6	4.8, 4.10, 8.5
Clamp and Support Rod	6	14.6
Clamp, Right Angle	6	14.6
Clamp, Test Tube, Stoddard, Opening to 25 mm	6	4.8
Clamp, Tubing, Hoffman Screw, 16 mm Tubing	6	11.5
Cylinder, Graduated, Borosilicate, 10 mL × 0.2 mL	12	Frequent Use
Cylinder, Graduated, Borosilicate, 100 mL × 1 mL	6	Frequent Use
Cylinder, Graduated, Borosilicate, 50 mL × 1 mL	12	Frequent Use
Cylinder, Graduated, Borosilicate, 1000 mL × 10 mL	6	1.9, 11.5, 13.1
Cylinder, Graduated, Borosilicate, 250 mL × 2 mL	6	1.9, 6.7, 8.3

Item Description	Class Qty.	Activity Number

LabWare Items Continued

Flask, Erlenmeyer, Pyrex, 250 mL	12	4.8, 8.5
Funnel, Plastic, 3.25"	12	4.8, 4.10
Petri Dish, 100 mm × 15 mm Sterile, Pkg/20	2	4.2, 4.8, 7.4
Pipet, Dropper, Flint Glass, 105 mm, 2 mL, Pkg/12	1	Frequent Use
Rack, Test Tube Support, Twelve Tube Capacity	12	2.3, 4.8
Ring, Support, w/Clamp, 9 cm ID, 11.5 cm OD	6	4.10, 8.3, 8.5
Stirring Rod, Glass, 5 mm × 200 mm	6	4.2, 4.10, 8.3
Stopper, Rubber, Size 2, Solid, 1 lb (454 g)	2	1.2, 2.3, 4.8
Stopper, Rubber, Size 6.5, 1 Hole, 1 lb (454 g)	1	8.5
Support Stand w/51 cm Long Rod, 13 cm × 20 cm	6	Frequent Use
Test Tube, SK, 20 mm × 150 mm, 34 mL	60	1.2, 2.3, 4.8
Test Tube, SK, 25 mm × 150 mm, 55 mL	6	8.5
Thermometer, −20 to 110 C, Partial Immersion, Yellow	18	Frequent Use
Thermometer, Plastic Back, −30 C − 110 C	8	1.3, 14.7
Tongs, Beaker, w/Rubber Covered Jaws	6	4.10, 11.1
Tubing, Rigid, Plastic, 29 cm (11.5") length	3	8.5
Tubing, Vinyl Plastic, 3/16" ID × 1/16" Wall	12	8.5
Wire Gauze, Galvanized, 13 cm × 13 cm (5" × 5")	6	4.10, 8.5

Large Equipment

Ammeter, Triple Range, 0-50 MA/500, 0-5A	6	11.7
Balance, Triple Beam, Low Form, 610 g, Ohaus	6	Frequent Use
Burner, Portable Butane Gas, for use w/Burner Fuel Cartridge (46712-01)	6	4.8, 8.5
Burner Fuel, Cartridge, 225 g	6	4.8, 8.5
Galvanometer (DC +/− 500 uA)	6	8.7
Geiger Counter, Portable, 17 × 8 × 3.5 cm	1	10.3, 10.8
Hot Plate, Scholar, 10.16 × 12.75 × 12.7 cm	6	Frequent Use
Microscope, Skope, LED, 40-400X	6	6.2
Voltmeter, Dual Range, 0-5V/15V DC	6	11.7
Weight, Attachment, Set/3, Increase Balance Capacity	6	16.9

*Ammeter and Voltmeter are found in the Solar Cell Kit and do not need to be purchased separately for that activity.

Safety Items

Apron, Vinyl, Student, 69 cm × 91 cm	30	4.10
Gloves, Clavies Biohazard Autoclave, w/28 cm Gauntlet, Pair	6	Frequent Use
Goggles, Safety Chemical Classroom Set (30 students)	1	Frequent Use

Locally Acquired Items

Angel Chimes with Unlit Candles	1	3.6
Apple Juice	1	14.3
Art Supplies, Assorted, Set	6	3.2, 3.5
Bottle, 2 L w/Cap	12	1.3, 10.8
Butter Patty	6	7.4
Paper, Butcher	6	3.2, 16.1
Candy, Piece	30	16.5
Cooler, Styrofoam	6	11.5
Cranberry Juice, Carton	1	14.3
Dictionary, American History Textbook	6	4.9
Dry Ice, Slab	6	10.3
Egg, Raw	6	10.8
Graph Paper, 10 sq/inch, sheet	60	Frequent Use
Grocery Sack Filled with Crushed Aluminum Cans	6	16.9
Honey	1	7.4

Item Description	Class Qty.	Activity Number
Locally Acquired Items Continued		
Hose or Source of Running Water	1	4.9
Ice Cubes, Bucket	6	2.1, 3.9
Ice, Crushed, Bucket	1	8.5
Juice Can, Cardboard	6	8.3
Macaroni, Elbow, 1 cup	6	6.6
Match, "Strike Anywhere"	6	14.4
Materials to Build Model Wind Generator, Assort, Student Designed	1	11.8
Microwave Oven (optional)	1	6.4
Milk of Magnesia	1	14.3
Motor, 12 V	6	11.8
Objects of Different Mass, Set	6	3.3
Onion Pieces	1	6.2
Orange Juice, Carton	1	14.3
Paper, Sheet	42	1.2, 4.5, 4.6
Paper, Sheet, 11" × 17"	30	10.7
Penny	600	2.1, 3.10, 4.3
Penny, New	6	10.1
Penny, Old	6	10.1
Plant, African Violet	1	14.5
Pond Water	1	2.3, 13.5
Potato	1	7.4
Refrigerator and Freezer	1	2.1
Resources about Ecosystems, Set	1	2.4
Resources about Energy Use, Set	1	3.13
Seed, Lima Bean, Fresh *Dried can be substituted if needed, pkg.	1	7.4
Seed, Corn, Fresh *Dried can be substituted if needed, cob	1	7.4
Seed, Soybean, Fresh *Dried can be substituted if needed, pkg.	1	7.4
Seed, Sunflower, pkg.	1	7.4
Shoebox	6	14.7
Siphon Bulb	6	11.5
Soft Drink, Carbonated	1	14.3
Soil Samples, 3 Different Types	6	7.1
Spray Bottle, Cosmetic, Small	6	6.7
Tape, Permanent Mending	1	Frequent Use
Tea Bag	12	3.11
Tin Can Chimney	8	8.3
Toothpicks	1	6.2
Turkey, Deli, Thin Sliced	1	7.4
Vinegar, 1 Qt.	1	2.3, 14.3, 14.4
Waste Container	6	1.3
Water Samples	2 to 4	13.4
Water, River (Pond)	1	13.4, 13.5
World Map, Political	6	4.12
World Population Data Sheet (www.prb.org)	2	3.13, 5.5, 7.6
Yarn, Ball	1	3.1, All Tied Up

THE GLOBE PROGRAM
(GLOBAL LEARNING AND OBSERVATIONS TO BENEFIT THE ENVIRONMENT)

Improved student achievement in science is a key goal in educational reform and in developing the diverse workforce necessary to meet the challenges of the 21st century. In science education reform efforts around the world, there is a push to have students become actively involved in doing science by creating questions and finding and utilizing the means to answer these questions. To support such efforts, there is a need for partnerships between scientists, teachers, and students. Information technology can enable linkages between scientists and students and provide a mechanism for students to relate their local environmental conditions and observations to other locations around the world.

These needs define the rationale for GLOBE, an international inquiry-based program designed to engage students with their teachers in partnership with research scientists to better understand the environment at local, regional, and global scales. GLOBE is an ongoing international science and education program that unites students, teachers, and scientists in the study of the Earth System. Students participating in GLOBE engage in hands-on activities, including the collection, analysis, and sharing of research quality scientific data with their peers around the world. Students interact with members of the science community who use the data collected from locations around the world in their research—data that would often not be available otherwise. As of August 2005, over 30,000 teachers representing over 16,000 schools worldwide have participated in GLOBE workshops resulting in over 13 million environmental measurements reported by students to the GLOBE Web site.

GLOBE is a cooperative effort of schools and scientists managed by the University Corporation for Atmospheric Research (UCAR) in partnership with Colorado State University and supported by the National Aeronautics and Space Administration (NASA), the National Science Foundation (NSF), and the U.S. Department of State. The program in the U.S. is organized in partnership with colleges and universities, state and local school systems, and non-government organizations. Internationally, GLOBE is a partnership between the U.S. and over 100 other countries. For more information on GLOBE visit the Web site www.globe.gov.

THE NATURE OF SCIENCE

LEARNING OUTCOMES

The student will:

1. **define** science based on past knowledge and experiences, the knowledge and experiences of others, and a quotation from a scientist.*(C)
2. **develop** a scientific process based on experiences in the activity "Asking Scientific Questions." (C,P)
3. **appreciate** that there are many ways to do science. (A)
4. **design** an experiment in an attempt to answer a scientific question by doing Activity 1.3. (C,P)
5. **model** the weathering process by **manipulating** lab materials and equipment and **completing** Activity 1.3. (C,P)
6. **identify** the characteristics of a scientific explanation. (A)
7. **realize** that humans have different ways to deal with the questions they face in life. (A)
8. **discover** that there are certain attitudes and behaviors that underlie good scientific work. (A)
9. **realize** that to do good science, a sufficient quantity of accurate data must be gathered. (A)
10. **recognize** that scientists are not perfect nor are their measurements. In spite of that, science performs a useful function. (A)
11. **develop** scientific skills by **manipulating** lab materials and equipment and **completing** Activity 1.9. (C,P) These skills include reading instruments, organizing and recording data, and searching for meaningful relationships.
12. **realize** that modern societies depend on quality data for their existence. (A)
13. **calculate** quantities by working in both the metric and U.S. Customary System. (C,P)
14. **realize** that the results of science affect everyone, so science must be used with care and respect. (A)
15. **develop** a brief history of environmental science by doing Activity 1.11. (C)

---

*C = cognitive, A = affective, and P = psychomotor. See the "Using the Teacher Guide" section at the front of this book for definitions and more information.

KEY TERMS

global science   hypothesis   scientific explanation   interpolate   U.S. Customary System
science   model   weathering   extrapolate   metric system

RECOMMENDED BLACKLINE MASTERS

1.1   Global Science
1.2   Openness to New Ideas
1.3   The Blind Men and the Elephant

1.4   Possible Elephant Model
1.5   Plotting Graphs
1.6   Comparisons: U.S. Customary to Metric

The Recommended Blackline Masters listed above are supplemental to the activity/reading, and can be found on the *Teacher Resource CD*.

ACTIVITIES FLOW CHART

CHAPTER 1: THE NATURE OF SCIENCE

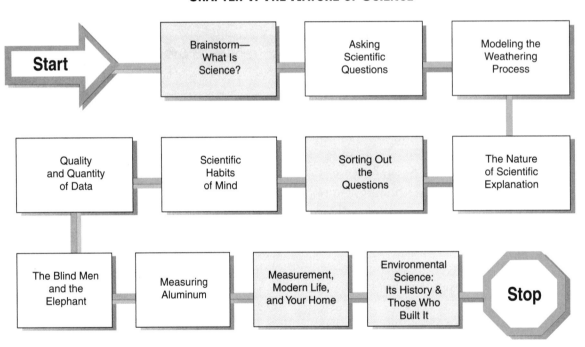

NOTE: Shaded items are lower priority.

TEACHING STRATEGIES AND ANSWERS FOR ACTIVITIES

 1.1

SCIENCE NOTEBOOKS

Because the activities for *Global Science* appear in the student textbook, ask your students to record the information for each activity in a science notebook. You may set up the notebooks based on your individual situation and preference; there is no one best method. If you don't use notebooks, many of the activities can be printed for classroom use by downloading from the *Teacher Resource CD*.

CHAPTER OPENER, See *Student Edition*, p.2.

 **1.1**

 READING 1.1 **WHAT IS SCIENCE?**

See *Student Edition*, p. 4.

 ACTIVITY 1.1 **BRAINSTORM—WHAT IS SCIENCE?**

See *Student Edition*, p. 4.

1. Students may describe science as medicine or what a doctor does, chemistry or "blowing up" things, or the field where people do experiments. They might describe a previous science class. At this time, accept all responses. This will give you a good idea of the fears, expectations, and preconceptions your students are bringing to class.

2. Students may suggest that scientists do experiments, collect data, find cures for diseases, launch rockets, clone organisms, mix chemicals, or design better cars and other products. Their responses are likely to combine both scientific work (answering questions about the natural world) and technological work (solving human problems). Accept all reasonable responses to learn more about your students' thinking.

3. Encourage students to listen closely to their partner. You may want to monitor the time each person talks and suggest a half-way point when students change who is sharing and who is listening.

4. Students should notice that science consists of *both* information and a way of obtaining that information.

5. **Science** is a body of information about the natural world and a way of examining that world. The examination involves observing, measuring, and interpreting the observations and measurements. Your students' definitions may be much simpler depending on their previous experience. Encourage them to incorporate their own experiences in their responses.

 READING 1.2 **WHAT SCIENTISTS DO**

See *Student Edition*, p. 5.

 ACTIVITY 1.2 **ASKING SCIENTIFIC QUESTIONS**

See *Student Edition*, p. 5.

ADVANCE PREPARATION

Conduct whatever prelab routine necessary to familiarize students with the layout and expectations of your classroom.

Note: Some of the test tubes should contain clear water. Others should have colored water obtained by adding food coloring.

Students should complete steps 1–3 quickly. At step 4, students will probably make the *observation* that the word URANIUM inverts but the word DIOXIDE does not. They may develop *questions* such as:

❧ Why does only one word invert (flip over)?
❧ Are there other words that won't flip over?
❧ Is this event based on words or letters and their shapes?

In step 5, students need to develop a hypothesis, or preliminary explanation. For example: *Hypothesis*: This happening is based on the shapes of the letters.

In steps 6 and 7, students invent their own plan of attack. Students may test their hypothesis by printing out the alphabet in capital letters and noting those letters that are vertically symmetric: B, C, D, E, H, I, K, O, and X. They can then try new words to see if they invert. The following words are vertically symmetric (the list is not exhaustive):

EH	HOD	EKE	HICK	EX	EXODE
COOK	BED	CODE	ODE	BE	EBB
BODE	BIKE	COB	OX	DECK	HI
HOCK	BOOK	DOCK	HIKE	OH	KID
DIB	BOX	BIB	HIDE	HO	DIKE
DIE	HOE	DEED	HID	COO	OXIDE

Some students may develop a hypothesis about the color of the water. Have extra test tubes available to allow students to try different colors of water. Also, have colored pens or pencils on hand to allow them to test the color of the print. Other students may test whether only certain words exhibit inversion.

If their first explanation fails, have the students test other ideas. Discourage students from giving their answer to other groups. It is important for all groups to experience the struggle of discovery. If some students solve the problem quickly, have them see how many words they can write that don't invert.

During the postlab, ask how many students discovered the answer on the first try, the second, and so on. Point out that explanations do not always come easily.

In step 8, students may respond to the questions as follows:

8. a. Certain capital letters invert when viewed through the water-filled test tube.
   b. You can write out words with letters that don't invert and see that the words do not invert.

In step 9, encourage students to develop a representation that makes sense to them. This may be a difficult task for some. You can offer this diagram as an example, if needed. Or share the first part of it to get them started.

Observation → Question → Hypothesis (possible explanation) → Test Hypothesis → Search for Exceptions → Revise Hypothesis or State an Explanation

For step 10, students may think that this process seems useful in situations where observations are followed by questions and explanations that can be tested. In step 11, this process would not work in situations where you cannot test the explanation to verify an answer. For example, the Broncos are the best team to ever play football. Sounds good, but the statement can't be verified. That's what makes arguments about much of athletics so fun; you can't settle them.

ACTIVITY 1.3 MODELING THE WEATHERING PROCESS

See *Student Edition*, p. 6.

STRATEGIES AND PROCEDURES

In step 1, be sure students understand the question they are attempting to answer and what materials are available. Then share your expectations about obtaining equipment, wearing safety goggles, exhibiting appropriate lab behavior, and cleaning up. Also discuss lab partners, groups, and write-ups. Who does what is an important issue that is best handled clearly and early on.

For step 2, provide time for students to brainstorm alone or with the lab partner(s) about how they should proceed. After a few minutes, you may wish to discuss possibilities with the class before the students begin.

Step 3 may be time-consuming. Encourage students to state a specific hypothesis and then write a numbered list of steps outlining their proposed experiment.

Do not allow students to proceed until you have reviewed their plan. As you review their procedures, look for safety issues. Safety considerations for this lab include:

* Wear goggles as soon as materials are collected.
* Use hot mitts or other protection when handling hot water to reduce the possibility of burns.
* Don't eat the antacid tablets.

Steps 5–7 will probably take a *full* class period. Allow students the latitude to amend their procedures so they can complete a table for data collection.

In step 8, students make a graph. Let them create their graphs based on prior experience. As you discuss the three questions, however, raise these graphing issues:

* Graph paper (as opposed to simply sketching the graph).
* What variables to plot (and what a variable is), and which axes to place them on.
* What units to use.
* How to choose a scale for the graph.
* Labeling and naming the graph.
* Drawing the graph curve (connect the points or draw a smooth curve).
* How many points do you need?

Appendix 2 of the student textbook contains a summary of those issues. The discussion of graphing may take a big chunk of a class period, especially if you pool class data and plot that information to culminate your lesson. You will revisit graphing issues in Activity 1.9. You can use that activity to check on how much students learned from this activity.

Make sure students understand the concept of a hypothesis. The idea of scientific explanation is the focus of the next activity.

ACTIVITY 1.4 THE NATURE OF SCIENTIFIC EXPLANATION

See *Student Edition*, p. 7.

STRATEGIES AND PROCEDURES

This activity encourages students to make connections between what they *did* and what they are *understanding*. From Activity 1.2, students may develop a short explanation about the property of water-filled test tubes to invert letters. In step 2, they should be able to identify the observations that led to their explanation (question 2a). Their explanation should explain multiple observations of words or letters (question 2b), and in question 2c, they may be able to connect their explanation to a natural phenomenon about how water under these conditions can change our perception of images (refraction).

For step 3, students may respond as follows:

3. a. They observed a difference in the rate at which antacid tablets dissolve in water of different temperatures.
    b. Answers will vary depending on the specific lab students designed or if they compared their results with other lab groups.
    c. Chemical weathering.

READING 1.3 SCIENTIFIC EXPLANATIONS

See *Student Edition*, p. 8.

ACTIVITY 1.5 SORTING OUT THE QUESTIONS

See *Student Edition*, p. 9.

STRATEGIES AND PROCEDURES

Although fairly short, this activity helps students apply their understanding of different ways of knowing. In step 1, encourage students to write a wide range of questions. In step 2, they can label each question with an "S" for scientific, "R" for religious, and "P" for philosophical.

After they have labeled their own list, step 3 asks students to exchange lists with a partner. They should attempt to justify their coding. For the purpose of this course, the distinction is primarily between scientific questions and non-scientific questions. The distinction between religious questions and philosophical questions is sometimes difficult to make. In your discussions with students, emphasize that scientific questions are those that ask about *how* things happen and can be answered by observing or experimenting in the real world.

READING 1.4 THINKING IN A SCIENTIFIC MANNER

See *Student Edition*, p. 10.

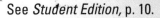

SAMPLE ANSWERS TO QUESTIONS

Dihydrogen Monoxide (DHMO):

1.& 2. Student opinions will vary. Encourage them to be thoughtful in their responses.
3. Students should go back through the bulletin and explain each statement using what they know about the properties of water.
4. Students should see that how something is presented can influence our view. That is, just because information is presented in a scientific format doesn't mean we should accept it without question. Political campaign literature and speeches are often filled with examples of using presentation to portray a particular perspective.

Summerlin Case:

1. There probably was a level of skepticism in the scientific community because other scientists had not been successful with similar experiments.
2. Possibly he wanted to be successful, be praised, get a promotion, or generate more money for his research.
3. The rewards for results are significant and cause some people to lose sight of what they know is the right thing. Students may agree that the pressure is similar because of the competition to get scholarships or receive parental approval. All people, not just scientists, are vulnerable to pressures.
4. Accept all responses that show depth of thought and specific examples or ideas.

Uncertainty in Science:

1. The admission of not knowing encourages others to contribute their ideas to the conversation.
2. Ideas may include: Is there life on Mars? How should cloning be pursued? Are human activities causing global warming? Can cures be developed for AIDS and cancer?

Openness to New Ideas:

The Blackline Master for this section shows how to connect all nine dots with four straight lines that all connect. It shows how to connect the dots with three connecting straight lines and with one line—if students are open to new and differing points of view. There may be other possibilities that are not shown on the Blackline Master. We recommend that you not show students the master right away; some will come up with these ideas if you encourage them. Their success will make the objective of this section even more powerful.

A book that can add more interest to this section is *Flatland: A Romance of Many Dimensions* by Edwin A. Abbott (1994, Harper Collins Publishers, ISBN 0-06-273276-6).

READING 1.5 Scientific Tools and Skills

See *Student Edition*, p. 14.

ACTIVITY 1.7 Quality and Quantity of Data

See *Student Edition*, p. 14.

STRATEGIES AND PROCEDURES

In step 1, be sure the person selected is not easily embarrassed by the collection of the six measurements outlined in step 2.

In step 3, discuss how accurately these data represent the class. To illustrate the inaccuracy of a small set of data, choose another student of the opposite gender and compare how well the representative data describe the second person.

Conduct steps 4 and 5 together as a class. Then let students work individually on step 6; they may respond as follows:

6. a. This data set is most likely more representative than the set based on one person; however, it still won't be very accurate.
   b. Answers may vary from data collected from everyone to data collected using some percentage of the class. Accept any response that students can reasonably justify.
   c. Students should make the distinction between measurable, exterior, superficial characteristics and the other traits that make a class what it is. The students in class have individual personalities, values, and ways of interacting that all contribute to the class personality. Those things are difficult to measure.

BLM 1.3, 1.4

Transparency 1.2

ACTIVITY 1.8 The Blind Men and the Elephant

See *Student Edition*, p. 15.

In step 2, students may respond as follows:

2. a. The blind men could represent any or all of the following:
   - scientists from different disciplines;
   - scientists, philosophers, and theologians;
   - individuals with different perspectives;
   - different people seeking information; or
   - any other response that students can justify.
   b. The elephant could represent any or all of the following:
   - a large and diverse set of data;
   - reality (the way things actually are);
   - truth;
   - an elephant; or
   - any other justifiable response.
   c. Each person obtained some accurate information about the elephant, but no one person had enough information to understand the complete set of data (picture).
   d. Like the blind men, scientists often attempt to describe things they have not observed directly. The pictures they draw are based on the information

available from observations and/or experiments. As the accuracy and amount of data (information) increases, the pictures (or models) change. Unlike the elephant, humans will never fully "see" an atom. But as technology changes, our models improve.

e. Encourage students to consider this question thoughtfully, rather than respond cynically. In general, science has a place in our lives and in school classrooms because it increases our understanding of the natural world. Hence, science provides the raw material for technological advances that often enhance our lives. Science also provides a form of enjoyment for amateur and professional scientists alike.

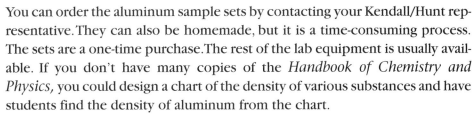

ACTIVITY 1.9 MEASURING ALUMINUM

 1.5

See *Student Edition,* p. 17.

You can order the aluminum sample sets by contacting your Kendall/Hunt representative. They can also be homemade, but it is a time-consuming process. The sets are a one-time purchase. The rest of the lab equipment is usually available. If you don't have many copies of the *Handbook of Chemistry and Physics,* you could design a chart of the density of various substances and have students find the density of aluminum from the chart.

Graph paper can be purchased at office supply stores, in the school supplies section at large drug and grocery stores (especially in the fall), at college bookstores, and from the large science equipment suppliers.

If you would like to have your students plot lab data using the computer, we recommend Graphical Analysis sold by Vernier Software, 8565 S.W. Beaverton-Hillsdale Hwy., Portland, OR 97225-2429, (503) 297-1760. It is available in both Mac and Windows. Students should plot their graphs on paper and understand this process completely before doing it on the computer. Appendix 2 on graphing is a good place to start.

SAMPLE ANSWERS TO ANALYSIS QUESTIONS

1. The mass *vs.* volume graph. The data allow a straight line to be drawn. The other two graphs consist of random points that indicate no meaningful relationship.
2. Density of aluminum = 2.7 g/mL.
3. Density = mass/volume.
4. Density of water = 1 g/mL.
5. Aluminum is more dense than water.
6. To float in water, the density must be less than 1 g/cm^3.
7. The graph is a straight line that passes through the origin of the graph.
8. Slope = approx. 2.7 g/mL.
9. The slope represents the density of aluminum.
10. Almost all groups obtained nearly the same value for the slope. Values were not exactly the same because of experimental errors.
11. *Interpolation* is no problem because if a sample were available that provided data between the points plotted, the new data point would also fall

on the graph line. *Extrapolation* is also permissible, without risk, because an aluminum sample more massive than any of those measured would have produced a point on the graph line if the line were extended upward. The same would also be true if a sample were provided that was less massive than any of those analyzed. It would have produced a point on the graph line that was extended down through the origin of the graph.

ACTIVITY 1.10 MEASUREMENT, MODERN LIFE, AND YOUR HOME

See *Student Edition,* p. 19.

1. As students look at the drawing, they should notice a variety of modern devices such as the clock, furnace, watt-hour meter, steel beams, and telephone. Encourage students to identify at least ten items related to the topic of measurement.

2. Students may respond as follows:
    a. length: the beams and boards were measured and cut by carpenters for a proper fit. The doors and door frames had to be measured and fitted carefully to prevent air leaks and to allow standard-size appliances to be moved in and out.
    b. time: the wall clock enables people to measure time accurately enough to coordinate their daily activities. The timer on the microwave helps the user to prepare good meals.
    c. temperature: the thermometer on the oven measures and displays the temperature inside the oven as meals are prepared. The thermometer on the patio fence informs those nearby of the current outdoor temperature.
    d. mass: the steel beams that support the floor above the basement were checked to determine what mass they can support. The bathroom scale can indicate the mass of the person who stands on it.
    e. electrical energy: the watt-hour meter measures the electrical energy used on location so the occupants of the home are billed properly. Electrical energy is changed to mechanical energy every time the phone rings. The average sound level of the ring was measured by the manufacturer so that it would not be too annoying to the occupants.

3. Assign this task as homework. This task encourages students to personalize their reliance on accurate measurements.

4. Locations should be similar to those students found in Figure 1.9.

5. Life would be much less sophisticated—possibly more like that of the 1940s and 50s. The cruder the measurements required, the more primitive the lifestyle. You may ask students how accurately tread wear is measured on tires, or how accurately the gap is measured on a sparkplug. Think of other examples.

SPECIAL FOCUS MEASUREMENT SYSTEMS

See *Student Edition,* p. 20.

1. 690 mm = 690 mm $\times$ 0.1 cm/mm = 69 cm
2. 7950 mL = 7950 mL $\times$ 1 L/1000 mL = 7.95 L
3. 38.2 kg = 38.2 kg $\times$ 1000 g/kg = 38,200 g
4. 465 mi = 465 mi $\times$ 1.6 km/mi = 744 km
5. 175 lb = 175 lb $\times$ 1 kg/2.2 lb = 79.5 kg
6. F = 9/5(21°) + 32 = 69.8°F
7. C = 5/9(180° − 32) = 82.2°C
8. 25 L = 25 L $\times$ 1.06 qt/L = 26.5 qt; 6.63 gal
9. 14 gal = 14 gal $\times$ 3.8 L/gal = 53.2 L
10. 120 hectare = 120 hectare $\times$ 2.5 acres/hectare = 300 acres
11. F = 9/5(37°) + 32 = 98.6°F = normal body temp. → a healthy person
12. F = 9/5(27°) + 32 = 98.6°F → a *hot* room
13. F = 9/5(100°) + 32 = 212°F = the *boiling point* of water at sea level. Yes.
14. 90 mi = 90 mi $\times$ 1.6 km/mi = 144 km
15. 2 L = 2 L $\times$ 1000 mL/L $\times$ 0.03 fl oz/mL = 60 fl oz
16. 24 in = 24 in $\times$ 2.5 cm/in $\times$ 1m/100 cm = 0.6 m

READING 1.6 USING THE RESULTS OF SCIENCE

See *Student Edition,* p. 23.

Read the first two paragraphs of this section to set up a discussion of the question on cloning. If there is another current scientific controversy in the news, substitute that issue in place of cloning.

After discussing the scientific issue, turn to the general question at the beginning of the third paragraph: "Should we try to restrict what scientists do or how certain ideas from science are applied?" Most people think there should be some restrictions, but there is great variation about how many and what kinds. If your students have difficulty engaging in this discussion, try posing these questions:

- What scientific projects would you consider to be unacceptable?
- What limits would you place on scientific research?
- How would you enforce those limits?

ACTIVITY 1.11 ENVIRONMENTAL SCIENCE: ITS HISTORY AND THOSE WHO BUILT IT

See *Student Edition,* p. 24.

The following are brief biographical sketches of each of the eleven people listed with this activity.

Rachel Carson (1907–1964). American marine biologist and science writer. She worked for many years with the U.S. Fish and Wildlife Service, during which time she began writing nature books for a general audience. *Under the Sea Wind* (1941), *The Sea Around Us* (1950), and *The Edge of the Sea* (1955) were all best sellers. She is best known for exposing the dangerous effects of widespread pesticide use in *Silent Spring* (1962), a book that sparked debate in Congress, stimulated a Presidential Advisory Committee, and still ranks as a classic in environmental history. An authoritative biography of Carson's life has recently been published: Linda Lear, *Rachel Carson: Witness for Nature* (New York: Henry Holt, 1995).

Paul and Anne Ehrlich (Paul b. 1932; Anne b. 1933). Husband and wife team of American evolutionary ecologists. Their early work focused on the growing negative impact on the environment caused by human population increases. In *The Population Bomb* (1968), they presented a bleak picture of the future. They considered countries with high birth rates no more to blame than countries like the United States, which has low birth rates but consumes natural resources and produces waste at much higher levels than less-developed countries. Although their most dire predictions have not come true, they continue to suggest that global warming, acid rain, ozone depletion, and other signs of environmental degradation mean that we may still face impending disaster. A useful article contrasting the Ehrlichs' work with that of one of their critics is David Berreby, "The Numbers Game," in *Discover Magazine*. (April 1990): 43–49.

Lois Gibbs (b. 1951). Activist at the Love Canal toxic waste site. She learned that her children's school was built on a site where 20,000 tons of hazardous chemicals had been dumped. Suspecting a connection with high rates of cancer, birth defects, miscarriages, and other health problems, she helped form a grass-roots organization to seek help for homeowners who wanted to move away from the area. After a two-and-a-half-year lobbying effort to the U.S. Congress, President Jimmy Carter stepped in and offered emergency aid to the residents of Love Canal. Gibbs went on to form the Citizens' Clearinghouse for Hazardous Waste, which would assist other communities to identify dump sites and seek help in cleaning them up or moving residents out. Gibbs has written an account of her efforts in *Love Canal: My Story* (New York: Grove, 1982). Another book on the episode is Adeline Levine, *Love Canal: Science Politics, and People* (New York: Lexington, 1982).

Aldo Leopold (1887–1948). American forester, game manager, and wildlife biologist. He began his career with the U.S. Forest Service in New Mexico. After identifying the need for a science of game management, he worked to apply principles of forestry and ecology to regulating wildlife populations, forging new principles in the process. He published countless essays throughout his life, including a series published the year after his death in *A Sand County Almanac* (1949). He increasingly emphasized preserving wilderness as the top goal in conservation. A definitive biography is available, (Curt Meine, *Aldo Leopold: His Life and Work*, Madison: University of Wisconsin, 1988), although a more accessible and excellent source is Marybeth Lorbiecki, *Aldo Leopold: A Fierce Green Fire* (Helena, Montana: Falcon, 1996). He is also discussed in Christian C. Young, *In the Absence of Predators: Conservation and Controversy on the Kaibab Plateau* (Lincoln: University of Nebraska, 2002).

James Lovelock (b. 1919). British chemist, biologist, and inventor. He proposed that the earth actually functions as a living organism, calling his idea the "Gaia hypothesis." The various living and non-living processes—including photosynthesis, respiration, volcanism, ocean currents, and air currents—respond to one another in the same way that an individual organism's systems interact and regulate temperature, pH, chemical balance, and the like. Based on his studies of the atmosphere of Mars, conducted for NASA's Jet Propulsion Laboratory, he concluded that life on Earth maintains the unique conditions that sustain life. His work is described in L.E. Joseph, *Gaia: The Growth of an Idea* (New York: St. Martin's, 1990), and in his own books: *Gaia: A New Look at Life on Earth* (Oxford: Oxford University, 1979), and *The Ages of Gaia: A Biography of our Living Earth* (New York: Norton, 1988).

Amory Lovins (b. 1947). American physicist and promoter of environmentally friendly energy sources. He founded the Rocky Mountain Institute in 1982 to promote the wise use of energy, water, and other resources. Some of his early writing promoted nuclear energy as a cleaner source of fuel. He later coined the term "soft path" to suggest that conserving energy, rather than producing more, is the key to solving the ongoing energy crisis. The primary aim of the Rocky Mountain Institute is to engineer appropriate technology for specific needs, in accordance with environmental and scientific principles. Studies based on these principles suggest that engineering for greater energy savings can offset the need for increased energy output from nonrenewable sources like oil and gas. His work includes *Soft Energy Paths* (San Francisco: Friends of the Earth, 1977), *Energy Unbound; Your Invitation to Energy Abundance* (San Francisco: Sierra Club, 1986) cowritten with his wife Hunter, and is described in H. Nash, ed., *The Energy Controversy: Amory B Lovins and His Critics* (San Francisco: Friends of the Earth, 1979).

George Perkins Marsh (1801–1882). American legal expert, entrepreneur, and diplomat. He wrote *Man and Nature* (1864), the first book-length critique of how human enterprise in the nineteenth century was having a large and rapid impact in America. Raised in New England, he also traveled extensively in Europe and saw that Americans could easily follow the destructive path of their European ancestors. In particular, his descriptions of how lumber operations depleted forests of their natural and economic value significantly influenced forest management in later decades. An introduction to *Man and Nature,* written by David Lowenthal (Belknap, 1965), provides an excellent overview of Marsh's life and work. Lowenthal has also written a complete biography, *George Perkins Marsh: Prophet of Conservation* (Seattle: University of Washington, 2000).

John Muir (1838–1914). American explorer, naturalist, and writer. He campaigned for the conservation of land, water, and forests in the United States. He helped establish Yosemite and Sequoia as national parks. He founded the Sierra Club in 1892, originally a hiking club and now a leading worldwide organization devoted to the promotion of conservation and environmental protection. Muir's life has been chronicled in many places, including Stephen Fox, *The American Conservation Movement: John Muir* *and His Legacy* (Madison: University of Wisconsin, 1981); Frederick Turner, *Rediscovering America: John Muir in His Time and Ours* (San Francisco: Sierra, 1985); and Steven J. Holmes, *Young John Muir: An Environmental Biography* (Madison: University of Wisconsin, 1999).

Eugene and Howard Odum (Eugene b. 1913; Howard b. 1924). Brothers and American ecologists. Together they helped define modern ecology. Eugene's textbook *Fundamentals of Ecology* (1953, 1959, 1971) became the standard for two generations of scientists. He emphasized the connections between communities as ecosystems. Recently, Eugene has compared life on Earth to the life support systems of the Apollo spacecraft in a book called *Ecology and Our Endangered Life-Support System* (1989). Howard focused on the flow of energy in ecosystems as the key to understanding those connections. He diagramed ecosystems much like electrical circuits. His most recent work, *Heavy Metals in the Environment: Using Wetlands for Their Removal* (2000), considers the ability of marshlands to clean up toxic heavy metals. An interesting account of Howard Odum's work is Peter Taylor, "Technocratic Optimism, H.T. Odum, and the Partial Transformation of Ecological Metaphor after World War II," in *Journal of the History of Biology,* 21:2 (summer 1988): 213-44. Eugene Odum's latest book is *Ecological Vignettes: Ecological Approaches to Dealing with Human Predicaments* (1998).

Theodore Roosevelt (1858–1919). Zoologist, U.S. president, hunter, and conservationist. He put conservation on the national agenda as part of the progressive reform policies of the early twentieth century. Under his administration, 150 million acres were added to the national forests. He also transferred administrative power over those forests by creating the Forest Service in the Department of Agriculture to replace the Division of Forestry in the Department of the Interior. The first chief of the new Forest Service, Gifford Pinchot, implemented a management policy of highest use for the forests. Roosevelt also established the first federal bird reservations and national game preserves, along with five new national parks. Roosevelt's conservation efforts are described in Paul Russell Cartwright, *Theodore Roosevelt: The Making of a Conservationist* (Urbana: University of Illinois, 1985).

Edward O. Wilson (b. 1929). American behavioral biologist, ecologist, and conservation biologist. He has contributed in several fields of biology, including island biogeography, sociobiology, and most recently, conservation biology. His recent books have called for an all-out reorientation of human attitudes toward nature that embraces the value of species diversity in a wide range of habitats. He has written an autobiography, *Naturalist* (Washington DC: Island, 1994), and his work includes *Biophilia* (Cambridge: Harvard University, 1984); *The Diversity of Life* (Cambridge: Harvard University, 1992); and *The Future of Life* (New York: Alfred A. Knopf, 2002), which focuses on endangered species, nature conservation, and environmental degradation.

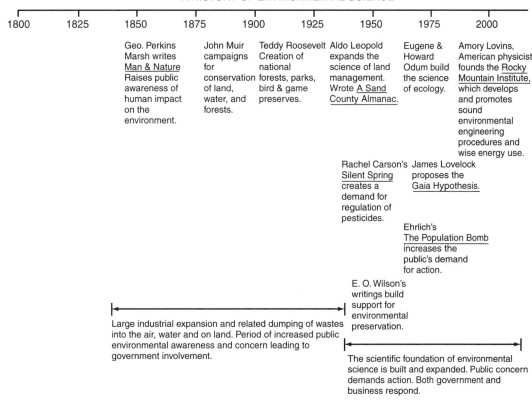

1800   1825   1850   1875   1900   1925   1950   1975   2000

Geo. Perkins Marsh writes <u>Man & Nature</u> Raises public awareness of human impact on the environment.

John Muir campaigns for conservation of land, water, and forests.

Teddy Roosevelt Creation of national forests, parks, bird & game preserves.

Aldo Leopold expands the science of land management. Wrote <u>A Sand County Almanac.</u>

Eugene & Howard Odum build the science of ecology.

Amory Lovins, American physicist founds the <u>Rocky Mountain Institute,</u> which develops and promotes sound environmental engineering procedures and wise energy use.

Rachel Carson's <u>Silent Spring</u> creates a demand for regulation of pesticides.

James Lovelock proposes the <u>Gaia Hypothesis.</u>

Ehrlich's <u>The Population Bomb</u> increases the public's demand for action.

E. O. Wilson's writings build support for environmental preservation.

Large industrial expansion and related dumping of wastes into the air, water and on land. Period of increased public environmental awareness and concern leading to government involvement.

The scientific foundation of environmental science is built and expanded. Public concern demands action. Both government and business respond.

SAMPLE ANSWERS TO QUESTIONS

1. All of the scientific specialties are included.
2. Public concern over environmental degradation lead to the development of a scientific response to the problem. The degree of the problem needed to be accurately measured and documented. Ways to eliminate or reduce the problems were developed. These strategies require input from all of the sciences including economic analysis.
3. Student answers will vary, but will center on efforts to rigorize environmental analysis as well as computer analysis (GIS) and technological developments (catalytic convertors, fuel cells).

CHAPTER 1 SUMMARY

See *Student Edition*, p. 25

UNDERSTANDING THE NATURE OF SCIENCE: THE RELATIONSHIPS AMONG FACTS, HYPOTHESES, LAWS, AND THEORIES

> "... those sciences are vain and full of errors which are not born from experiment, the mother of all certainty ..."
>
> Leonardo da Vinci, 1452–1519

WHAT IS THE WORK OF SCIENCE?

Determining how the natural world works is the domain of science. Students should understand that science is a way of knowing.[1] As a form of human endeavor, the *process* of science is characterized by the systematic gathering of information (data) via direct and indirect observations and the subjection of patterns inherent in those data to empirical (experimental) testing. It is assumed that the natural world follows discernable rules and that there is predictability. Further, the scientific process is cyclic; it involves the persistent refinement and revision of our understanding of nature through continual questioning and active investigation. To formulate laws and theories is the primary goal of the process of science.

The primary *product* of science is a body of knowledge—one that is growing by leaps and bounds as even casual science students have observed by note of the increasing mass of their science textbooks! The scientific knowledge base includes naturalistic concepts, principles and laws, and, of course, theories. Precluded from the knowledge base are the constructs of the supernatural and the occult, pseudoscience, dogma, and beliefs related to religion and philosophy. Scientific knowledge is in a state of constant flux because scientific understanding can always be challenged and changed, if necessary, by the availability of new data and different interpretation.

THE ROMAN ARCH MODEL OF SCIENCE

Learning much of their engineering capabilities from the Etruscans, the Romans applied their knowledge of the keystone or voussoir (voo'- swar: brick) arch to build extremely strong and enduring bridges and aqueducts. Figure 1.1 is a sketch of a typical bridge designed for pedestrian and chariot traffic. The secret of the arch's strength lies in the redistribution of forces through the semicircular structure. The weight from above is directed outward and downward through stone piers into a concrete foundation. In fact, the greater the load, the more compressed the voussoirs become, rendering the arch an extremely strong component that allowed army legions and loaded carts to cross without collapsing the bridge. The structures were so durable, having survived the ravages of time and erosion, that several of the original Roman arch bridges actually lasted through the Middle Ages into modern times. Thus, the Roman arch provides us with an appropriate model of the work of science that can assist your students in distinguishing among the various components that reflect the very nature of the scientific process: theories, laws and principles, hypotheses, facts, and observations (data).

Like spectacular Roman arches, the semicircular structures made usually of stone that span openings and support weight from above or the sides, the theories of science stand

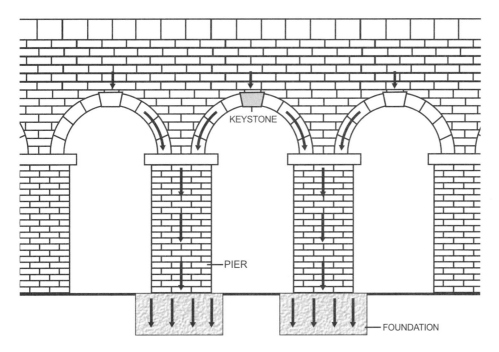

FIGURE 1.1 An arcade of Roman arches. The weight of the stone and concrete of the bridge itself compressed the tapered stones together, making the arch an extremely strong structure. The keystone voussoir (center, top of arch) directs the load sideways and downward through the piers and into the foundation.

over and encompass a vast body of natural information. Overarching an extensive body of observations, empirical data, and facts, scientific theories overshadow all that is science. Theories *explain and unify,* combining facts with creative reflection, skepticism, and logical inferences. Theories are the end-points of science;[2,3] they are the goals to which scientists strive.

Supporting the arch are the piers, which provide strength and solid foundations to anchor the structure. Like the piers, laws and principles, as well as models and hypotheses that have passed the validity test via observation and experiment, provide support for the theory that overshadows and encompasses them. Laws and principles *describe* relationships, patterns, rules, regularities, and generalizations that have proven to be invariant under the same conditions. Tested hypotheses, like theories and models, have the ability to lead to testable deductions that, if verified, can result in additional insight. Hypotheses and models *predict.* Of course, no amount of experimentation will prove the validity of laws, models, and hypotheses absolutely; however, they represent the best support currently known.

As time progresses, our scientific arch increases in height and strength. Its width reflects the breadth and diversity of the body of knowledge it currently encompasses, while its height is a measure of the level of scientific confidence it embraces. The Heliocentric Theory, the Cell Theory, the Kinetic Molecular Theory, and the Theory of Evolution are examples of powerful theories that have stood the test of time and, consequently, inspire the utmost confidence. These scientific theories are so well substantiated by an abundance of observational and empirical evidence that their validity is no longer questioned in science.

To minimize linguistic confusion, we offer the following definitions fully cognizant that popular and casual usages have blurred the lines of distinction. Definitions are presented in ascending order of scientific confidence in Table 1 which follows.

TABLE 1 NATURE OF SCIENCE: A GLOSSARY OF TERMS

Beliefs:	Ideas, accepted as true, based on religious faith, authority or dogma, trust, pseudoscience, or philosophy. They are concepts that cannot be subjected to empirical testing and, consequently, possible refutation. Their acceptance requires no proof; consequently, they are not included as part of the scientific process.
Observations:	Qualitative or quantitative information collected via our senses, possibly with the aid of scientific instruments designed to "hone" our senses. They can never be trusted entirely.
Facts:	Observations that have been confirmed repeatedly. The word is used infrequently in science; often, "facts" and "observations" are referred to as "data." Although facts can be strongly supported "conclusions," they occupy the third tier from the bottom in our model; hence, facts represent a low level of scientific confidence. Nevertheless, they serve as a data base from which inferences can be drawn.
Patterns:	Logical inferences drawn from a substantial data base. Patterns (also referred to as rules, regularities, or generalizations) may emerge from a data base when scientists reflect creatively on facts, usually with a healthy dose of skepticism. They generally arise through a process of inductive reasoning, and are *considered valid within the bounds defined by the experiments* that led to them. Patterns may support tested hypotheses and models; they may suggest new hypotheses to test or refinements of the model. If repeatedly confirmed, patterns can eventually become laws or principles.
Hypotheses:	Tentative, albeit testable, statements about the natural world. Hypotheses represent an early level of understanding, yet they extend thinking beyond the factual and inference levels. They are usually written in "if-then" format, thus implying a cause/effect relationship that has been framed as a testable prediction. Hypotheses are explanations on trial: if they are judged valid, they can be used to build more complex inferences, which must also stand trial before being accepted. Further, a hypothesis that has *not* been proved true is considered to be *probably* true until and unless evidence to the contrary is found. In fact, a scientific hypothesis must imply a "test" for proving it *wrong*. If there is no test for its "wrongness," it is not a scientific hypothesis; it is pure speculation.[4] Hypotheses that do not pass validity testing are modified (and retested) or rejected.
Laws:	Declarative statements of what always happens under certain conditions. Although laws (principles) are based on patterns and facts, they may be altered with new data; yet no amount of experimentation can prove them absolutely. They support theories and hypotheses[5] and, in turn, are supported by extensive validating evidence and logical arguments. Laws can be described via paragraph or equation.
Models:	Deliberately simplified constructs of nature. Models can be pictorial, computer, laboratory, mental, or working models. They may be conceptual or mathematical in nature. Like theories, models demonstrate and explain (but at a less abstract level) and may have to be modified or replaced as new knowledge emerges. Those that provide broad, fundamental explanations of many facts, tested hypotheses, patterns, and laws can be "promoted" to the highest status of theory.
Theories:	Offer overarching, unifying explanations developed from extensive observation, experimentation, and creative reflection. Theories are well-supported, time-tested, and substantiated by facts, tested hypotheses, models, laws, and principles. Continually subjected to skepticism, testing, modification, and possible refutation, theories must be capable of organizing a broad range of natural phenomena. They incorporate and encompass scientific facts, logical inferences, tested hypotheses, and laws, and they have predictive capabilities. In fact, the ultimate test of a theory is how well its predictions fare. Theories do not become laws (they explain laws), nor do they turn into facts via the accumulation of more evidence. Supported by a base of overwhelming evidence that makes their abandonment extremely improbable, they are, rather, truly the pinnacles of science—science's greatest achievements!

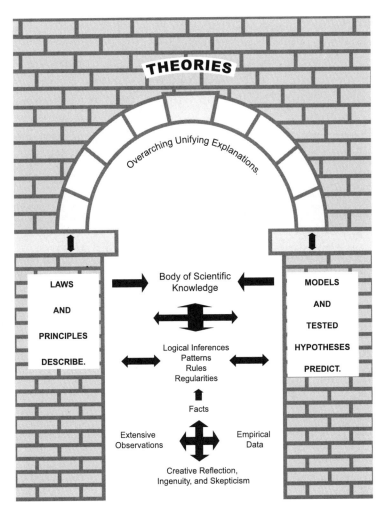

FIGURE 1.2. The Roman Arch Model of Science. Scientific confidence increases as one moves upward from ground level to theories—the ultimate achievements of science.

THE MODEL AS APPLIED TO THE KINETIC MOLECULAR THEORY OF MATTER

The Kinetic Molecular Theory of Matter (KMT) is not likely to be abandoned because it *explains and links* the laws[6] and principles, inferences, tested hypotheses, facts, and observed phenomena and, thus, embraces a high degree of scientific confidence. That is not to say the KMT is infallible. There is a possibility, albeit a very remote one, that it will have to be modified or even completely discarded in light of future empirical evidence. Said in another way, the KMT is supported and validated by the laws and principles, inferences, tested hypotheses, facts, and observations that lend strength to the piers of the arch and the foundation into which they are grounded.

ENTER MISUNDERSTANDINGS AND MISCOMMUNICATIONS

Given that beginning science students have limited backgrounds and understandings of science, they can become mired quickly in a morass of terms used to describe the nature of the scientific process. Adding further to student confusion and misunderstanding are the quite different connotations of scientific terms popular in common usage today, as well as careless usage of those same terms by science teachers and members of the scientific community themselves.

Misunderstandings arise when certain terms are used in casual conversation. For example, when someone says, "I have a theory that there will be a pop quiz today in science," or when another comments, "Yes, but evolution's only a theory," each is implying nothing more than a hunch, a notion, an assumption, an idea, or a guess. Unfortunately, in casual usage the word "theory" connotes a minimally supported speculation. Its confidence level may be tantamount to that of a belief. Sometimes even scientists lack linguistic precision, using "theory" loosely by applying the word to tentative explanations that lack well-established evidence (i.e., to untested hypotheses). Yet, theories are the ultimate achievements of science.

Similarly, the word "fact" is used in quite a different context in everyday language. "It's a fact, not a theory," someone might say, implying that facts are the ultimate truths and that theories lack supporting evidence. To most, "facts" are indisputable claims or ideas. Recall that "facts," however, occupy a niche in the scientific hierarchy that mirrors a low level of scientific confidence, just the opposite of the word's connotation in casual usage. No wonder students (and others) seem confused!

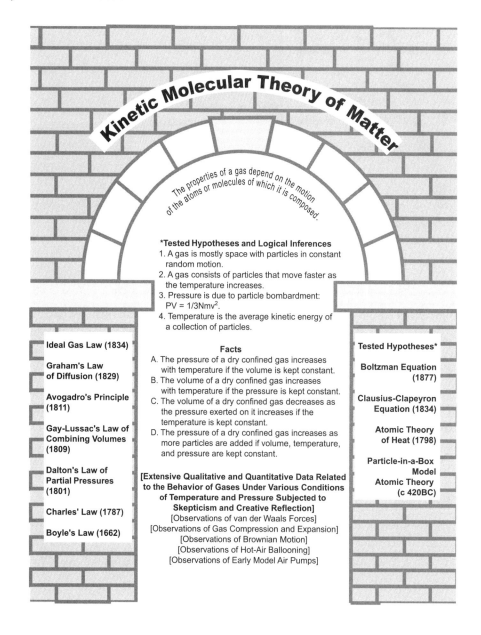

Kinetic Molecular Theory of Matter

The properties of a gas depend on the motion of the atoms or molecules of which it is composed.

*Tested Hypotheses and Logical Inferences
1. A gas is mostly space with particles in constant random motion.
2. A gas consists of particles that move faster as the temperature increases.
3. Pressure is due to particle bombardment: $PV = 1/3Nmv^2$.
4. Temperature is the average kinetic energy of a collection of particles.

Facts
A. The pressure of a dry confined gas increases with temperature if the volume is kept constant.
B. The volume of a dry confined gas increases with temperature if the pressure is kept constant.
C. The volume of a dry confined gas decreases as the pressure exerted on it increases if the temperature is kept constant.
D. The pressure of a dry confined gas increases as more particles are added if volume, temperature, and pressure are kept constant.

[Extensive Qualitative and Quantitative Data Related to the Behavior of Gases Under Various Conditions of Temperature and Pressure Subjected to Skepticism and Creative Reflection]
[Observations of van der Waals Forces]
[Observations of Gas Compression and Expansion]
[Observations of Brownian Motion]
[Observations of Hot-Air Ballooning]
[Observations of Early Model Air Pumps]

Ideal Gas Law (1834)

Graham's Law of Diffusion (1829)

Avogadro's Principle (1811)

Gay-Lussac's Law of Combining Volumes (1809)

Dalton's Law of Partial Pressures (1801)

Charles' Law (1787)

Boyle's Law (1662)

Tested Hypotheses*

Boltzman Equation (1877)

Clausius-Clapeyron Equation (1834)

Atomic Theory of Heat (1798)

Particle-in-a-Box Model Atomic Theory (c 420BC)

[1]There are other ways of knowing but they are not science-based if they do not include the empirical testing of falsifiable hypotheses. In other words, a hypothesis must be capable of being proven false. Unless the hypothesis is verified by experiment, it must be modified or rejected.

[2]National Academy of Sciences. 1998. *Teaching About Evolution and the Nature of Science.* National Academy Press, p. 6.

[3]Berra, Tim M. *Evolution and the Myth of Creationism.* 1990. Stanford University Press, p. 4.

[4]Hewitt, Paul G. 2002. *Conceptual Physics.* New Jersey: Prentice Hall, p. 4.

[5]Sometimes laws can be derived from theories (e.g., Kepler's Laws of Planetary Motion were derived from Newton's theory of universal gravitation).

[6]The laws/principles listed as the left supporting pillar of the KMT arch are, in reverse chronological order:

The Ideal Gas Law: This equation of the state of an ideal gas can be derived *from* the KMT and has been *validated* via experiment: $PV = nRT$, where P is pressure, V is volume, n is the number of moles of gas, R is the universal gas constant, and T is the absolute temperature.

Graham's Law of Diffusion: The rate of diffusion of a gas is inversely proportional to the square root of its molecular weight.

Avogadro's Principle (Law)[‡]. Equal volumes of gases at the same temperature and pressure contain equal numbers of molecules.

Gay-Lussac's Law of Combining Volumes: At a given temperature and pressure, gases combine in simple proportions by volume, and the volume of any gaseous product bears a whole number ratio to that of any gaseous reactant.

Dalton's Law of Partial Pressures: The total pressure exerted by a mixture of gases is equal to the sum of the partial pressures of the various gases.

Charles' Law: At constant pressure, the volume occupied by a fixed weight of gas is directly proportional to the absolute temperature.

Boyle's Law: At constant temperature, the volume occupied by a fixed weight of gas is inversely proportional to the pressure exerted on it.

[‡]Formerly known as Avogadro's Hypothesis. Note how this principle extends Gay-Lussac's Law to the molecular level.

REFERENCES

Academic Press. 1992. *Dictionary of Science and Technology.*

American Association for the Advancement of Science (AAAS). 1990. The Nature of Science. Chap. 1 in *Science for All Americans: Project 2061.* Oxford: Oxford University Press, pp. 1–12.

Berra, Tim M. 1990. *Evolution and the Myth of Creationism.* Stanford University Press,

Chemical Education Material Study (CHEM Study). *Chemistry–An Experimental Science.* 1963. San Francisco: Freeman & Company, pp. 1–37.

Hewitt, Paul G. 2002. *Conceptual Physics.* New Jersey: Prentice Hall, p. 4.

National Academy of Sciences. 1998. *Teaching About Evolution and the Nature of Science,* National Academy Press.

National Science Teachers Association. 2000. *NSTA Reports.* "NSTA Position Statement: The Nature of Science," May–June, p. 15.

Sienko, Mitchell J., and Robert A. Plane. 1961. Gases. Chap 6 in *Chemistry.* 2nd Ed. New York: McGraw-Hill, pp. 127–160.

State Board of Education. "Policy on the Teaching of Natural Sciences," *California,* January 13, 1989, p. xi.

Trefil, James. 2003. *The Nature of Science,* New York: Houghton Mifflin.

Name_____ Date_____

MULTIPLE CHOICE

1. _____ Science begins with
   A. answers to questions about the natural world.
   B. measurements of various quantities.
   C. observations and questions about those observations.
   D. explanations of things that happen around us.

2. _____ Which one of the following is *not* a scientific question?
   A. What is the effect of temperature on the process of chemical weathering?
   B. Which is more dense, copper or zinc?
   C. Why do some trees lose their leaves in the winter?
   D. What is the purpose of human life?
   E. Why do the lights go on when I push the *on* button?

3. _____ All of the following are behaviors and attitudes of good scientists *except*
   A. honesty.
   B. open to new ideas.
   C. acceptance of uncertainty.
   D. skepticism.
   E. intolerance.

4. _____ In the fable *The Blind Men and the Elephant,* the blind men could represent
   A. scientists from different disciplines (like biology, chemistry, and physics).
   B. scientists, philosophers, and religious people all seeking information.
   C. different people all seeking information on a subject.
   D. all of the above.

   This graph is a plot of mass *vs.* volume for five samples of copper. The line was drawn after the five points were plotted. The letters A, B, C, D, and E were added to the graph to represent different locations on the graph.

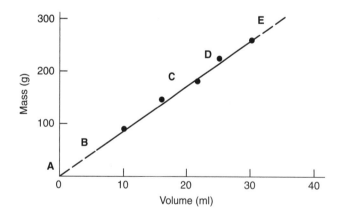

5. _____ Which letter is nearest a point that was actually plotted on the graph?

6. _____ Which letter is in the region representing the *extrapolation* of the graph to obtain information on samples smaller than those analyzed in the experiment?

7. _____ Which letter is nearest a point that can be used to *interpolate* information about copper samples?

8. _____ From the graph, one can determine that the density of copper is approximately
A. 4.5 g/mL.
B. 90 g/mL.
C. 32 g/mL.
D. 61 g/mL.
E. 8.9 g/mL.

9. _____ A scientific investigation includes a hypothesis because
A. a hypothesis is an explanation you can test.
B. it is a tradition to have one.
C. it is fact not fiction.
D. you then don't have to do the experiment.
E. it is required by your teacher.

10. _____ When doing an experiment, which *one* of the following is *not* important?
A. Honesty, data collection, and a scientific question.
B. Creativity, honesty, and observation.
C. Questioning, information gathering, and accurate measurements.
D. Uncertainty, skepticism, and openness to new ideas.
E. Partial answers, quickness, and finishing early.

MULTIPLES AND PREFIXES

These Prefixes May be Applied to All SI Units*

Multiples and Submultiples		Prefixes	Symbols
1 000.000 000 000 000 000 000 000	=	10^{24} yotta	Y
1 000 000 000 000 000 000 000	=	10^{21} zetta	Z
1 000 000 000 000 000 000	=	10^{18} exa	E
1 000 000 000 000 000	=	10^{15} peta	P
1 000 000 000 000	=	10^{12} tera	T
1 000 000 000	=	10^{9} giga	G
1 000 000	=	10^{6} mega	M
1 000	=	10^{3} kilo	k
100	=	10^{2} hecto	h
10	=	10^{1} deka	da
1	=	10^{0}	
0.1	=	10^{-1} deci	d
0.01	=	10^{-2} centi	c
0.001	=	10^{-3} milli	m
0.000 001	=	10^{-6} micro	μ
0.000 000 001	=	10^{-9} nano	n
0.000 000 000 001	=	10^{-12} pico	p
0.000 000 000 000 001	=	10^{-15} femto	f
0.000 000 000 000 000 001	=	10^{-18} atto	a
0.000 000 000 000 000 000 001	=	10^{-21} zepto	z
0.000 000 000 000 000 000 000 001	=	10^{-24} yocto	y

*apply to gram in case of mass

COMMON CONVERSIONS (APPROXIMATE CONVERSIONS)

Symbol	When You Know	Multiply By	To Find	Symbol
		Length		
in	inches	2.5	centimeters	cm
ft	feet	30	centimeters	cm
yd	yards	0.9	meters	m
mi	miles	1.6	kilometers	km
mm	millimeters	0.04	inches	in
cm	centimeters	0.4	Inches	in
m	meters	3.3	feet	ft
m	meters	1.1	yards	yd
km	kilometers	0.6	miles	ml
		Mass (Weight)		
oz	ounces	28	grams	g
lb	pounds	0.45	kilograms	kg
g	grams	0.035	ounces	oz
kg	kilograms	2.2	pounds	lb
		Volume		
fl oz	fluid ounces	30	milliliters	mL
qt	quarts	0.95	liters	L
gal	gallons	3.8	liters	L
mL	milliliters	0.03	fluid ounces	fl oz
L	liters	1.06	quarts	qt
L	liters	0.26	gallons	gal
		Temperature		
°F	degrees Fahrenheit	{ subtract 32, then multiply by 5/9 }	degrees Celsius	°C
°C	degrees Celsius	{ multiply by 9/5 and add 32 }	degrees Fahrenheit	°F

NOTE: Most symbols are written with lower case letters; exceptions are L for liter and units named after persons for which the symbols are capitalized. Periods are not used with any symbols.

SHORT ANSWER

11. Convert 2.8 meters to centimeters. SHOW YOUR WORK!

12. Five (5) gallons of gasoline is how many liters? SHOW YOUR WORK!

13. If science cannot provide a perfect picture of the natural world, why have science?

_____

_____

_____

_____

_____

_____

14. Write a scientific question and explain why it is scientific.

_____

_____

_____

_____

_____

_____

_____

15. As a modern society, should we try to restrict what scientists do or how certain ideas from science are applied? Justify your answer.

_____

_____

_____

_____

_____

_____

_____

CHAPTER 1 ASSESSMENT

1. C
2. D
3. E
4. D
5. D
6. B
7. C
8. E
9. A
10. E
11. 2.8 m = 2.8 m × 100 cm/m = 280 cm.
12. 5 gal = 5 gal × 3.8 L/gal = 19 L.
13. Science enables us to do all kinds of things even though our picture is not perfect. Modern societies find science and technology useful and desirable.
14. Student answers will vary. A scientific question can be tested by making observations, gathering data under controlled conditions, and openly interpreting and debating the data and related inferences.
15. Student answers will vary. Grade on depth of thought and clarity of the justification.

CHAPTER

2

A GRAND OASIS IN SPACE

LEARNING OUTCOMES

The student will:

1. identify key features of Earth that allow life to survive on this planet. (C)
2. explain why those key features are unique to Earth. (C)
3. select and evaluate six important items needed for survival on a trip to Mars by reading and discussing the activity "A Voyage to Mars." (C,A)
4. design and conduct a controlled experiment. (C,P)
5. recognize and describe some ecosystems and their biotic and abiotic components. (C,A)
6. suggest associations among the living and nonliving things in an ecosystem. (C)
7. observe a photo of Earth surrounded by space and explain its uniqueness. (C,A)
8. realize that the amount of space available for life on Earth is small and finite. (A)

9. realize that the limited resources of Earth's crust and atmosphere can support a huge quantity and diversity of life. (A)
10. describe the process of ecological succession and explain how understanding it can be useful. (C,A)
11. become aware of the basic needs of humans. (C,A)
12. become aware of the social requirements of human survival. (C,A)
13. identify personal basic needs and additional wants in the human quest for the "good life" by completing the activity "Our Quest for the 'Good Life'." (A)
14. realize that to live the "good life" various energy and mineral resources are required. (A)

KEY TERMS

Earth	lithosphere	biosphere	heat capacity	soil nutrients
crust	atmosphere	solid	control	environment
mantle	hydrosphere	liquid	controlled experiment	ecosystem
core	ecosphere	gas	surface tension	habitat

niche	levels of organization	oragan system	tundra	ecological succession
photosynthesis	atom	organism	coniferous	primary succession
oxygen	molecule	species	decidous	secondary succession
respiration	protoplasm	population	marine	
producer	cell	community	aquatic	
consumer	tissue	biome	estuary	
carbon dioxide	organ	terrestrial	succession	

RECOMMENDED BLACKLINE MASTERS

2.1 Mars Lab—Important Items (15 Groups Summarized)
2.2 Ecosystem Dynamics
2.3 Earth's Solar Budget
2.4 Interaction between Photosynthesis and Respiration
2.5 Investigating Ecosystems—The Indicator
2.6 Investigating Ecosystems—Experimental Design
2.7 Investigating Ecosystems—Summary of Findings

The Recommended Blackline Masters listed above are supplemental to the activity/reading and can be found on the *Teacher Resource CD*. Blackline Masters 2.8-2.11 are essential to teaching the activity/reading, and so are included in the *Teacher Guide* (pp. 44-47) as well as on the *Teacher Resource CD*.

ACTIVITIES FLOW CHART

CHAPTER 2: A GRAND OASIS IN SPACE (THE NEEDS OF LIVING THINGS)

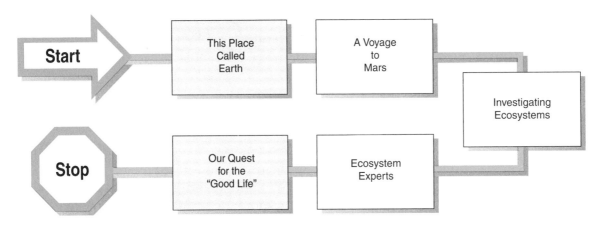

NOTE: Shaded items are lower priority.

TEACHING STRATEGIES AND ANSWERS FOR ACTIVITIES

CHAPTER OPENER, See *Student Edition*, p. 27.

Ask students to look at the photograph of Earth that opens this chapter and imagine that they are in a spacecraft looking at Earth. Ask them what they think Earth looks like from that perspective. If your students are familiar with metaphors, ask them to think of a metaphor for Earth.

Read astronaut Lovell's statement aloud in a dramatic voice. Ask the students to identify the metaphor that Lovell used. (Earth is a grand oasis.) Discuss the quotation by asking the students such questions as:

* Do they like this metaphor? Why or why not?
* Do they think it is appropriate? Why or why not?
* What do they think Lovell meant by "a grand oasis"?

READING OUR UNIQUE PLANET

See *Student Edition*, p. 28.

This introductory reading provides a context for the science content in *Global Science*. This course emphasizes the relationship between humans and the use of Earth's resources. You may want to spend some time discussing this key idea. Ask students what content they think they may learn more about as they proceed through the program. These ideas may help you identify special areas of interest or concern for your students.

ACTIVITY 2.1 THIS PLACE CALLED EARTH

 2.8

See *Student Edition*, p. 28.

ADVANCE PREPARATION

Collect materials for the stations. Make or buy ice cubes and arrange access to a freezer.

STRATEGIES AND PROCEDURES

This activity will take several class periods because of the lab stations included in Part B. As you set up the stations, think about whether you will need duplicate stations to keep students in smaller groups. Encourage student exploration at the stations. This activity helps students explore their understanding of the features of Earth.

SAMPLE ANSWERS TO STATION QUESTIONS

Station 1
1. Student ideas may include comparisons such as
   * the crust is thinner than the other layers;
   * scientists know much more about the crust; and
   * we can see the crust.
2. Responses include logical connections between the need for oxygen and water by all living organisms (plants and animals); the essential role of minerals (solid materials) for life processes; the use of solid materials to create shelter for many animals; and the protection from UV rays afforded us by the atmosphere.
3. Responses may overlap with those to question 2. Students should understand that humans need air (oxygen, in particular) for respiration, water to stay hydrated, and solid materials for food and shelter.

Station 2

1. Use this question to prompt the students to use the math skill of estimating. If their estimates and calculations are very different, ask students to review their estimates. **Note:** The oceans cover about 70% of the earth's surface.
2. Accept thoughtful responses.
3. This response will help you identify students' prior knowledge about other planets. One of the unique characteristics of Earth is the high percentage of water in the atmosphere compared to other substances.
4. Students should understand that water is essential for the hydration of humans and other living organisms. Therefore, the greater percentage of water on Earth makes it relatively easy for us to stay alive.

Station 3

1. Accept thoughtful responses. Remind students that being "right" before an experiment is not the goal. Instead they should focus on what they predicted and how that compared to the actual results. Sometimes people are so sure of their predictions, they are unable to collect reasonable data and make valid conclusions.
2. This question provides an opportunity for students to recognize the use of their prior knowledge in this science class. A variety of life experiences may have informed students as they made their predictions, including having lived in a northern climate, working on a car with radiator problems, or having the pipes freeze in a house.
3. Water expands when it freezes, and as a solid it floats on top of the liquid.
4. Ice is the only substance in the world that expands when it freezes. This is inconvenient to a car owner whose radiator freezes and cracks. However, if water did not expand when it freezes, ice would not float on water, and the world would become a gigantic ice ball. Lakes would freeze from the bottom up, and icebergs would sink to the bottom of oceans where they could not melt. Each winter would add more layers of ice until even the oceans would freeze.

Station 4

1. Water holds heat better than other substances. As a result, it warms up slowly and cools down slowly compared to other surfaces.
2. This question asks students to apply the concept of heat capacity. They should recognize that the desert changes temperatures dramatically because dry sand does not hold heat the way a large body of water does.

Station 5

This activity demonstrates the ability of water molecules to stick together.

Station 6

1. Students may note that Earth is close to the sun, or they may respond from the perspective of where Earth and the sun are located in the galaxy or universe.

2. Students may respond specifically by saying, for example, Earth is the third planet from the sun or Earth is between Venus and Mars. Or the students may respond in general by saying it is close to the Sun.

3. Hopefully students will realize they have only partially answered the question because the answer varies greatly based on the relative position from which one is responding.

4. Earth's distance from the sun is thought to be critical for the survival of living organisms. It allows for a moderate temperature range and the formation of an atmosphere that is protective but not too thick. There are other characteristics that support these ideas such as the amount of gravitational force and the rotation of Earth. These features in combination with our distance from the sun result in a livable environment.

SPECIAL FOCUS SCIENTIFIC EXPLANATIONS CHANGE OVER TIME

See *Student Edition,* p. 38.

This short reading highlights a key feature of the nature of science: explanations change over time. Sometimes people think that because a scientific explanation changes it was wrong and that they should not pay attention to scientific explanations. It is rare for scientists to discard an explanation completely. It is quite common for scientists to refine and revise their explanations based on new information or evidence.

Reviewing historical information can provide numerous examples of how scientific explanations have changed over time. Many of these changes are attributed to the invention and use of a new tool or the development of a completely new way of thinking about an idea. The example in this reading connects to the students' work at Station 1 when they examined the composition of Earth.

Assign this reading as homework or as class reading for students who have finished their station work early. After everyone has read the feature, ask students to think about the questions posed at the end. Conduct a class discussion focused on students' observations about how the illustrations differ and about the implications for understanding scientific explanations.

SAMPLE ANSWERS TO QUESTIONS

1. Students should identify changes such as a greater number of layers, the solid nature of the materials, and the water inside the earth in Descartes's drawing. The 1974 drawing is much more similar to our current models; the inner layers are the more dense materials, and there are fewer layers than shown in Descartes's drawing.

2. Students will probably not have much knowledge about the tools that were available to collect data at the time each illustration was developed. But after completing the reading, they should be able to comment in general about the increased sophistication of the data collected from earthquakes that has helped scientists determine the relative density of Earth's layers as well as the depth of each layer.

3. The most obvious difference is the addition of transition zones. The idea of distinct layers fell out of favor as scientists discovered evidence that the

layers of Earth were not distinctly separate, but rather had zones comprised of the minerals from the layer above and the layer below.

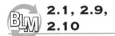
2.1, 2.9, 2.10

ACTIVITY 2.2 A Voyage to Mars

See *Student Edition*, p. 41.

ADVANCE PREPARATION

Make one copy per student of Figure 2.15 "Confidential Classified Government Document" (optional) and Blackline Master 2.9 "Earth-Mars Data." Make three copies per student of Blackline Master 2.10 "Judging Sheet."

STRATEGIES AND PROCEDURES

You can tailor this activity to be as simple or complex as you or your students wish. The information included in the student textbook and on the Blackline Masters will provide sufficient background to complete the activity. The websites listed in the student textbook provide a starting place for those who want additional information to complete the activity.

Organize the students into groups of three, which will facilitate a high-quality discussion among the students. We recommend groups of three because groups of two may not have enough breadth of response to foster lively discussions.

Give students a copy of one of the judging sheets before they begin planning their posters or oral presentations. Discuss your expectations of their work.

The five key items (components of an ecosystem) are water, air mixture, variety of food, soil nutrients, and decomposers. On Mars, these will need to be contained within a shelter. The sun will provide the energy for photosynthesis and for maintaining a livable inside temperature.

2.2, 2.3, 2.4

Transparency 2.1, 2.2

READINGS 2.1 and 2.2 The Basic Needs of Living Organisms and Ecosystems Are Dynamic Systems

See *Student Edition*, p. 43 and p. 44.

Reading 2.1 reiterates the ideas that the students discussed in the activity "Voyage to Mars." Their understanding of these key ideas will allow them to participate more fully in the next activity where they design an experiment. Assign both readings as homework or as in-class assignments, and use students' responses to the questions at the end of Reading 2.2 to assess their understanding.

SAMPLE ANSWERS TO QUESTIONS

1. Answers will vary, but probably all students planned for oxygen in some form. If they planned to take bottled oxygen, they will quickly run out of oxygen. It is likely that someone in the group realized the need for plants.
2. It is unlikely that anyone accounted for the accumulation of carbon dioxide because we do not generally discuss it as a common waste product. If their plans incorporated plants, then they are less likely to have toxic accumulations of carbon dioxide.

Describe the relationship between plants and animals in terms of ecosystems and the six basic needs of living organisms.

At this time, students should recognize the following relationships: (1) animals require oxygen, which is produced by plants; (2) all organisms release carbon dioxide; (3) all organisms die, and these wastes are converted into other usable matter by decomposers; and (4) water is essential to all living organisms.

Depending on their prior experiences and knowledge, students may even realize that unique combinations of organisms are found in different ecosystems to carry out these relationships and interactions.

SPECIAL FOCUS LEVELS OF ORGANIZATION OF MATTER

See *Student Edition*, p. 47.

ACTIVITY 2.3 INVESTIGATING ECOSYSTEMS

See *Student Edition*, p. 49.

 2.5, 2.6, 2.7

Transparency 2.2

ADVANCE PREPARATION

Make the bromthymol blue solutions. A 0.05% solution can be prepared by dissolving 0.25 g of bromthymol blue powder in 500 mL of water. Drop by drop, add a very dilute solution of ammonium hydroxide until the solution turns blue. If the tap water in your community is slightly alkaline, you won't need to add the ammonium hydroxide. (*Note:* If you purchase a bromthymol blue solution from a commercial supplier, make sure you purchase a *water* solution. The alcohol-based solutions could kill your organisms.)

Acquire snails and elodea from a supply house or local pet store, or raise them yourself. Assemble the materials for the activity.

STRATEGIES AND PROCEDURES

This activity allows students to design their own controlled experiments. Based on the amount of materials available, keep the groups as small as possible, so students have direct experience designing the experiment.

Students may struggle with step 1. Encourage them to think of easy or simple questions. Try not to give students the actual questions. Encourage them to think of their own. Provide hints as necessary, for example:

- What do you think the snail does?
- Why do we seal the test tubes?
- What comparisons might you make?

Some questions that might lead to reasonable experiments include:

- Is light necessary for photosynthesis?
- Does the plant use the carbon dioxide produced by the snail?
- If there is no snail, will the plant conduct photosynthesis?

Do a short demonstration with the bromthymol blue to help students design their experiments (see Blackline Master 2.5). Blackline Master 2.6 should help them plan their experiment. Blackline Master 2.7 can be used during postlab discussion.

Students will need at least one day to design their experiment and another day to set it up. You can begin the next activity while you are waiting for the reactions to occur. The following description may help you guide students to an understanding of the reaction that could have occurred in their lab setups: Bromthymol blue turns yellow or green when the pH of the water drops below 7.6. This color change is the result of CO_2 mixing with the water to form a weak acid. This acid reduces the pH. If the solution is more yellow than green or blue, then the pH is near 6.0.

Note: If you wish to conduct another laboratory activity related to the role of microorganisms in an ecosystem, try "Microorganisms: Friend or Foe?" This activity appears in the Additional Materials section of this chapter.

 2.11

ACTIVITY 2.4 ECOSYSTEM EXPERTS

See *Student Edition,* p. 50.

In this activity, students become very familiar with one ecosystem and learn a bit about a number of others. You can craft the activity to fit your setting by determining whether students will work in groups or individually, what options they will have for creating their brochures and commercials, what resources will be available besides the textbook, and how much time students will have to work on their projects. The textbook provides background information on ten ecosystems. Add more or delete some as you wish.

The criteria for the activity are included in steps 2 and 3. You can use these criteria to evaluate students' work. If you modify the activity, let the students know what additional criteria you will be using for assessment.

Some teachers make this activity into a library/Internet research project and have the students make posters like the one shown here. Posters on 11″ × 17″ sheets of paper fold nicely and can be placed in a portfolio. Use Blackline Master 2.11 to help students make a food web.

READING 2.3 TERRESTRIAL ECOSYSTEMS (BIOMES)

See *Student Edition,* p. 51.

Life-forms (animals, plants, birds, insects) ↓	ECOSYSTEM (name) General description	Physical Features (land and water forms on the earth's surface) ↓	Food Web (Natural Energy Flow) (diagram goes here)
Location Map (colored map goes here) Climate (description goes here)		Endangered Species (found in this ecosystem) Human Impact (list and/or describe)	Bibliography

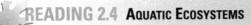

READING 2.4 AQUATIC ECOSYSTEMS

See *Student Edition,* p. 58.

READING 2.5 ECOSYSTEMS CHANGE OVER TIME

See *Student Edition,* p. 61.

READING 2.6 DO HUMANS HAVE SOME SPECIAL NEEDS?

See *Student Edition,* p. 64.

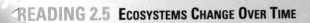

SPECIAL FOCUS SURVIVING AN ANTARCTIC WINTER

See *Student Edition,* p. 64.

This feature is designed to help the students think about the human side of science. Science is conducted by people who are very similar to the students in your classroom. Students should be able to connect this reading to their lives and to their work on the Voyage to Mars activities.

SAMPLE ANSWERS TO QUESTIONS

1. It is long term and dark. People stay in small, closed quarters. The ability to get along with others is critical. Accept other ideas, as long as students can justify their responses.
2. Both Mars and Antarctica are extreme environments compared to where humans live normally. It is essential to attend to scientific information about food, shelter, and dress if one is to survive.
3. In this article, stress brought out anger, depression, violence, jealousy, and divisions between people who had been friends. Encourage students to share their own stories of stress and how they change under stress.
4. In Antarctica, the people who do the best are those who tend to be more aloof than most, higher than average intelligence and education, focused on work, without close family ties, and tolerant of different viewpoints.
5. Accept any responses that students can justify.
6. If we do not work to reduce these environmental stresses, for example, we may see an increase in the types of behaviors described in this story.

ACTIVITY 2.5 OUR QUEST FOR THE "GOOD LIFE"

See *Student Edition,* p. 65.

STRATEGIES AND PROCEDURES

This activity helps students look at the connections between characteristics known for contributing to a positive "quality of life" and the value of understanding the earth and its resources. Students will answer most of the questions based on personal opinion, but they should work on developing thoughtful responses, even when those responses are based on their opinions.

In step 7, students may respond as follows:

7. a. Yes, more people need more resources. When resources are in short supply, competition increases.
   b. Students may have many creative responses. Classic societal responses include military action (war), mediation, passing new laws, or international treaties.
   c. Student responses may vary, but some will realize after one's basic needs are met that comfort and well-being transcend material wealth.
   d. Encourage students to share their ideas. Support all responses.
   e. Depending on one's definition of "large," students may argue that life without large quantities of energy and minerals is still "good." Accept all responses that students can justify.
   f. What is the "good life"? Accept thoughtful responses.
   g. Students may suggest making good financial investments, getting an education, taking care of those around you, or other actions that are important to them.
   h. Responses will vary depending on which standard of living students use to define the good life, but generally the percentage is less than many realize.
   i. Most definitions of the good life require increasing the use of resources, which means more environmental degradation, a greater need for more space, more higher-paying jobs, and so on. This question sets up later discussion of world population changes.

CHAPTER 2 SUMMARY

See *Student Edition*, p. 66.

EXTENSION MICROORGANISMS: FRIEND OR FOE?

See *Teacher Guide*, p. 39.

TEACHING STRATEGIES

This lab emphasizes the role microorganisms play in the functioning of an ecosystem. It builds on what was learned in "A Voyage to Mars." Special emphasis is placed on discovering the conditions under which microorganisms grow best, the helpful and harmful aspects of microorganism growth, and strategies of food preservation.

The lab is best run in a seven-day sequence. The first day is spent preparing and labeling the samples. Students also start their observation charts, which takes about 20–25 minutes. The remaining observations are made during the first 15 minutes of each class. We recommend that you start on a Monday. You will then complete the lab on Thursday of the following week. Students can then complete the write-up and turn it in on Friday.

The best containers are small baby food jars and lids. Have students bring them in during the weeks before the lab is run, or ask a neighbor who has a small baby or a day-care center. Wash and sterilize the jars and lids in a dishwasher before use.

It is best to have students work in groups of five or six. With smaller groups, you have so many jars to hand out and collect that you won't be able to get anything else done—and this makes class boring. Collect and store the jars in cut-down boxes. Label the boxes by type (cool dry breads, cool moist breads, vegetable, meat, etc.) so you can hand out and collect the jars rapidly and also note what is happening as you pass them out each day. The cool breads need to be placed in a refrigerator *immediately* after each class.

The information in the observation chart was obtained using hamburger, apples, and peas. For three classes, purchase a half pint of milk, ⅓ pound of ground beef, one apple, and a *tiny* can of peas. Bring a couple slices of bread (no preservatives added) from home. You'll need two sets of plastic measuring spoons and a can opener.

After students complete the lab, empty the jars with the bread and apples, clean them in a dishwasher, and store for the following year. Place the jars of meat, milk, and peas in a plastic garbage bag and dispose of them in the trash. You'll need to replace these jars next year.

Sample results and answers to questions follow. A control (an empty, sterilized baby jar) is not part of the observations because the lack of growth in an empty jar does not *prove* that microorganisms are not in the "sterilized" jar. One could argue that microorganisms are in there, they just lack the nutrients to grow and multiply.

RESULTS

The containers should not be stored in direct sunlight because certain frequencies of sunlight (solar radiation) kill microorganisms. Also, the greenhouse effect may cause unnatural warming of the containers.

SAMPLE ANSWERS TO QUESTIONS

1. a. Your hands.
   b. The air.
   c. The equipment that was used to prepare the food samples.
   d. The food itself.
   e. From the walls of the containers.
2. a. Food (nutrients)
   b. Warmth
   c. Moisture
3. Wherever dead plants and animals are decaying.
4. From the bodies of dead plants and animals.
5. As decomposers feed on the scraps, they break down the scraps and return minerals (nutrients) to the soil. These nutrients are used by growing plants. The decomposing scraps also help build humus, which aids in soil aeration and water retention.
6. *Harmful:* Some microorganisms cause disease, and others damage plants, food, and clothing.
   Helpful: Decomposers break down dead organic materials and return nutrients to the soil. Sewage treatment is essentially microorganisms in action. Some microorganisms are involved in making wines, cheeses, breads, and medicines. Some mushrooms are edible.

7. a. Drying (removal of moisture)
   b. Salt and sugar curing (dehydrates the bacteria)
   c. Canning (heating kills microorganisms and vacuum packing seals the container to prevent contamination)
   d. Smoking (removes moisture and adds preservatives)
   e. Pickling (changes the chemical environment)
8. One of the most effective ways to inhibit the growth of microorganisms is by keeping the temperature low. Refrigeration doesn't change the taste of foods as much as drying, salting, or canning. It is also much easier.
9. Cooking food before it is canned and sealed kills the microorganisms. After cooking (heating), the food is placed in a sterile container and sealed. The vacuum maintains the seal.

Note: The "hiss" when a can or jar is opened is an indication that the seal has remained intact. If a container doesn't hiss when it is opened and/or if a bulge develops in the lid as it sits on the shelf, something is wrong and the contents *must* not be eaten!

OBSERVING THE GROWTH OF MICROORGANISMS

Day	Bread		Milk	Meat	Fruit	Vegetables
	moist	dry				
0	wm____ cl____	____ ____	____	____	____	____
1	wm____ cl____	____ ____	slightly curdled	turned brown	turned brown	____ ____
2	wm____ cl____	____ ____	thickened	even more brown	brown	some fuzzy mold
3	wm start to mold cl____	____ ____	thickened	about the same	brown	more mold
4	wm mold cl____	____ ____	thickened	appears moist	brown	more mold
7	wm mold cl____	____ ____	separated	a slimy coating	brown	more mold & liquid
10	wm mold cl____	____ ____	separated	a slimy coating	some mold appeared	more mold & liquid

Key: wm = warm; cl = cool;———= no reaction

Name _____ Date _____

MICROORGANISMS: FRIEND OR FOE?

TASK

To grow some microorganisms and speculate about their role in ecosystems. To determine what conditions are best for the growth of microorganisms. To relate what we learn to food preservation practices.

MATERIALS

(per lab group of five or six students)

8 containers with lids
medicine dropper
marking pencil, masking tape
4 pieces of bread, small

1½ tbsp milk
sandwich meat or hamburger, 1 cm × 1 cm
piece of acidic fruit, apple or orange
cooked green vegetables, 2 peas, beans

Time required: About two weeks

PROCEDURE

Before you begin, read through all the directions. Notice that you will prepare two sets of containers.

A. Gather eight containers and make sure they are clean and dry. Put a piece of bread into each of four containers.

B. Use a medicine dropper to put 3 or 4 drops of water on two of the pieces of bread.

Adapted from *Food and Microorganisms* of Individualized Science Instructional System (ISIS), 1976, The Florida Board of Regents. Some of the materials incorporated in this work were developed by Florida State University with the financial support of the National Science Foundation. Any opinions, findings, conclusions, or recommendations expressed herein do not necessarily reflect the view of the National Science Foundation or Florida State University.

C. Cover each of the four containers with a lid or plastic wrap. Label the containers and store them as shown.

name date bread moist, warm	name date bread dry, warm	name date bread moist, cool	name date bread dry, cool

NOTE: *Don't store any of the prepared containers in direct sunlight.*

Why? _____

_____

_____

D. Prepare the four remaining containers. Put 3 to 5 drops of water on the fruit and vegetables if they are dry.

E. Cover each container with a lid or plastic wrap. Label and store each container as indicated.

name date vegetable warm	name date meat warm	name date milk warm	name date fruit warm

WARNING

Most, perhaps all, of the microorganisms that will grow in this investigation are harmless. But there is a small chance that one or more could cause an allergic reaction, an infection, or even a serious illness. There is no danger, however, if you follow these safety rules:

1. Don't remove the lids.
2. Don't taste, touch, or smell spoiled food. Keep all odors inside the containers.
3. Follow your teacher's instructions for throwing away all unopened containers.

F. Check the containers regularly for two weeks to see what changes are taking place. Record your observations in the table provided. Good observations are extremely important in scientific investigations. Observe carefully. Record what you see in an understandable way. Accurate observations are critical to discovering changes and making meaningful interpretations of what occurred.

QUESTIONS

Microorganisms are everywhere—bacteria, yeasts, molds. Often they are so small that they are almost invisible unless you use a microscope. This explains why they are called *microorganisms*. Microorganisms, whether you can see them or not, are on your hands, inside your body, and in the air, water, soil. They are almost everywhere you can think of.

1. Where might the microorganisms come from that are growing in your containers?
   a.
   b.
   c.
   d.
   e.

2. In this lab, you observed three things that are necessary for the rapid growth of microorganisms. List them.
   a.
   b.
   c.

3. Where do you look to find decomposers? _____

4. Where do decomposers (bacteria and fungi) get the food they need to grow?
   _____

   Note: Fungi are organisms such as yeasts, molds, smuts, rusts, mildews, and mushrooms.

5. Why do some people bury food scraps in the ground where they plan to have a garden?

   _____

   _____

6. Microorganisms are both harmful and helpful. Explain.

   harmful: _____

   _____

   _____

   _____

   helpful: _____

   _____

   _____

   _____

   _____

Observing the Growth of Microorganisms

Elapsed Time (Days)	Bread			Milk	Meat	Fruit	Vegetables
	moist/warm	moist/cool	dry/warm	dry/cool				
0								
1								
2								
3								
4								
7								
10								

NOTES: 1. Record the beginning appearance in the Day 0 row.

2. If no change is noted, record a dash:—.

BACKGROUND

The following information may help you explain some of the things you observed in this lab. This information will also help you answer the next few questions.

In general, microorganisms grow best where they have:

* moderate temperatures (not too hot or cold);
* moist surroundings;
* available nutrients; and
* oxygen (air) present.

Growths of molds in general look fuzzy and threadlike. Compared to molds, bacteria grow where it is wetter and less acidic; bacterial growths usually look more waxy and jellylike. Growths of yeasts look very much like those of bacteria, but the odor of yeasts is easy to identify. (However, *don't smell* the containers.) The odor is similar to the smell of baking bread. When yeasts grow in a liquid, they make it look cloudy.

7. What did the pioneers do to preserve food in the days before refrigeration was common?

_____

_____

8. Why is refrigeration used so widely in our modern society? _____

_____

9. Why are canned goods vacuum-packed? _____

_____

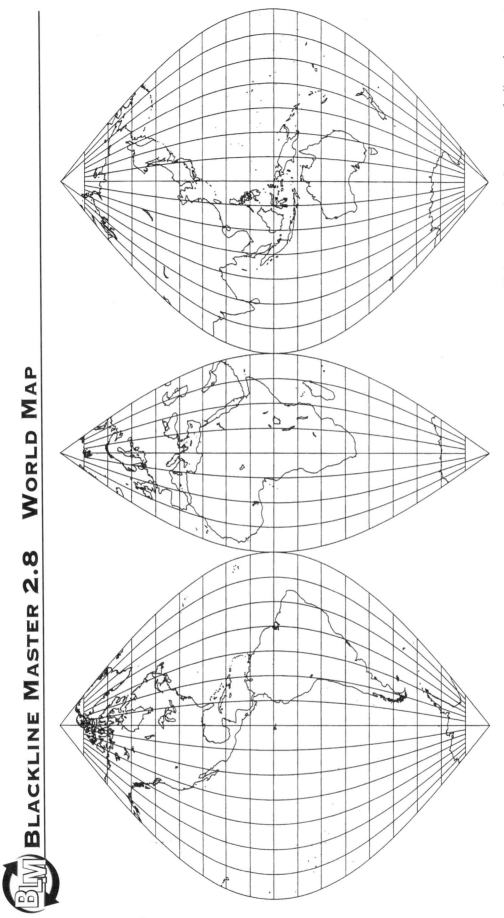

This interrupted sinusoidal projection of the earth with shorelines is an equal-area projection, which means that the areas of all regions are shown in the same proportion to their true areas. (SOURCE: An Album of Map Projections. U.S. Geological Survey Professional Paper 1453.)

Characteristic	Earth	Mars
Composition of Soil	Silicate minerals, organic compounds in organic matter.	Weathered volcanic soil.
Biological Activity	Abundant, many life-forms, heavily dependent on water and oxygen.	Unknown, but probably scarce. Little protection from the Sun's UV rays. Scarcity of water.
Magnetic Field	Strong.	Weak to none.
Cosmic Radiation	Insulated by thick atmosphere, ozone, and magnetic field.	Lack of magnetic field—does not deflect cosmic radiation. Is about 100 times greater than on Earth.
Position in Solar System	3rd planet	4th planet
Natural Satellites	Moon	Phobos and Deimos
Mass	1	0.11
Volume	1	0.15
Surface Gravity	1	0.38
Density	5.52 g/cm^3	3.95 g/cm^3
Distance to Earth	0	Closest: 56,000,000 km Farthest: 400,000,000 km
Revolution around the Sun	365 days = 1 Earth year	687 days = 1.9 Earth years
Tilt of Axis	23.5°	24°
Seasons	Yes	Yes
Solar Input (at surface)	1000 watts/m^2	595 watts/m^2
Average Temperature	10°C (50°F)	−63°C (−81°F)
Temperature Range	Low: −89°C (−128°F)	Low: −140°C (−220°F)
Atmosphere	High: 58°C (136°F) N_2 78% O_2 21% Ar 0.93% CO_2 0.31%	High: 21°C (70°F) N_2 2.7% O_2 0.13% Ar 1.6% CO_2 95.3%
Weather	Variable: wind, rain, snow, clashing 5air masses, cyclones, etc.	No precipitation, only wind, dust storms, seasons, pink skies during daytime. Patches of frost and high clouds.
Average Wind Speed	5 m/sec	2–7 m/sec in summer; 17–30 m/sec during dust storms
Average Atmospheric Pressure	1000 mb	7 mb (near vacuum)
Water Cover	71%	0%
Behavior of Water	Remains a liquid above 0°C (32°F).	Boils easily above freezing because of near vacuum conditions.
Ice Cover	17%; ice caps at poles. Ice made of solid water. Water ice.	Variable; ice caps at poles. Ice made of frozen CO_2. Dry ice. Possible water ice below surface near equator.
Highest Point	Mt. Everest: 8800 m (29,000 ft)	Olympus Mons: 28,000 m (78,000 ft)
Lowest Point	Mariana Trench: 11,000 m (36,000 ft)	Valles Marineris: 7000 m (23,000 ft)
Crust	Silicon, oxygen, aluminum (silicate minerals).	Silicon, oxygen, aluminum (silicate minerals).
Geologic Activity	Plate tectonics and associated earthquakes and volcanoes. Active weathering and erosion. Perpetual "resurfacing."	Currently only wind deposition and erosion. No evidence of plate tectonics. Dormant volcanoes, evidence of 4-billion-year-old lakes, oceans, streams within large basins.

Source: NASA

A Grand Oasis in Space

FORM A

Directions: *Decide how well the team met the criteria. A "5" indicates that students met the criteria very well; a "1" means that the team did not address that criterion at all.*

Team names:

Criteria	Score				
Clearly indicated which five items selected.	1	2	3	4	5
Briefly described why those five items are important enough to be selected.	1	2	3	4	5
Identified ten people.	1	2	3	4	5
Justified the selection of the ten people.	1	2	3	4	5
Made presentation short, interesting, creative, and colorful.	1	2	3	4	5

Total Score

 BLACKLINE MASTER 2.10
JUDGING SHEET (ALTERNATIVE FORM)

FORM B

	Needs Work	Okay	Good	Excellent
Selection of Five Items	Five items selected with little thought.	A mixture of items, some with thought, others seem randomly selected.	Effort and thought put into the selection, but some major categories missed.	Each item is carefully selected so that no major categories are missed.
Description of Importance	Descriptions are missing for some items and do not address the importance of each item.	Descriptions are somewhat vague and do not always address importance.	Items described in detail, but multiple purposes are missing.	Each item described in detail: why it is important and what its multiple purposes are on the voyage.
Identification of Ten People	A few groups people identified, rather than ten unique individuals; no thought about the mixture of skills, ages, etc.	Some groups identified and some individuals; lack of thought about who would be useful on voyage.	Ten different people identified, but range of skills, ages, genders, or sizes not varied.	Ten distinctly different people identified with a variety of skills and ages; both genders represented.
Justification of Ten People	Selection of people justified in general only.	A couple of people justified specifically, but most supported by general ideas.	Most people clearly justified.	Clear justification for each person.
Appeal	Not colorful, many mistakes and misspellings; too long, messy, and disorganized.	Neat and well organized; not colorful, too long, and several mistakes.	Colorful, right length or size, neat, interesting to view or listen to, few mistakes.	Exciting, makes me want to know more; colorful, creative, no mistakes in spelling or grammar.

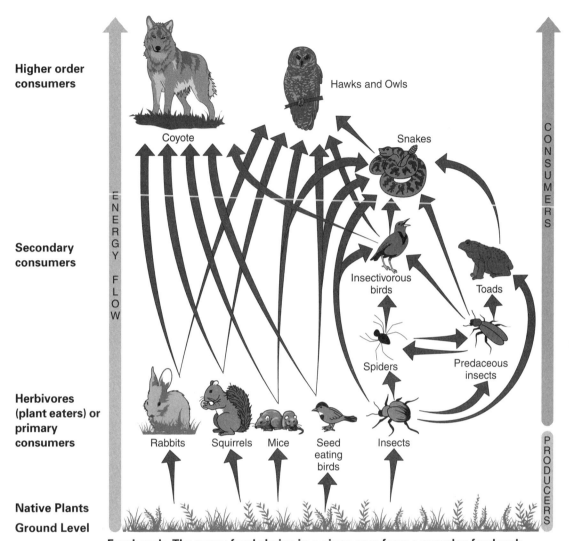

Food web. The many food chains in a given area form a complex food web.

The numbers shown at the left are the order in which items are to be done:

1. Draw a horizontal line representing the ground.
2. Draw some plants (grasses to trees) native to your ecosystem. Label the plants (not shown).
3. Draw some herbivores (plant eaters) native to your ecosystem. Label them (as shown above).
4. Draw some secondary consumers (animals that eat herbivores) native to your ecosystem. Label them (as shown above).
5. Draw some higher order consumers native to your ecosystem. Label them (as shown above).
6. Draw in arrows to show the flow of energy (food) from plants to herbivores. Then draw in more arrows to show energy (food) flow from prey to predator.

Name _____ Date _____

MULTIPLE CHOICE

1. _____ Viewing Earth from outer space forces us to conclude that
   A. there is intelligent life on Earth.
   B. Earth and its resources are finite.
   C. Earth is made of three main layers.
   D. the United States and Russia are the dominant world powers.

2. _____ What is the original source of all energy used by living organisms?
   A. plants
   B. chlorophyll
   C. photosynthesis
   D. the sun

3. _____ Almost half of all the solar radiation that reaches Earth is
   A. used by plants in photosynthesis.
   B. absorbed and reradiated into space.
   C. involved with the production of wind and waves.
   D. reflected back into space.

4. _____ Which of the following relationships shows movement from smallest to largest?
   A. atoms—cells—earth—ecosystem
   B. atoms—organism—earth—ecosystem
   C. molecules—cells—populations—organs
   D. cells—organs—population—ecosystem

5. _____ The science of ecology includes which of the following levels of organization?
   A. atoms—molecules—protoplasm—cells
   B. Earth—planets—stars—galaxies
   C. organisms—populations—communities—ecosystems
   D. organs—organ systems—organisms—populations

6. _____ An ecosystem has two major components, nonliving and living. The nonliving or abiotic
   component includes all of the following *except*
   A. an energy source.
   B. minerals.
   C. physical factors (humidity, rainfall, etc.).
   D. scavengers.
   E. none of these.

7. _____ On land, large major ecosystems, such as forests, grasslands, tundra, and deserts, can be
   called
   A. biomes.
   B. populations.
   C. communities.
   D. none of the above.

8. _____ Animals that eat plants are called
   A. producers.
   B. first order consumers.
   C. second order consumers.
   D. third order consumers.

9. _____ Organisms *usually* classified as consumers include
   A. some plants and no animals.
   B. all animals but no plants.
   C. some animals and all plants.
   D. some plants and all animals.

10. _____ Which of the following is a consumer-producer relationship?
    A. foxes eat rabbits
    B. rabbits eat young plant shoots
    C. plant shoots grow in soil
    D. leaves grow on trees

11. _____ Organisms that obtain food material and energy from the breakdown of animal wastes and the remains of dead organisms are called
    A. decomposers.
    B. producers.
    C. consumers.
    D. critters.

12. _____ All of the following fit into the general category of *decomposers except*
    A. vegetables.
    B. fungi.
    C. earthworms.
    D. bacteria.

13. _____ Respiration is carried out by
    A. plants only.
    B. animals only.
    C. both plants and animals.
    D. neither plants nor animals.

14. _____ What does carbon dioxide form when it is dissolved in water?
    A. acid
    B. base
    C. neither an acid nor a base
    D. both an acid and a base

15. _____ When you metabolize food while eating at home or in the school's cafeteria, which of the following gases in the air mixture that surrounds us are you using?
    A. oxygen
    B. nitrogen
    C. carbon dioxide
    D. carbon monoxide

16. _____ Arctic and alpine tundras would be represented by
    A. low precipitation and high temperature.
    B. low precipitation and low temperature.
    C. high precipitation and high temperature.
    D. high precipitation and low temperature.

17. _____ An ecosystem can function properly because it has
   A. a one-way flow of energy.
   B. a recycling of chemicals.
   C. both a and b.
   D. neither a nor b.

18. _____ If one is to survive in a closed system, that system must contain *all* of the following *except*
   A. a gaseous mixture similar to the air in our atmosphere.
   B. fruits and vegetables—including sources of protein.
   C. a variety of poultry and fish.
   D. bacteria to break down dead material.
   E. soil nutrients.

19. _____ Water is a basic human need. It helps satisfy our metabolic requirements and the requirements of plants and animals. What other important function does water perform?
   A. source of energy
   B. enrichment of the soil
   C. waste transport
   D. fixation of nitrogen

20. _____ Which of the following types of food are required for tissue building or rebuilding?
   A. fats
   B. vitamins
   C. carbohydrates
   D. proteins

21. _____ As outlined in your textbook, the "good life" includes all of the following *except*
   A. ridding the world of war, pestilence, and disease.
   B. cigarettes, liquor, pot, and wild parties.
   C. variety in our diets, including some milk, meat, poultry, and fish.
   D. some "creature comforts" such as stoves, refrigerators, washing machines, and so on.
   E. a chance to relax and enjoy life periodically.

22. _____ The thin layer of living matter that is associated with the exterior of the earth is called the
   A. hydrosphere.
   B. atmosphere.
   C. lithosphere.
   D. epcot sphere.
   E. biosphere

23. _____ The *niche* of an organism describes
   A. what the organism does in an ecosystem.
   B. the place where it lives.
   C. its role as a predator.
   D. its role as prey.

24. _____ An ecosystem *can* survive without
   A. water.
   B. atmosphere (air).
   C. decomposers.
   D. animals.
   E. minerals (nutrients).

25. _____ When a forest is logged, remnants of the community (i.e., seeds and saplings) are left on site and contribute to site recolonization.
This is an example of _____ succession.
   A. residual
   B. cyclic
   C. primary
   D. secondary
   E. tertiary

26. _____ Plants make their bodies primarily from
   A. carbon monoxide and heart.
   B. sunlight.
   C. soil nutrients and oxygen.
   D. fertilizer and oxygen.
   E. carbon dioxide and water.

27. _____ A population is
   A. a group of organs performing a similar function.
   B. a group of different organisms living in a given area.
   C. a group of the same type of organisms living in a certain area.
   D. none of the above.

28. _____ Early successional plants have all of the following characteristics *except*
   A. fast growth.
   B. shade intolerance.
   C. they are called "climax species."
   D. they require soil rich in nutrients.
   E. their seeds are widely dispersed.

29. _____ A glacier has been retreating from the ocean landward since the late Ice Age. A correct description of the succession from the ice boundary to the ocean would be
   A. tundra, shrubs, beach.
   B. shrubs, forest, beach.
   C. lichens, shrubs, forest.
   D. bare rock, lichens, shrub, forest.
   E. grasses, shrub, lichens, forest.

30. _____ Ecologists separate aquatic ecosystems into three major groups. These include all of the following *except*
   A. freshwater.
   B. marine.
   C. estuary.
   D. tributary.

31. _____ In which of the following are the water molecules the farthest apart?
   A. ice cube
   B. puddle
   C. fog
   D. glass of water
   E. rain

32. _____ Oceans moderate climate because of water's large

    A. surface tension.

    B. heat capacity.

    C. boiling point.

    D. capillarity.

    E. dew point.

SHORT ANSWER

33. In the activity "A Voyage to Mars," you identified a number of key components (parts) of an ecosystem. List them here and describe the role each plays in a functioning ecosystem.

CHAPTER 2 ASSESSMENT

1. B	9. D	17. C	25. D
2. D	10. B	18. C	26. E
3. B	11. A	19. C	27. C
4. D	12. A	20. D	28. C
5. C	13. C	21. B	29. D
6. D	14. A	22. E	30. D
7. A	15. A	23. A	31. C
8. B	16. B	24. D	32. B

33. An ecosystem has six components (if the energy source is not implied). Several are listed here in outline form.

1. *Energy:* A source, such as the sun, must be a part of an ecosystem to drive life-sustaining processes such as photosynthesis.
2. *Water*
    a. to satisfy the metabolic requirements of the colonists and their plants and animals.
    b. to provide for nutrient and waste transport.
3. *Air mixture* (oxygen, nitrogen, CO_2)
    a. oxygen—for the metabolizing of food.
    b. nitrogen— (1) for the building of protein, enzymes, and DNA.
            (2) for the dilution of oxygen, that is, to provide an inert gaseous buffer against combustion.
            (3) for the prevention of certain respiratory problems.
    c. carbon dioxide—for plant metabolism.

Note: The ratios need not be identical to those on Earth. One can get by with less nitrogen. The carbon dioxide content can be increased somewhat to stimulate plant growth.

4. *A variety of foods*—including some nitrogen-fixing plants. The plants and animals provide:
    a. carbohydrates and fats—for energy.
    b. proteins—for energy and tissue building.
    c. vitamins—organic substances that are indispensable for life but are not required as a source of energy.
    d. minerals—inorganic substances that are indispensable for life but are not required as a source of energy.
    e. fertilizer—for the soil.
    f. regeneration of the atmosphere.
5. *Minerals*—to enrich the soil and hence provide healthy plants to keep the colonists healthy. If wastes are properly recycled, the minerals will be recycled continually.
6. *Decomposers*—to recycle sewage and dead plants and animals and keep the soil fertile. In addition, it can be argued that we need metals, fibers, space, and portable energy sources. We also have certain psychological needs such as love and a feeling of purpose. Humans would have to construct a shelter on any planet other than Earth to create and sustain an ecosystem.

ENERGY FLOW AND MATTER CYCLES

LEARNING OUTCOMES

The student will:

1. manipulate materials and observe the feeding interactions among organisms in an artificial marine ecosystem by completing the activity "What Eats What?" (A,P)

2. develop a model of feeding interactions in a marine ecosystem by observing a demonstration and constructing a diagram. (C,A)

3. explain why there is less energy available to secondary consumers than to primary consumers in a food chain. (C)

4. identify a food chain and predict the order of population sizes. (C)

5. differentiate between energy "lost" and energy retained in the various levels of a food chain. (C)

6. design an ecodome that uses the components identified in the activity "A Voyage to Mars" and the four major cycles of nature by manipulating materials. (P)

7. realize that resources are recycled in nature through cycles (water, carbon, nitrogen, and mineral). (C,A)

8. observe the relationships between mass, inertia, and forces by doing the activity "Exploring the Meaning of Mass." (P)

9. draw conclusions about the relationships between mass, inertia, and forces by answering fill-in-the-blank statements based on doing the activity "Exploring the Meaning of Mass." (C)

10. define energy, mass, and matter. (C)

11. classify examples of energy into a potential category or a kinetic category and explain why each fits in that category. (C)

12. compare a closed system, an open system, and a steady state system. (C)

13. manipulate materials and equipment, record data, and calculate the conservation of mass by completing the activity "The Conservation of Mass." (C,P)

14. list and give examples of the six forms of energy. (C)

15. construct a table of possible energy transformations between the six forms of energy by writing responses and/or conducting a discussion. (C)

16. state the laws of conservation of mass and energy. (C)

17. realize that matter on Earth is in a closed system and energy from the Sun is in an open system. (C,A)

18. realize that the six forms of energy can be represented with different units that can be changed from one unit to another by using conversion factors. (A)

19. use conversion factors to change from one measurement to another by calculating problems from the activity "Conversion Factors." (C)

20. define and give examples of the five sources from which all energy comes. (C)

21. observe an application of the second law of thermodynamics and use it to define useful energy by completing the task "The Agony of (da) Heat" in the activity "Examining the Second Law." (C)

22. state the second law of thermodynamics and explain why it represents a "kink" in our quest for the "good life." (C)

23. realize that disorder is a natural occurrence by completing the activity "It's a One Way Street." (C,A)

24. realize that energy is needed to overcome disorder (entropy, chaos, randomness) by completing the activity "It's a One Way Street." (C,A)

25. examine the definition of efficiency and realize by examining a table that efficiencies of different energy convertors (i.e., motors and lightbulbs) vary widely. (C,A)

26. manipulate materials to make a cup of tea and calculate the efficiency of the process by completing the activity "Let's Have Tea!" (C,P)

27. explain how system efficiency and the conversion of energy are related. (C,A)

28. calculate system efficiency by completing chapter problems. (C)

29. state the concept of net energy and realize its importance in physical and biological systems. (C,A)

30. define energy quality and state how it relates to the "good life." (C)

31. realize we face a quality crisis and not an energy crisis and suggest personal ways that she or he can "stretch out" our energy quality losses. (A)

KEY TERMS

efficiency	precipitation	inertia	mechanical energy	foot-pound
primary consumer	infiltration	kinetic energy	heat energy	joule
secondary	transpiration	potential energy	radiant energy	conversion factor
consumer	hydrologic	work	electrical energy	second law of
carnivore	groundwater	closed system	magnetic field	thermodynamics
herbivore	aquifer	open system	chemical energy	entropy
omnivore	carbon cycle	steady state	nuclear energy	efficiency
decomposer	carbohydrate	conservation law	fusion	heat engine
tertiary consumer	nitrogen cycle	law of conservation	fission	system efficiency
food chain	mineral/nutrient	of matter	tides	net energy
energy pyramid	cycle	law of conservation	geothermal power	quality energy
water cycle	mass	of energy	remote sensing	end-use
runoff	matter	first law of	calorie	quad (Q)
evaporation	energy	thermodynamics	Btu	ambient

RECOMMENDED BLACKLINE MASTERS

3.1 Nature's Cycles
3.2 Generic Ecodome
3.3 Various Energy Transformations
3.4 The Second Law of Thermodynamics
3.5 The Agony of (da) Heat

3.6 Photosynthesis Implies Order
3.7 Energy Quality (Usefulness)
3.8 Behavior and the Second Law
3.9 Strategies for Resource Users

The Recommended Blackline Masters listed above are supplemental to the activity/reading, and can be found on the *Teacher Resource CD*. Blackline Masters 3.10–3.11 are essential to teaching the activity/reading, and so are included in the *Teacher Guide* (pp. 80–81) as well as on the *Teacher Resource CD*.

ACTIVITIES FLOW CHART

CHAPTER 3: ENERGY FLOW AND MATTER CYCLES

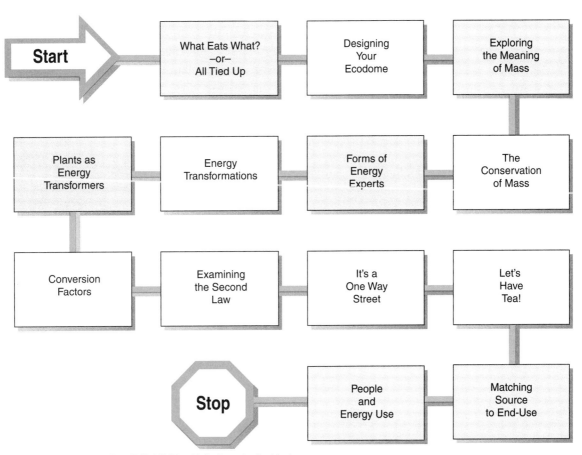

Start → What Eats What? –or– All Tied Up → Designing Your Ecodome → Exploring the Meaning of Mass

Plants as Energy Transformers → Energy Transformations → Forms of Energy Experts → The Conservation of Mass

Conversion Factors → Examining the Second Law → It's a One Way Street → Let's Have Tea!

Stop ← People and Energy Use ← Matching Source to End-Use

NOTE: Shaded items are lower priority. "All Tied Up" is with the Extension for this chapter.

TEACHING STRATEGIES AND ANSWERS FOR ACTIVITIES

CHAPTER OPENER, See *Student Edition,* p. 70.

The opening photograph of Earth reminds students that our planet is a closed system in terms of resources and that our energy originates from a source outside that closed system, namely the sun. Ask students what the image makes them think of.

READING THE GEOSPHERE IMAGE

See *Student Edition,* p. 70.

READING ENERGY AND MATTER—THE BIG PICTURE

See *Student Edition,* p. 70.

ACTIVITY 3.1 WHAT EATS WHAT?

See *Student Edition,* p. 71.

ADVANCE PREPARATION

If possible, arrange for access to a large, open area to do this activity. Make enough role cards so that each student has one. For a class of 30 students, we recommend the following assortment: 8 plankton, 5 mullet, 5 shrimp, 3 crab, 3 redfish, 3 dolphin, 2 heron, and 1 crocodile.

Role Cards	
Role: plankton Eats: nothing Is eaten by: mullet, shrimp	Role: heron Eats: mullet, crab, shrimp, redfish Is eaten by: crocodile
Role: shrimp Eats: plankton Is eaten by: crab, heron, redfish	Role: redfish Eats: shrimp Is eaten by: heron, crocodile, dolphin
Role: mullet Eats: plankton Is eaten by: crab, heron, dolphin	Role: dolphin Eats: mullet, redfish Is eaten by: nothing
Role: crab Eats: shrimp, mullet Is eaten by: heron	Role: crocodile Eats: redfish, heron Is eaten by: nothing

STRATEGIES AND PROCEDURES

This activity depicts food webs and food chains in a very visual and physical manner. The students will quickly form a tangled web that represents the complicated relationships in real ecosystems.

Sometimes students have difficulty understanding the directions for the string. You may want to set up a demonstration. Explain that you have the role of a crab, and your role card says that you can eat either mullet or shrimp. You can be eaten by heron. Approach a student who will play the role of a mullet. Since the crab can eat the mullet, you take the loose end of that student's string in your hand. That student retains his or her ball of string. Now approach the heron. Since the heron can eat the crab, you must give your loose end of the string to the heron. Point out that, should you encounter another heron, you would roll out the string from your ball and allow the second heron to grasp another section of your string (in addition to the one already held by the first heron). As students move around the area, they will have to roll out their strings, and they will be pulling along sections of the strings they have grasped previously. After a while it becomes difficult to move.

In step 8, students may respond as follows:

8. a. The students became tangled in a web.
   b. There are many different feeding relationships, all going on simultaneously.
   c. The string represents the feeding relationships. Later in the chapter, remind students of this activity and see if they can connect the string to the idea of energy flow in an ecosystem.

d. Only students who ate other organisms got string. Plankton did not get any string because they make their own food and do not eat other organisms. Plankton are the base of this marine ecosystem.

e. The dolphin and crocodile never gave away any string because they are not eaten by any of the other organisms. They represent the end point in this food web.

f. Theoretically the dolphin, heron, and crocodile are most vulnerable to changes in the ecosystem because they are affected by anything that affects the other levels. Any disruption at the beginning levels diminishes the food supply available to the higher-level consumers.

For the demonstration in step 9, ask four volunteers to assemble in the front of the class. Hand out these four cards: plankton, mullet, heron, and crocodile. Have the students follow the same basic procedure with their strings. Students may respond to the questions as follows:

9. a. Students should see the set of feeding interactions.

b. This pattern is more like a chain than a web. A food web is actually many food chains.

You may want to reproduce the aquatic food chain provided to give students a picture of what their organism looks like. (The drawings are not to scale.)

Aquatic Food Chain

Source: Crenshaw, Neil. Food Webs in the Classroom. *The American Biology Teacher* 43(2) (1981): 100–102.

READING 3.1 ENERGY FLOW IN NATURE AND HUMAN-BUILT SYSTEMS

See *Student Edition,* p. 72.

SAMPLE ANSWERS TO QUESTIONS _____

1. Vegetarians consume food at the source of the food chain, directly from the garden or field. Only one energy transformation is involved in changing the plant energy to energy the human can use. Eating meat

involves intermediate steps from the plant to what is placed in the mouth. The amount of useful energy that becomes unavailable for further use in a food chain is directly related to the number of transformations involved.

2. Lions don't hunt mice because the energy they would expend in the process would be more than the nutritional energy they would gain by eating the mice. Hence, exclusively mice-eating lions would soon starve.

3. More energy is available in plant than in animal material. Large amounts of energy are consumed in hunting, more than in grazing or browsing.

4. Rabbits are herbivores. Herbivores are closer to the bottom of the food chain where most of the useful energy is; therefore, the greater food source supports a larger population.

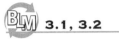 3.1, 3.2

Transparency 3.1

ACTIVITY 3.2 DESIGNING YOUR ECODOME

See *Student Edition,* p. 76.

This activity provides an excellent summary of the ecosystem concept. Divide the students into groups of four or five. Use the following rubric to improve student presentations.

Rubric: Designing your ecodome

TASK NO. 1: Draw Dome
Check off items completed.

_____ Work as a group. Everyone must participate.

_____ Include the five basic components of an ecosystem.

_____ Place N_2, O_2, CO_2, and H_2O in the atmosphere.

_____ Include nature's four cycles.

_____ Include high-tech monitoring devices.

TASK NO. 2: Presentation to the Class
Each group member must speak on one of the following topics. All topics must be covered. If a group member is absent, someone else must present that part. Know all parts well.

1. Components of an Ecosystem (_____ points)

   _____ Define MODEL.

   _____ Define ECOSYSTEM.

   _____ Explain how your *model* helps you understand how an *ecosystem* functions.

   _____ Point out the FIVE MAJOR COMPONENTS of an ecosystem.

   _____ Point out any *high-tech monitoring* you use.

2. Water Cycle (_____ points)

   Explain how water cycles in your dome. Use these terms correctly:

   _____ Evaporation   _____ Precipitation

   _____ Transpiration   _____ Runoff

   _____ Condensation   _____ Infiltration

3. Carbon/oxygen Cycle (____ points)
Explain how oxygen cycles in your dome. Use these terms correctly:
____ Photosynthesis   ____ Carbon Dioxide
____ Respiration   ____ Oxygen
____ Solar Energy

4. Mineral Cycle (____ points)
Explain how minerals cycle through your dome. Use these terms correctly:
____ Minerals/soil nutrients   ____ Digestion
____ Photosynthesis   ____ Animal/plant wastes
____ Eating/nutrition   ____ Decomposers

5. Nitrogen Cycle (____ points)
Explain how nitrogen cycles in your dome. Use these terms correctly:
____ Nitrogen Gas   ____ Nitrogen-Rich Foods
____ Legume   ____ Digestion
____ Nitrogen-Rich Fertilizer   ____ Decomposers/Waste

READING 3.2 RESOURCE RECYCLING IN NATURE

See *Student Edition,* p. 77.

READING MATTER AND ENERGY—A CLOSER LOOK

See *Student Edition,* p. 82.

READING 3.3 SO WHAT ARE ENERGY AND MATTER?

See *Student Edition,* p. 83.

ACTIVITY 3.3 EXPLORING THE MEANING OF MASS

See *Student Edition,* p. 84.

ADVANCE PREPARATION

You can purchase the inertia ball by contacting your Kendall/Hunt representative or make it if you have the time, materials, and tools. Use a weaker variety of packaging string. Place a piece of thick cardboard or something similar under the demonstration so the inertia ball doesn't dent the floor. Pull the string a little to the side and not straight down to prevent the ball from hurting your hand.

STRATEGIES AND PROCEDURES

Conduct the teacher demonstration so that everyone gets to see it clearly. The students should be surprised when you jerk the bottom string and that string breaks, but when you pull the bottom string slowly, the top string breaks.

After the demonstration, the students conduct their own inquiry about the relationships between force, mass, and energy. At this point in the chapter, encourage the students to trust their own experiments and use their own evidence to develop their explanations.

In step 1, students may respond as follows:

1. c. The inertia of the metal object is large because the mass of the chunk of metal is relatively large. It takes time to overcome this inertia. When string B is jerked, there is too little time to influence the metal object. The mass doesn't move, so the force exerted focuses its effect on string B and it breaks. When B is pulled slowly, the unbalanced force has time to influence the metal mass and move it slightly downward. This in turn stretches string A and relieves tension on B. Finally, string A breaks.

   This is more detail than most students are likely to include in their responses; however, you can use this information to prompt the students to think deeper about their responses.

In step 2, students may respond as follows:

2. a. & b. Responses will vary depending on what materials are available and which ones students use. Watch that students are making connections that are similar to the explanation for step 1c. If they are way off, check their inquiry.

In step 4, students may respond as follows:

4. a. If the students can connect this activity to the information in Reading 3.3, they should describe mass as the measure of an object's resistance to change. The more mass an object has, the longer it takes for a change to occur.
   b. Forces are applied to the systems the students build. If their systems have a large mass, then it takes more force to produce a change. It takes energy to exert a force.

READING 3.4 KINETIC AND POTENTIAL ENERGY

See *Student Edition,* p. 85.

SAMPLE ANSWERS TO QUESTIONS

1. The rocks have potential energy due to the energy stored in their position. If the rocks are given a push to start them rolling down the hill, the potential energy is converted to kinetic energy.
2. Objects b and f have kinetic energy due to their motion. Objects a, c, d, and e have potential energy due to the energy stored in their position (c) or chemical bonds (a, d, e).

READING 3.5 CLOSED AND OPEN SYSTEMS

See *Student Edition,* p. 86.

SAMPLE ANSWERS TO QUESTIONS

1. a. Tub 4 (More people are born than die.)
   b. Tub 2 (Amount of water is relatively constant, but it cycles.)
   c. Tub 3 (Water comes in and goes out, but the relative amount remains constant.)

d. Tub 3 (Energy comes in from outside, but there is not much change over time. One also could argue for tub 4 if students reason that there is a gradual increase in the average temperature.)

e. Tub 3 (Births and deaths are equal.)

f. Answers will vary; for teenagers, tub 4 probably represents their growth.

g. Tub 2 (Materials are used over and over.)

2. Answers will vary. It is important at this point that the students understand the difference between a closed system and an open system. On Earth, mineral/resource cycles are closed systems—no new materials come in from outside. But our energy flow on Earth is an example of an open system because the Sun shines in from outside the system. Students' ecodomes should reflect these features of Earth.

3. Students should point out that sunshine comes to the earth from outside our closed system. This energy is converted into resources that are part of the closed system.

READING 3.6 CONSERVATION LAWS

See *Student Edition*, p. 87.

SAMPLE ANSWERS TO QUESTIONS

1. Even when we get rid of our garbage from our homes or schools, the trash has to go somewhere. The conservation of mass means that all mass, such as garbage, is always here in some form. Trash is buried, but it is many years before it breaks down enough to be unrecognizable. Also, some of the chemicals that come from buried garbage can be harmful if they enter the water we drink.

2. There will not be a source of energy to power the machine. Even if students take a source of energy along, it will not last indefinitely.

3. Students should realize that the device is just transforming the pollutants, not eating them up and making them disappear.

4. Natural litter is broken down quickly by decomposers into minerals and resources that are quickly used again and recycled. This is the basic action underlying all of the mineral/resource cycles, except the water cycle.

5. In everyday life, trash that is buried is not destroyed. Responses to this question will be similar to those for the first question.

6. It does not change the total amount. Aluminum is economically more valuable when it is concentrated and easily accessible. Recycling helps keep it in this condition.

ACTIVITY 3.4 THE CONSERVATION OF MASS

See *Student Edition*, p. 89.

ADVANCE PREPARATION

To make the solutions:

* 0.1M Na_2CO_3; Mass out 10.60 g of Na_2CO_3. Add distilled water to the sodium carbonate and build the volume to 1 liter.

* 0.1M $Ca(CH_3COO)_2$: Mass out 17.62 g of $(CH_3CO)_2 Ca.H_2O$. Add distilled water to the calcium acetate and build the volume to 1 liter.

Prepare the lab stations before you teach this activity. Review or teach how to use the balance, as necessary.

You may want to reproduce the data table from Figure 3.17 to save time during class.

Review the safety precautions for this lab.

STRATEGIES AND PROCEDURES

This activity demonstrates the conservation of mass nicely, but it is very dependent on attention to detail. Students need to measure the mass precisely and record their data carefully in the correct spot on the data collection table.

In step 15, students may respond as follows:

    a. Matter can be rearranged, changed, reused, or altered.

    b. This was a closed system because everything stayed within the same system.

ACTIVITY 3.5 FORMS OF ENERGY EXPERTS

See *Student Edition,* p. 90.

ADVANCE PREPARATION

Gather art supplies to encourage student creativity. Ask students to bring in materials that might be useful for making posters such as old magazines, colored paper, ribbon, and so forth.

STRATEGIES AND PROCEDURES

This activity relies on the jigsaw strategy. If students did not do well teaching other members of their group in earlier activities, you may want to have them make their presentations to the whole class, so you can monitor what is happening.

Remind students that they will have to make use of Readings 3.7 and 3.8 to do well in this activity. The creation of the posters can be a homework assignment.

READING 3.7 THE SIX FORMS OF ENERGY

See *Student Edition,* p. 91.

READING 3.8 ENERGY SOURCES

Transparency 3.2

See *Student Edition,* p. 95.

SAMPLE ANSWERS TO QUESTIONS

    1. The sun, tides, geothermal, fission, and fusion.

    2. The sun produces energy by a fusion reaction.

    3. Plants for food (short term), wood fiber, methane gas, petroleum, coal, oil shale, and tar sands.

    4. Petroleum.

ACTIVITY 3.6 ENERGY TRANSFORMATIONS

See *Student Edition*, p. 97.

 **3.3, 3.10, 3.11**

ADVANCE PREPARATION

Set up stations for as many of the following devices as possible:

- flashlight battery (D-cell)
- digital thermometer
- solar collector
- battery charger
- small firecracker, defused
- camera
- electric fan (or other electric motor)
- chemical light stick
- solar cell (or calculator powered by a solar cell)
- radiometer
- angel chimes with unlit candles
- toaster (or other heating appliance)

Make one copy each of Blackline Masters 3.10 and 3.11 "Forms of Energy Chart" and "Devices/Processes Grid" for each student. (See pages 80–81). Sample answers to BLM 3.10 are on page 86.

STRATEGIES AND PROCEDURES

Ask students to identify the energy transformations that are possible with the device at each station. To extend this part of the exercise, introduce the Devices/Processes Grid in step 4 with illustrations of transformations that are difficult to represent in the classroom.

Step 1 answers will vary depending upon classroom stations.

Step 2 helps students connect the discussions of energy to their lives. Students should think of many everyday transformations. In step 3, the only form of energy not shown in Figure 3.26 is nuclear (unless students remember what is happening at the sun; however, that is not the form of energy depicted).

In step 6, students may respond as follows:

- Electric furnaces, ovens, and toasters are examples of household appliances that change electrical energy into heat.

An example of a process with at least three energy transformations is eating a meal (chemical energy) provides energy to ride a bike (mechanical energy). The movement of the bike allows the generator headlight to light up (electrical energy).

ACTIVITY 3.7 PLANTS AS ENERGY TRANSFORMERS

See *Student Edition*, p. 98.

The first step in this activity is a very useful type of formative assessment for determining what students know and how they are connecting the information. Based on the webs or maps students create, you may need to review certain concepts.

The rest of this activity guides the students through the process of conducting their own scientific inquiry about plants and energy. A simple experiment based on the question if plants need sunlight to grow will actually demonstrate the principle of converting sunlight into chemical energy that produces growth. Encourage students to keep their questions simple so that their inquiries are manageable and controllable.

In step 9, students should recognize that animals would not survive very long without plants. Even if we could survive for some time eating only other animals, we also rely on plants for the generation of oxygen.

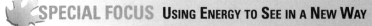

SPECIAL FOCUS Using Energy to See in a New Way

See *Student Edition*, p. 99.

READING 3.9 Energy Units and Conversion Factors

See *Student Edition*, p. 101.

ACTIVITY 3.8 Conversion Factors

See *Student Edition*, p. 102.

This is a good activity to team teach with a math teacher. Try grouping students by math ability to do this activity. You will need to work directly with students who have limited math skills.

ANSWERS TO QUESTIONS

1. 15.3 cm/6.0 in = 2.55 cm/in
2. Answers will vary.
3. 10 yards $\times$ 3 ft/1 yard = 30 ft $\times$ 12 in/1ft = 360 in $\times$ 2.5 cm/1 in = 900 cm
4. 30 cm $\times$ 1 in/2.5 cm = 12 in
5. 25 kg = 55 lbs
6. Number of calories = (temp. change in Celsius degrees) $\times$ (no. grams of water) = 8 g $\times$ 7C° = 56 calories
7. 150 g $\times$ 7C° = 1050 calories
8. 200 g $\times$ 60C° = 12,000 calories
9. 4.4 lbs $\times$ 20F° = 88 Btu
10. 50 lbs $\times$ 23F° = 1150 Btu
11. 4300 g $\times$ 60C° = 258,000 calories
12. 258,000/860 = 300 watt-hours
13. 300/1000 = 0.3 kWh
14. 0.3 kWh $\times$ 7 cents/kwh = 2.1 cents
15. 1022/365 = 2.8 years
16. 210/42 gal per barrel = 5 barrels
17. 750 lbs $\times$ 7F° = 5250 Btu
18. 6 barrels $\times$ 5.8 $\times$ 10^6 Btu/bbl = 34.8 $\times$ 10^6 Btu

19. 75 lbs × 4 ft = 300 ft-lb
20. 193 ft-lbs × 1 Btu/772 ft-lbs = 0.25 Btu

 READING 3.10 THE SECOND LAW OF THERMODYNAMICS (FORMS 1–3)

See *Student Edition,* p. 104.

 3.4

SPECIAL FOCUS THE KINETIC THEORY OF MATTER

See *Student Edition,* p. 105.

ACTIVITY 3.9 EXAMINING THE SECOND LAW

See *Student Edition,* p. 106.

3.4, 3.5

STRATEGIES AND PROCEDURES

This is a very thought-provoking experiment. Students will need to think abstractly to respond to the questions. Some students will find that difficult, but for others it will be a welcome change from more concrete activities.

In step 2 for task 1, students may respond as follows:

2. a. The molecules of the hot gas move faster than the cold ones and force the paddle wheel to rotate clockwise.
    b. & c. The bulb gets dimmer. In a given amount of time, more hot gas molecules enter the right-hand chamber than cold gas molecules enter the left. The temperatures slowly equalize and the paddle wheel slows down.
    d. The bulb gets dimmer, the paddle wheel goes slower, and the hot side gets cooler as the cool side gets warmer.
    e. The heat flows from hot to cold; this is spontaneous.
    f. Turned the paddle wheel and lit the bulb.
    g. Energy that can easily be used to move objects or generate electricity is considered useful.
    h. Energy is not lost. The box is perfectly insulated. Usefulness decreased because the paddle wheel slows down and the brightness of the bulb gets dimmer. Also, the temperature in the two chambers equalizes as time goes by.

In step 1 for task 2, students may respond as follows:

* *Flaw #1:* Because there are more balls on the ascending side of the wheel, the clockwise and counterclockwise torques (or turning tendencies) cancel out and the wheel remains motionless. (There is also a little friction in the main bearing.)

* *Flaw #2:* No magnet powerful enough to pull a ball up the ramp would permit the ball to drop through the hole. It would zoom past the hole and stick to the magnet.

For Task 3: Choosing Disorder

1. Puddle = Most Disordered
2. Random Blocks = Most Disordered
3. Luke Warm = Most Disordered
4. Random Pool Balls = Most Disordered
5. Salt Water = Most Disordered

True Natural systems have a natural tendency to move toward (or become) a more disordered state.

BLM 3.4, 3.6
Transparency 3.3

ACTIVITY 3.10 IT'S A ONE WAY STREET

See *Student Edition,* p. 108.

ADVANCE PREPARATION

You will need 100 pennies for each team of students. You can substitute any small, flat object that has a "head" side and a "tail" side. Alternatively, you can conduct this activity as a demonstration and use volunteers to shake and dump the pennies.

STRATEGIES AND PROCEDURES

This activity takes seemingly unrelated events—dumping pennies, growing plants, and questions about cars, silver, and children—to help demonstrate the universal nature of the second law of thermodynamics. Make sure your students are making this connection.

In step 6, students may respond as follows:

6. a. The pennies are part of a system that includes the tray, the desktop/floor and the people.
   b. The pennies are less ordered as they fall.
   c. Energy must be added to the system to restore the order.

In step 7, students may respond as follows:

7. a. Plants cannot create order without sunlight powering the photosynthesis process. The sun is the outside energy source that drives the plant system.
   b. We are disposing of silver in a disorderly manner that requires too much energy to retrieve it from our dumps. The silver is "lost" from an economical point of view.
   c. An automobile breaks up orderly gasoline molecules as it extracts energy from them. It requires energy to put those molecules back together again (recycle them), and this would not make economic sense.
   d. Parents usually like their living space picked up and neat. This is order. Children have a tendency to take toys and other things out and not put them away. This is disorder.
   e. Form 3; the iron in the mine is more concentrated (less random) than the iron that is spread out in landfills.
   f. Energy.
   g. Plants create order in their structures as they grow. Animals (including humans) destroy that order as they extract energy from the plants they use for food and fuel. In the process, animals give back to plants the carbon

dioxide and water they need for growth. Humans dominate this equation. When we maintain a balance, these energy relationships can be maintained indefinitely.

READING 3.11 ENERGY AND EFFICIENCY

See *Student Edition,* p. 110.

ACTIVITY 3.11 LET'S HAVE TEA!

See *Student Edition,* p. 111.

ADVANCE PREPARATION

Collect the necessary materials for this activity. If you do not have enough immersion heaters for pairs of students to do the activity, consider coordinating this activity with another, such as Activity 3.10, and have students trade off who is working with the immersion heaters. Many hardware and drug stores sell immersion heaters.

STRATEGIES AND PROCEDURES

After the students complete step 1, discuss the variables they identified. Then discuss which ones they can control in the classroom. Review the protocol and safety issues in step 2 with the students. Remind them that a protocol is an established procedure that scientists use to help them move more efficiently through an experiment. It is not the same thing as the experiment.

After the students finish their experiments, conduct a discussion to help them relate their experiences to the concept of efficiency.

In step 6, students may respond as follows:

6. a. Some of the energy was lost as heat to the air and through the sides of the cup.
    b. One possibility is to put a top on the system; another would be to insulate the sides of the cup.
    c. No loss of heat; all heat energy from the heater would go into changing the temperature of the water.
    d. Answers will vary depending on the student's point of view, but in general it is not considered a very efficient system.
    e. The system is convenient, which outweighs concerns about efficiency.

SAMPLE ANSWERS TO QUESTIONS

1. The system would be creating energy.
2. Generally, the bottom portion lists heat engines, devices that convert heat into mechanical energy. This energy is used to counteract the natural entropy flow, as well as in changing energy from one form to another.
3. These devices lose a lot of heat as they operate. Their purpose is not to heat the space around them. This lost heat greatly reduces their efficiency.
4. At each step, energy is transformed and heat is lost. This lost energy is not available for accomplishing the desired task.

5. 50%.
6. {150,000 ft-lbs / [3,000,000 calories × (1 ft-lb / 0.3239 cal)]} × 100 = 1.62%

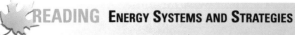 **READING** **ENERGY SYSTEMS AND STRATEGIES**

See *Student Edition*, p. 113.

Transparency 3.4

READING 3.12 **SYSTEM EFFICIENCY**

See *Student Edition*, p. 113.

SAMPLE ANSWERS TO QUESTIONS

1.

Step	Efficiency	Cumulative
a. Produce coal	96%	96%
b. Transport coal	97%	93%
c. Generate electricity	33%	31%
d. Transmit electricity	85%	26%
e. Charge storage battery	93%	25%
f. Operate large electric motor	93%	23%

2. From a total energy use perspective, natural gas uses energy most wisely.

Step	Efficiency	Cumulative
Electric (coal fired)		
a. Coal production	96%	96%
b. Coal transportation	97%	93%
c. Electricity generation	33%	31%
d. Electricity transmission	85%	26%
e. Heater efficiency	95%	25%
Fuel Oil		
a. Crude oil production	96%	96%
b. Fuel oil refining	90%	86%
c. Fuel oil transportation	97%	83%
d. Furnace efficiency	63%	52%
Natural Gas		
a. Natural gas production	96%	96%
b. Natural gas transportation	97%	93%
c. Furnace efficiency	75%	70%

READING 3.13 **NET ENERGY**

See *Student Edition*, p. 117.

 3.7   **READING 3.14** **THE CONCEPT OF ENERGY QUALITY**

See *Student Edition*, p. 119.

1. When energy is concentrated, it is more useful because we do not need to use more energy to collect it.

 **ACTIVITY 3.12** MATCHING SOURCE TO END-USE

 3.7

See *Student Edition,* p. 120.

You may want to assign this activity for homework and then discuss in class.

Pair I: Choice 2. Heating a home is a low-quality task, and so it should require a low-quality source for its accomplishment. Fossil fuels rank below nuclear energy on a quality scale, so natural gas makes the better source.

Pair II: Choice 1. Heating a home is a low-quality task. Electrical and electronic devices are high-quality gadgets. High-quality energy should be used for electrical/electronic applications and lower-quality sources, such as solar, should be devoted to the heating of buildings.

READING 3.15 ANOTHER ENERGY UNIT

See *Student Edition,* p. 121.

ACTIVITY 3.13 PEOPLE AND ENERGY USE

See *Student Edition,* p. 122.

STRATEGIES AND PROCEDURES

1. Use Figures 7.30 and 7.31 to help choose a variety of countries to compare.
2. The World Book Encyclopedia and other resources recommended by a social studies teacher can provide general information about each country.
3. Use the following website to obtain primary energy consumption per person for each country: http://www.eia.doe.gov/emeu/international/contents.html. Select "Total Energy" and click "Population." Then click "Per Capita (Person) Total Primary Energy Consumption All Countries, 1980–2003 (Million Btu/Person)."
4. The efficiency of energy use per country can only be a wild guess unless a dedicated student commits to do some difficult research on the subject.
5. Quality of life is introduced here for purposes of discussion. This item will mean more if you did Activity 2.5. It will take on more meaning as you progress through the course.
6. You may choose to do only selected portions of this activity.

This activity helps students visualize how life changes based on how we use energy. It is not intended to judge other cultures. Help students understand the pros and cons of different types of energy use. Make sure that students do enough background research that they do not revert to ill-informed stereotypes for their skits.

READING 3.16 STRATEGIES FOR RESOURCE USERS

See *Student Edition,* p. 123.

SAMPLE ANSWERS TO QUESTIONS

1. It is lost in the form of heat. It escapes up smokestacks, out tailpipes, off the fins on engines, and out poorly insulated walls.
2. Conservation; insulation; improve the efficiency of engines, lightbulbs, and appliances; and examine our energy systems.
3. Encourage students to think of personal actions they are willing to take.

CHAPTER 3 SUMMARY

See *Student Edition,* p. 124.

ACTIVITY 3.X A "VITAL COMMODITY" IN ECOSYSTEMS

See *Teacher Guide,* p. 77.

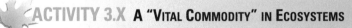

STRATEGIES AND PROCEDURES

Purpose

The purpose of this activity is to roughly model energy flow through an ecosystem. Do *not* reveal this purpose ahead of time. The student's directions suggest that the beans represent some "vital commodity" that is transferred through the food web. Use that phrase throughout the activity, until the concept of energy flow is introduced in the later questions. Some students will realize that energy is the vital commodity. Encourage discussion and explanations between students. Do not use the term "energy" yourself until the time comes.

Procedure

Follow the procedure given in the student activity. Use the role cards as shown on the next page. Have one empty box or jar labeled "LOSSES" in the center of the room or simulation area. Place a large box or jar full of beans marked "SUPPLY" near the center of the room so it is in easy reach of the students. Large dried beans work well for this activity.

Fill and label paper bags (one per student) before class. For a class of thirty, the following numbers of bags and beans are recommended. (Adjust the number of bags proportionately for smaller or larger classes.)

If you plan to use this activity with more than one class, have students return the bags to their original count before leaving class.

You may choose to make a transparency of the chart to aid in recording class data. Note that multiplying the number of students by the number of

Plankton:	8 bags with 30 beans each	
Mullet:	5 bags with 15 beans each	
Shrimp:	5 bags with 15 beans each	
Crab:	3 bags with 10 beans each	Total bags = 30.
Redfish:	3 bags with 10 beans each	
Dolphin:	3 bags with 10 beans each	
Heron:	2 bags with 5 beans each	
Crocodile:	1 bag with 5 beans	

beans in the bag (the first and second columns) gives the total number of beans in the system at the *beginning* of the simulation. Thus, the students will need to count the beans in their bag at the end to fill in the final column. You should supply the data for the first column. This is determined by the size of your class and the number of students you assign to each role.

You may wish to project the marine food web shown on page 74 to help students visualize the food web they are modeling.

Doing the simulation and recording class data requires about 45-50 minutes. Additional time is required for discussion of the questions.

ANSWERS TO THE QUESTIONS

1. The plankton finish with the most beans. The heron and crocodile will probably get the least, although some of the other organisms that are subject to frequent predation may have been the losers. Some deaths of individuals or even all members of a species are possible. This happens because (a) the plankton is the largest population and (b) the plankton population has the most of the "vital commodity" available. The other populations are progressively smaller, depending on the position they occupy in the food web. They are vulnerable to predation (except for the crocodile and the dolphin) and may have a hard time finding food. They also tend to lose the "vital commodity" in living and in searching for food.

2. The jar full of beans represents the basic supply of the "vital commodity" (energy from sunlight). Only the plankton have the ability to capture and use the "vital commodity" from its basic source (i.e., energy from sunlight).

3. The crocodiles would have gotten more of the "vital commodity." (This demonstrates the favored position of herbivores over carnivores in the food web.)

4. The mullet has an advantage. It eats plankton, and therefore, has a greater food supply (energy supply) available.

5. This models a real ecosystem. There are more plants than animals. (Technically, the plant population represents a greater biomass and a greater energy reservoir than do the various animal populations. This is the classic energy pyramid. The pyramid with which we began—assuming a class of thirty students—is depicted below. You may wish to share this pyramid with the class as the discussion develops.) This is the pyramid they make for item 10.

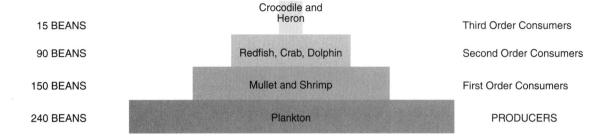

15 BEANS	Crocodile and Heron	Third Order Consumers
90 BEANS	Redfish, Crab, Dolphin	Second Order Consumers
150 BEANS	Mullet and Shrimp	First Order Consumers
240 BEANS	Plankton	PRODUCERS

Note: The diagram of a food web of a marine ecosystem used in this activity and in "What Eats What?" shows both plant and animal forms of plankton at the base. It is the phytoplankton (plant forms of plankton) that are the producers. Zooplankton (animal forms of plankton) are first order consumers. So, technically, there is one additional level in this pyramid that is not shown by the web. For the purposes of this discussion, it is permissible to consider plankton as producers and ignore the exchange that occurs between phytoplankton and zooplankton.

Note: Depending on the particular food chain one examines, the heron and the dolphin may be considered either second order or third order consumers. In the pyramid shown, the heron has been placed at the third level and the dolphin at the second. This choice has been made only for convenience, and other arrangements are possible.

6. They might represent the total body weight of all members of a population. They might also represent the amount of energy tied up in the bodies of all members of the population of each species. Each answer is correct, and both relationships apply.
7. Organisms use up some of the "vital commodity" in living and moving about. So, some of the vital commodity is lost before it has a chance to be passed on to other organisms.
8. (Same as #7)
9. Student responses will vary, depending on whether they have caught on to the fact that energy is the "vital commodity." Review the questions and explain energy flow as needed.

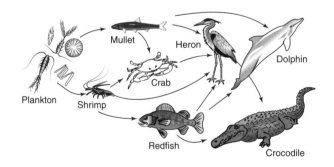

SOURCE: Crenshaw, Neil. Food Webs in the Classroom. The American Biology Teacher 43(2) (1981): 100–102.

Role: plankton
Eats: nothing
Is eaten by: mullet, shrimp

Role: heron
Eats: mullet, crab, shrimp, redfish
Is eaten by: crocodile

Role: shrimp
Eats: plankton
Is eaten by: crab, heron, redfish

Role: redfish
Eats: shrimp
Is eaten by: heron, crocodile, dolphin

Role: mullet
Eats: plankton
Is eaten by: crab, heron, dolphin

Role: dolphin
Eats: mullet, redfish
Is eaten by: nothing

Role: crab
Eats: shrimp, mullet
Is eaten by: heron

Role: crocodile
Eats: redfish, heron
Is eaten by: nothing

ALL TIED UP: (A FOOD WEB ACTIVITY)*

This animated exercise illustrates the concept of a food web in a particular ecosystem.

MATERIALS

large ball of heavy-duty string
signs to be held by students (or photos mounted on poster board) depicting typical members of a familiar ecosystem

Suggested representatives for a grassland-forest ecosystem would be grass, shrub, tree (producers); insect, squirrel, rabbit, deer, mouse (first order consumers); snake, hawk, wolf, mountain lion, eagle (second and third order consumers); and a vulture (scavenger).

STRATEGIES AND PROCEDURES

a. Choose several students to play the grass, shrub, and tree. Have them sit in the center of the room holding their role card. You may introduce the word *producer* at this time. Continue to distribute the role cards to other students, saving the vulture card for the class clown (each class has one).

b. Hand one end of the string to the "grass" and unroll the string as you move toward the "rabbit"; hand the string to the rabbit. You can introduce the terms *herbivore or first order consumer* at this time.

c. Continue unwinding the string as you move toward the wolf. Introduce *second order consumer and carnivore* at this time.

d. Make a true web by connecting the wolf to a mouse that eats the bush that also produces food for the insect that is consumed by the snake that also eats the mouse. Continue this intertwining until every member except the vulture is involved. Make sure that you show that some animals may serve as food for several others and that your first and second order consumers eat a variety of food.

e. While the students are holding their strings up high and fairly tight, you may wish to quiz several of them about what they eat and what eats them. *Predator* and *prey* can be introduced.

f. Suggest that a housing developer moves into the area and cuts down the trees, digs up the bushes, and plows under the grass.

g. Instruct the other members of the community that since their source of food is gone, they too must die and release their string.

h. Remind the students that amid all of the death and destruction there is one organism that is happy with all of this. That is the vulture that has been patiently observing the whole event. It is the scavenger that now gets to clean up the mess as you hand him or her the ball of string.

i. Collect the role cards as the vulture winds up the cord.

j. How would the results of this activity change if the developer saved some open space, planted a tree in front of each new home, and required all new home owners to landscape their yards within six months?

k. Review all vocabulary introduced.

*Developed by Thomas Messner, Global Science Teacher, 12711 W. Edgemont Avenue, Avondale, Az. 85323.

Name_____ Date _____ Period _____

ACTIVITY 3.X   A "VITAL COMMODITY" IN ECOSYSTEMS

PURPOSE

1. To model the transfer of a "vital commodity" through a food web.
2. To see how much of that "vital commodity" is available to different organisms in an ecosystem.

INTRODUCTION

In the activity "All Tied Up" you examined food chains and food webs. Perhaps you realized that all the interconnections mean something important. They mean that a "vital commodity" is transferred from one organism to another. Obviously, the transfer involves food. But what is so important about food? In this activity, you will have a chance to find out.

MATERIALS

Per student: One role card
One bag of beans (your teacher will provide)

Per class: One large box or jar full of beans marked "SUPPLY"
One empty box or jar marked "LOSSES"
One light source placed over the supply box area

PROCEDURE

Your teacher will give you a role card and a paper bag with some beans in it. The number of beans you start out with will be different from the number held by other students. Don't worry about that difference now. Its meaning will become clear later on.

Stand up and approach another student that is holding a role card. If your role card allows you to eat the organisms represented by that student, you may take five beans from that student. If that student's organisms can eat your organisms, you must give up five beans. After you have "eaten," you cannot eat again until you have placed two beans in the box marked "LOSSES." If your encounter with another student results in no transfer of beans (because that student's organism cannot eat your organism and vice versa), simply move on to another student. But first place one bean in the "LOSSES" box. Both you and the other student should do this.

If your role is *plankton,* you may go to the box or jar of beans marked "SUPPLY" and remove ten beans after each encounter with another student. This box is located under a light. No other students are allowed to remove beans from the "SUPPLY." After removing ten beans from the box, plankton must go immediately to the "LOSSES" box and deposit one bean.

If you lose all the beans in your bag, you are dead and must withdraw from the simulation.

One organism eats another.	Take five beans, put two in the "LOSSES" box.
Plankton.	Remove ten beans from "SUPPLY" after each encounter, place one in the "LOSSES" box.
Neither organism eats the other.	Each student places one bean in "LOSSES" box.
An organism loses all beans.	Withdraw from the simulation.

Do the simulation for 10 to 15 minutes. Then follow the directions given to complete the following chart:

Organism	Number of Beans at Start		Number of Students Representing Organism		Total Number of Beans at Start	Total Number of Beans at Finish
Plankton	30	×		=		
Mullet	15	×		=		
Shrimp	15	×		=		
Crab	10	×		=		
Redfish	10	×		=		
Dolphin	10	×		=		
Heron	5	×		=		
Crocodile	5	×		=		

After completing the chart with data provided by everyone in class, answer the following questions:

QUESTIONS

1. Which organisms finished with the most beans? Which got the least? Why do you think this happened?

2. What does the "SUPPLY" represent in a real ecosystem? Why were the plankton the only organisms allowed to withdraw beans from the box?

3. What do you think would have happened to the crocodiles if they could have taken beans from the plankton?

4. Do you think the mullet has an advantage in the game over the dolphin? Why or why not?

5. You may have realized that there were more plankton in the simulation than there were crocodiles or herons. Why was the simulation set up this way?

6. Dolphins are much larger organisms than mullet. Yet the dolphins started out with fewer beans than did the mullet. Thus, the beans do not represent the body weight of a single organism. What might the beans represent?

7. Why were all of the organisms in the simulation required to place beans in the "LOSSES" box?

8. Why were you required to place a bean in the "LOSSES" box after encountering an organism that you could not eat and that could not eat you?

9. At the beginning of this activity, we talked about a "vital commodity." Perhaps you realize that the "vital commodity" is energy. Go back and recast your answers to questions 1–8 with this in mind. Explain how the beans represent energy flow through the ecosystem.

10. Make an energy pyramid for the food we examined at the start of this activity. Place the plankton at the bottom of the pyramid as indicated in the following chart. Complete to scale on another sheet of paper.

_____ Beans	Crocodile and Heron	Third Order Consumer
_____ Beans	Redfish, Crab, Dolphin	Second Order Consumer
_____ Beans	Mullet and Shrimp	First Order Consumer
_____ Beans	Plankton	Producers

Extra Credit: Make a similar energy pyramid for the finish of this activity.

Energy Flow and Matter Cycles

Energy can be converted from one form to another. We do this when we use energy.

In each of the empty boxes below, write the number of the device or method that could convert energy from the form listed on the left side to the form named at the top. An example is done for you. The numbers for the devices and methods appear on Blackline Master 3.11. Place only one number in a box; no number is used more than once. Sample answers for this chart can be found on p. 86 of the *Teacher Guide*.

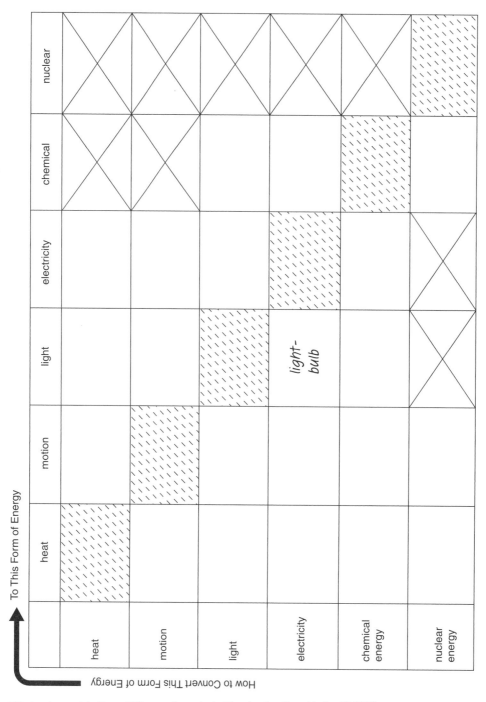

This chart is part of the Energy 80 Program, Enterprise for Education, Inc., Santa Monica, CA 90401.

These boxes show examples of devices and processes in which one form of energy is converted to another form. Place the number of the example in the appropriate box on the energy chart. You may need to use a dictionary or an encyclopedia to find a description of some of these examples.

1. flashlight battery

2. electron falling to lower orbit

3. thermocouple, digital hospital thermometer

4. nuclear reactor

5. solar collector

6. battery charger

7. firecracker, dynamite

8. friction (rub hands together)

9. radiation treatment

10. red-hot branding iron

11. photographic film

12. electric fan (electric motor)

13. light stick, firefly

14. solar cell

15. nuclear blast

16. wind generator

17. Crooke's Radiometer

18. combustion (fire)

19. Angel chimes

20. electric toaster

Name _____ Date _____

MATCHING

Match the terms and definitions below.

A. calorie   B. joule   C. kilowatt-hour   D. foot-pound   E. Btu

1. _____ Electricity is normally bought and sold in these units.

2. _____ The energy content of food is most often expressed in these units.

3. _____ In the United States, heating systems and air conditioners are rated in terms of their ability to provide or withdraw so many of these units per cubic foot.

4. _____ The amount of heat necessary to raise the temperature of one gram of water one Celsius degree.

5. _____ The nonmetric unit for mechanical energy or work.

MULTIPLE CHOICE

6. The ability to move matter around is the definition of

   A. mass.   B. oil.   C. system.   D. energy.   E. unit.

7. Which of the following would be an example(s) of kinetic energy?
   A. flying arrow   D. a and b only
   B. thrown baseball   E. a and c only
   C. charged battery

8. _____ A system where nothing enters or leaves is called a(n)
   A. steady state.   D. closed system.
   B. static system.   E. random state.
   C. open system.

9. _____ Which of the following is the correct order for a food chain?
   A. herbivore—producer—secondary consumer
   B. producer—herbivore—secondary consumer
   C. secondary consumer—producer—herbivore
   D. producer—secondary consumer—herbivore

10. _____ Which of the following is *not* a form of energy?
   A. mechanical   D. chemical
   B. photosynthesis   E. light (radiant)
   C. electrical

11. _____ Using gasoline to run a car and eating food so that you can make it through the day would be examples of
   A. heat energy.   D. geothermal energy.
   B. radiant energy.   E. chemical energy.
   C. nuclear energy.

12. _____ All of the following are primary *sources* of energy *except*
   A. chemical.
   B. geothermal.
   C. solar.
   D. tidal.
   E. fission.

13. _____ We currently use uranium and thorium as materials for our nuclear power plants in the United States. What type of nuclear power plants do we have?
   A. fission
   B. hydro
   C. fusion
   D. a mixture of fission and fusion
   E. none of the above

14. _____ All of the following are statements of the second law of thermodynamics *except*
   A. in any conversion of energy from one form to another, there is always a decrease in the amount of *useful* energy.
   B. in any closed system, disorder (entropy) always tends to increase toward a maximum.
   C. heat is work and work is heat.
   D. in a closed system, heat will spontaneously flow from hot to cold.

15. _____ All of the following words mean the same thing *except*
   A. entropy.
   B. chaos.
   C. randomness.
   D. disorder.
   E. arrangement.

16. _____ The "agony of the heat" refers to the fact that
   A. heat is a form of energy.
   B. heat is uncomfortable when one's surroundings become too hot.
   C. heat can be changed to work (mechanical energy) and from work (mechanical energy) back to heat.
   D. all energy ultimately ends up as relatively worthless low-temperature heat.
   E. the relationship between high heat and high humidity creates a stressful environment for living things.

17. _____ Iron is mined from an area of concentrated iron ore and made into thousands of products, which eventually end up in landfills and dumps. Which form of the second law of thermodynamics does this represent?
   A. In any conversion of energy from one form to another, there is always a decrease in the amount of useful energy.
   B. Heat cannot flow from cold to hot.
   C. In any closed system, randomness tends toward a maximum.
   D. Humans, with a high standard of living, tend to waste energy.

18. _____ We are running out of useful energy for all of the following reasons *except*
   A. the energy sources we rely on most are presently nonrenewable sources.
   B. energy cannot be recycled.
   C. energy can neither be created nor destroyed.
   D. as energy is used, it ultimately ends up as low-temperature heat.
   E. heat spontaneously flows from hot to cold.

19. _____ The most efficient device listed below is a(n)
   A. large electric motor.
   B. steam electric power plant.
   C. incandescent lightbulb.
   D. diesel engine.
   E. automobile engine.

20. _____ Twenty-five (25) calories of energy are put into a device that does 10 calories of useful work. The efficiency of this device is
A. 35%.   D. 100%.
B. 15%.   E. 2.5%.
C. 40%.

21. _____ Coal is burned in most of the electric power generating plants in the United States. It requires several steps to get the electrical energy to your home. The chart below show those steps and the efficiency of each.
The overall efficiency of providing electrical energy by this method is
A. 97%.   D. 76%.
B. 85%.   E. 26%.
C. 33%.

Step	Efficiency (%)
Production of coal	96
Transportation of coal	97
Generation of electricity	33
Transmission of electricity	85

22. _____ How much energy represented by a standing tree ends up warming a cabin that is heated with a wood-burning stove? Base your answer on these data.

Step	n
Production of wood (cutting and trimming)	66
Transportation of logs	98
Wood-burning stove	25

A. 7%   C. 16%
B. 10%   D. 189%

23. _____ In the following food chain, where is the greatest about of energy contained?

grain→mice→snakes→hawks

A. grain   D. hawks
B. mice   E. none of these
C. snakes

24. _____ Why are there more rabbits than coyotes on Earth?
A. Rabbits are herbivores.
B. Rabbits are closer to the bottom of the food chain.
C. A greater source of food supports a larger population.
D. All of the above.

25. _____ Why do vegetarians use food energy more efficiently than nonvegetarians?
A. Only one energy transformation is involved.
B. Many transformations are required to change the plant energy to human energy.
C. Some intermediate steps are necessary after the food is placed in the mouth.
D. More useful energy is lost by vegetarians.
E. You can eat fruits and vegetables quickly because they do not require preparation like meats do.

26. _____ Respiration is the process by which the majority of living organisms form these two by-products.
   A. nitrogen and water
   B. carbon and water
   C. oxygen and water
   D. carbon dioxide and water

27. _____ Energy is most usable where it is concentrated, such as in
   A. low temperatures.
   B. chemical bonds.
   C. automobile exhaust.
   D. none of the above.

28. _____ The *least* useful form of energy is
   A. mechanical.
   B. ambient temperature heat.
   C. gasoline.
   D. electrical.
   E. hot water.

29. _____ All of the following strategies are useful for taking care of our energy resources *except*
   A. changing lifestyles so we consume less energy.
   B. redesigning technology to be more efficient.
   C. perfecting the use of nontraditional energy sources.
   D. matching the quality of the energy source to the task being performed.
   E. storing energy in preparation for an economic depression.

30. _____ Food chains start with producers and end with
   A. carnivores.
   B. herbivores.
   C. omnivores.
   D. insects.
   E. decomposers.

SHORT ANSWER

Write a brief response to each item.

31. Why are we "running out" of silver? _____

_____

_____

32. Energy can neither be created nor destroyed, but it can be _____

_____

33. Matter can neither be created nor destroyed. It can, however, be _____

_____

SAMPLE ANSWERS FOR BLACKLINE MASTER 3.10

To This Form of Energy (rows) / **How to Convert This Form of Energy** (columns)

To This Form of Energy ↓ \ How to Convert →	heat	motion	light	electricity	chemical energy	nuclear energy
heat	(shaded)	8	5	20	18	4
motion	19	(shaded)	17	12	7	15
light	10	2	(shaded)	light-bulb	13	✗
electricity	3	16	14	(shaded)	1	✗
chemical	✗	✗	11	6	(shaded)	9
nuclear	✗	✗	✗	✗	✗	(shaded)

This chart is part of the Energy 80 Program, Enterprise for Education, Inc., Santa Monica, CA 90401.

CHAPTER 3 ASSESSMENT

1. C
2. A
3. E
4. A
5. D
6. D
7. D
8. D
9. B
10. B
11. E
12. A
13. A
14. C
15. E
16. D
17. C
18. C
19. A
20. C
21. E
22. C
23. A
24. D
25. A
26. D
27. B
28. B
29. E
30. E
31. It is being scattered around the globe.
32. Transformed from one form to another.
33. Rearranged.

CHAPTER

4

MINERAL RESOURCES

LEARNING OUTCOMES

The student will:

1. know what a mineral is by completing the activity "Grow Your Own." (C,P)

2. identify common rock-forming minerals by manipulating materials and equipment and completing the activity "What Mineral Is It?" (C,P)

3. classify rocks by manipulating rock samples, examining information, and completing the activity "What Rock Is It?" (C,P)

4. construct a scale model of Earth's cross section and analyze its significance by completing the activity "What's Inside Earth?" (C,P)

5. compare the orientation of the five continents bordering the Atlantic Ocean and speculate about how they may have been arranged centuries ago by manipulating materials and completing the activity "Matching Continents." (C,P)

6. use maps to provide evidence for plate tectonics by completing the activity "Map Evidence for Plate Tectonics." (C)

7. identify relationships between tectonic plates and the existence of volcanoes, earthquake activity, and so forth by completing the activity "Map Evidence for Plate Tectonics." (C)

8. model some of the processes by which minerals become concentrated in Earth's crust by manipulating materials and equipment and completing the activity "Concentrate on Your Minerals." (C,P)

9. summarize the major ways in which ore bodies form. (C)

10. state why gold would be more likely to be found in a rapidly flowing stream than in a slow one. (C)

11. list the kinds of devices used to locate ore bodies. (C)

12. define the following terms: ore, gangue, tailing, placer, refining, smelting, and flotation. (C)

13. explain where the useful mineral is separated from the gangue. (C)

14. plan a procedure for milling an unknown crushed ore sample by manipulating materials and equipment and completing the activity "Milling Lab." (C,P)

15. write a group report based on the results of separating the minerals from an unknown crushed ore sample by completing the activity "Milling Lab." (C)

16. realize the importance to our society of twelve key minerals by completing the activity "Importance of Minerals Revisited." (A)

17. name the three elements essential to nonorganic fertilizer production. (C)

18. explain how agriculture is affected by the mineral industry. (C)

19. examine major mineral issues by completing the activity "Mineral Issues." (C)

20. appreciate why it is important for an industrial country to maintain trade relations with other countries of the world. (A)

21. realize that using substitutes for minerals in short supply will extend the date of a shortage crisis. (A)

KEY TERMS

natural resources	metamorphic	plate tectonics	seismic	refining
mineral resources	magma	rift	magnetometer	alloy
crystal	lava	seafloor spreading	remote sensing	fertilizer
mineral	extrusive	subduction	mine	ceramics
physical weathering	intrusive	uplift	underground mining	steel
chemical weathering	foliation	ore bodies	open pit mining	strategic
rock-forming minerals	clastic	ore	solution mining	reclamation
element	crust	secondary enrichment	gangue	conservation
rock	mantle	residual enrichment	tailing	substitution
igneous	core	placer	milling	recycling
sedimentary	lithosphere	mechanical concentration	smelting	severance tax

RECOMMENDED BLACKLINE MASTERS

4.1 Minerals

4.2 Pangaea

4.3 Map Evidence—Plate Tectonics

4.4 Map Evidence—Plate Tectonics

4.5 Convection Cell Models

4.6 Milling Lab

4.7 Milling Lab—Separation Scheme

4.8 Steps in Metal Production

The Recommended Blackline Masters listed above are supplemental to the activity/reading, and can be found on the *Teacher Resource CD*.

CHAPTER 4: MINERAL RESOURCES

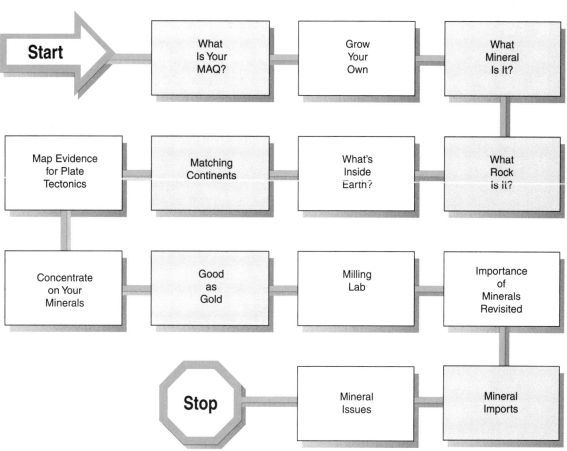

Start → What Is Your MAQ? → Grow Your Own → What Mineral Is It?

Map Evidence for Plate Tectonics → Matching Continents → What's Inside Earth? → What Rock is it?

Concentrate on Your Minerals → Good as Gold → Milling Lab → Importance of Minerals Revisited

Stop → Mineral Issues → Mineral Imports

NOTE: Shaded items are lower priority.

TEACHING STRATEGIES AND ANSWERS FOR ACTIVITIES

READING 4.1 WHERE DOES IT ALL COME FROM? MINERALS!

See *Student Edition,* p. 130.

ACTIVITY 4.1 WHAT IS YOUR MAQ?

See *Student Edition,* p. 130.

STRATEGIES AND PROCEDURES

Teachers should approach this activity as a way to help students think beyond the unconscious grabbing a snack from the refrigerator, switching on a light, or hopping on a bike. We can't fully appreciate creature comforts without some awareness of where they come from. Remind students that the science of resources—both agricultural and mineral—is not simply academic, it is also the basis for many exciting careers.

PART A

In step 1, students can record their initial list on a separate sheet of paper or in their science notebook. Determine the amount of time appropriate for your students. Make sure their lists follow a format similar to the one shown in Figure 4.1.

In step 2, students should select five items from their initial list. Point out that although pencils, desks, and other objects may be made primarily of wood, they have non-wood components (rubber, aluminum, steel, etc).

For step 3, accept all reasonable answers. This step will help you assess students' current state of understanding on this topic.

SAMPLE ANSWERS TO QUESTIONS

Object	Ingredient(s)	Sources
Metal cabinet	Steel	Iron, carbon (coal), manganese
Light bulb	Glass, metal	Silica, tungsten, aluminum
Computer	Plastic, glass	Petroleum, mica, silica, tungsten, nickel, + about 30 trace elements
Linoleum floor	Plastic	Petroleum, limestone, kaolin

PART B

In step 1, students should acknowledge that we often take for granted many of the things we use each day.

In step 2, understanding that food must be grown, harvested, and processed may be a more familiar concept to students than mining. Emphasize that everything we use to survive must be mined *or* grown. Although we can't grow minerals (as we grow living plants), they still must be extracted and processed for them to be useful. Challenge students to think of something *not* derived from any living or nonliving resource. This will help students refine their understanding of a natural resource.

In steps 3–5, have students score their own MAQ. Tabulate the scores and share them with the class or simply ask students to record their personal MAQ in their science notebook. You can repeat this activity at the end of the chapter or at the completion of the course.

For step 6, have students write a definition in their science notebook. This is a good opportunity to assess understanding through class discussion.

READING 4.2 THE IMPORTANCE OF MINERALS

See *Student Edition*, p. 131.

READING 4.3 WHAT IS A MINERAL?

See *Student Edition*, p. 132.

ACTIVITY 4.2 GROW YOUR OWN

BLM 4.1

See *Student Edition*, p. 132.

This activity is best done before a long weekend or holiday to allow the solution to evaporate to a dry state. If sunny, solar heating on a windowsill will aid in drying. If humid or cool, the heat lamp apparatus will accelerate evaporation.

STRATEGIES AND PROCEDURES _____

This activity deemphasizes obtaining the "right" answer, but rather encourages learning by observing and doing. Emphasize that arriving at tentative answers or definitions is always the first step of scientific inquiry. Point out that minerals can "grow" in their own way—inorganically through crystallization, but never through the biological processes of cell division.

In steps 4–7, students may respond as follows:

4.   a. & b. Encourage students to observe details objectively. Point out that good science relies on the use of sketches to aid in understanding. If students simply write "crystals," make sure they describe what the crystals look like to them.

   c. Plants grow by increasing their mass and size, but minerals "grow" through the organization of their atoms (usually in a liquid state) into more ordered structures (usually in a solid state). Think of water freezing into ice as a way minerals "grow" from a cooling melt. The key difference is that many minerals freeze at temperatures of about 1000°C.

5.   Accept only the answers that incorporate students' *own* observations into a working hypothesis (which can and should be revised as new information is learned).

6.   See the glossary for a definition. A quick definition is *A mineral is any naturally occurring crystalline, inorganic Earth material.*

7.   *Charcoal:* Once living is not as relevant as the fact that charcoal briquettes are shaped by machines. Coal is a fossil fuel mineral, but not a true mineral according to the definition from step 6. *Sugar cube:* Not a mineral nor a crystal; is factory pressed into cubes from granular sugar. *Snowflakes:* Although it fits most of the criteria, it is not a true mineral. *Diamond* is a mineral because it is found in nature as a crystal and its arrangement of atoms is ordered and predictable. *Salt* is a mineral for the same reasons as diamond. *Fool's gold* is a common name for pyrite, which is a mineral.

Test students' understanding with your own examples. *Note:* Help students distinguish between nutrient minerals, which refer to chemicals used by living things to grow (e.g., nitrogen, potassium, sodium, etc.) and geologic minerals, which are the solid ingredients of rocks and soil. They are related because nutrient minerals are derived ultimately from geologic minerals.

READING 4.4 MINERAL PROPERTIES: CLUES FROM CHEMICALS

See *Student Edition*, p. 134.

 4.1

ACTIVITY 4.3 WHAT MINERAL IS IT?

See *Student Edition,* p. 136.

ADVANCE PREPARATION

For a good introduction to minerals, mineral identification, and mineral resources, have students watch the video "Minerals: Building Blocks of the Earth" as a preview to this lab.

STRATEGIES AND PROCEDURES

For this activity, again emphasize the need for careful observation and following directions. Make sure students study Figure 4.6 first, which gives examples of physical and chemical properties of minerals. This chart will have more meaning as students work through the exercise.

NOTES ON IDENTIFICATION

The simplified hardness scale that uses fingernails, glass, and a dull pocket knife or nail is adequate for this lab. Remind students that hardness is more a measure of "scratchability" than toughness. Make sure the powder you obtain from a streak test belongs to the mineral and not to the porcelain (which will occur if minerals harder than 7 are tested for streak). Advise students not to bite the samples when they check for hardness. Dilute solutions of HCl (10–15%) should be available at various locations around the classroom. Instruct students about its careful use. A nail and an inexpensive hand lens or magnifying glass are useful tools and should be placed with each mineral collection.

You should be able to gather some of the minerals locally. However, most teachers find it both convenient and economical to purchase commercially available mineral sets designed for classroom use. The following materials can be purchased by contacting your Kendall/Hunt representative:

biotite mica	hornblende
calcite	limonite
feldspar	magnetite
fluorite	muscovite mica
galena	pyrite
graphite	quartz (clear or white)
gypsum	quartz (Jasper or smoky quartz)
halite	talc
hematite	

It is also helpful to have larger specimens on display for students to examine. These examples can illustrate a particular mineral property (e.g., crystallinity vs. cleavage) or simply provide a reference or key for more hard to identify minerals. Photos from books or magazines are useful, but remind students that color alone should not be used to identify an unknown mineral.

READING 4.5 ROCKS: THE SOLID MATERIALS OF EARTH'S CRUST

See *Student Edition,* p. 139.

Transparency 4.2

ACTIVITY 4.4 WHAT ROCK IS IT?

See *Student Edition,* p. 143.

Transparency 4.3

ADVANCE PREPARATION

For a good introduction to rocks and the rock cycle, have students watch the video "The Rock Cycle" as a preview to this lab. Also, many students and their families may collect rocks as a hobby. Ask them to bring some in for identification.

STRATEGIES AND PROCEDURES

It is more difficult to teach students to identify rocks than to identify minerals. One reason is that rocks are named for their origin and not just for their mineral content. Spend one or two classes describing the system. One effective method is to prepare a collection of 15 different rock specimens as shown in the key "What Rock Is It?" Segregate them according to the three rock types. Allow students to examine the labeled specimens and record their observations. In a few days, let them work with the key to identify unknown samples that you supply. The following materials can be purchased by contacting your Kendall/Hunt representative:

basalt	granite	rhyolite
breccia	limestone	sandstone
conglomerate	marble	schist
gabbro	obsidian	shale
geiss	phyllite	slate

The biggest challenge for students is their frustration in discriminating among different kinds of fine-grained rocks. Similarly colored rocks all "look alike," so help students discern subtle, but important clues such as layering, presence or absence of crystals, and reactivity with dilute HCl. Make sure students have reviewed Figure 4.16, which explains many of these subtle differences.

READING 4.6 A LAYERED LOOK AT EARTH

See *Student Edition,* p. 146

ACTIVITY 4.5 WHAT'S INSIDE EARTH?

See *Student Edition,* p. 148.

STRATEGIES AND PROCEDURES

This activity helps students to appreciate how relatively thin Earth's crust is. This is the layer from which we obtain virtually *all* our mineral resources and all our food resources (soil). Make available references such as Earth science textbooks, encyclopedias, or electronic media for students to consult. This activity also dispels the common misconception that we drill or mine for Earth materials at impossible depths (where temperatures and pressures would melt and crush drills or mining equipment).

In steps 3–12, students may respond as follows:

Layer Name	Actual Thickness	Model Thickness	Compass At
Inner core	1250 km	2.0 cm	2.0 cm
Outer core	2250 km	3.6 cm	5.6 cm
Lower mantle	2100 km	3.4 cm	9.0 cm
Upper mantle	700 km	1.1 cm	10.1 cm
Crust	70 km	0.1 cm	10.2 cm

Demonstrate the correct use of a compass. Remind students to use a radius of 2 cm (r = 2 cm) on the compass's scale since the diameter of the circle will be 4r or 4 cm.

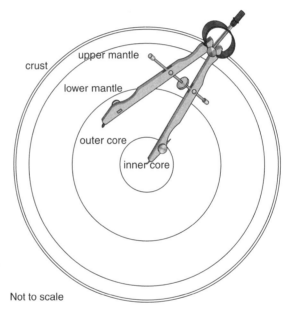

Not to scale

9. Check for accuracy; the table that follows is representative of the data students will find. CD-ROMs, encyclopedias, and library reference materials will provide the necessary data on Earth's interior.

10. Make sure students correctly identify and label each layer. Coloring the scale model using shades of brown, yellow, and red will help reinforce the concept of increasing heat and pressure with depth. The other key concept deals with the progressive density of materials with increasing depth. As a variation or for extra credit, have students plot density as a function of depth. Make sure their choice of colors is consistent and has a legend or key.

11. The depth shown will be miniscule with respect to Earth's radius.

12. Nickel and iron are abundant throughout most of Earth's internal mass. It is impractical to obtain them from such deep layers due to engineering problems of drilling through weak, hot rock. The problems encountered would prevent direct removal of the mineral resources.

Layer Name	Density	Temperature	Solid/Liquid/Other	Elements/Minerals Present
Inner core	12 g/cm³	8600°F	Solid	Iron-nickel, sulfur
Outer core	10–12.1 g/cm³	7000°F	Liquid	Iron-nickel, sulfur
Inner mantle	3.3–5.7 g/cm³	2700–5400°F	Solid	Iron and magnesium oxides and silicates
Outer mantle	3.3 g/cm³	2300–2700°F	Plastic, mobile	
Crust (oceanic)	2.9–3.1 g/cm³	O–hundreds degrees F	Solid	Silicon, aluminum, potassium, magnesium, iron oxides, and silicates
Crust (continental)	2.7 g/cm³			

 READING 4.7 PLATE TECTONICS: UPPER CRUST ON THE MOVE

See *Student Edition,* p. 150.

 ACTIVITY 4.6 MATCHING CONTINENTS

See *Student Edition,* p. 150.

 4.2

The supercontinent that students construct should look similar to Blackline Master 4.2. Note that continental drift (as conceived prior to the 1960s) is now considered an outdated, incomplete interpretation of why continents shift over time. The theory of plate tectonics is more inclusive and accounts for many other phenomena as well as continental drift.

SAMPLE ANSWERS TO QUESTIONS

1. Matching continental shelf boundaries yields a better fit than sea level borders. Over time, sea level borders fluctuate due to weathering and erosion, local uplift, and climate change. A physical map of the world reveals relatively shallow ocean water that "hides" the true edges of continents. These submerged portions of continental margins are called **continental shelves.**
2. These areas did not exist before drifting.
3. Europe and Africa are drifting *away* from North and South America.
4. Some type of collision and piling up of continents and/or collision and subduction must be taking place. Essentially, some form of "crustal recycling."
5. Accurate surveying to measure distances from fixed points on opposite land masses. Accept other thoughtful responses.

 ACTIVITY 4.7 MAP EVIDENCE FOR PLATE TECTONICS

See *Student Edition,* p. 152.

 4.3, 4.4

This activity can be done individually or by cooperative learning groups.

SAMPLE ANSWERS TO QUESTIONS

1. Plate Tectonic Theory is the name given to the idea that the earth's surface consists of six large plates and several smaller ones. These plates move on a pliable layer called the asthenosphere.

2. Map A shows the boundaries of the plates that cover the earth's surface.

3. The greatest earthquake activity is along the Pacific perimeter, in the eastern Mediterranean, and in Turkey.

4. Most of the world's volcanoes occur along the Pacific perimeter, along the northeastern edge of the Mediterranean, just west of the horn of Africa, in Iceland, and by the Sunda Islands.

5. The volcanoes of the Hawaiian Islands may be due to a hole, crack, or thin spot on the Pacific Plate. It is believed there is a hot spot below the moving plate that melts through the plate at various times.

6. The seafloor is youngest here because plates are moving apart. The seafloor that forms as magma moves into the void and hardens is the youngest. The seafloor gets older as one moves directly away from this boundary.

7. Earthquakes are more common where plates move together. In these regions, pressures build to high levels until slippage occurs (causing earthquakes).

8. More dense minerals are closest to the surface near plate boundaries. This is where magma is cooling and mineral deposits form.

9. Earthquakes occur most often along plate boundaries. This is where pressures focus and slippage occurs.

10. Magma is most likely to surface where plates collide and separate. During collision, cracks form and pressures are relieved. Magma then moves into the lower pressure region.

READING 4.8 ORIGIN OF ORE MINERALS

See *Student Edition,* p. 154.

ACTIVITY 4.8 CONCENTRATE ON YOUR MINERALS

See *Student Edition,* p. 156.

STRATEGIES AND PROCEDURES

This lab gives students an opportunity to see how nature concentrates minerals. Emphasize that without these processes, minerals would exist in concentrations too low to mine profitably. There is a lot of new vocabulary here, so encourage students to keep detailed notes and sketches in their science notebook.

Gather the following materials, which will likely take you portions of a couple of days. You will have to make some of the items. Give each lab group a title: A, B, C, and so on.

MATERIALS (PER LAB GROUP)

5 mL 0.3M $CuSO_4$ solution (see Activity 10.1 for directions)

2 50 mL beakers

1 iron nail

1 100 mL graduated cylinder

1 test tube and stopper

2 10 mL graduated cylinders

1 bottle of cooking oil

1 small bottle, KMnO$_4$ crystals
1 test-tube rack
1 250 mL Erlenmeyer flask of
    concentrated NaCl solution
1 10 mL graduated cylinder
1 petri dish
1 ringstand
2 utility clamps
1 glass column
1 500 mL beaker
minerals deposit #1 (90% sand, 10%
    copper sulfate crystals)
1 Bunsen burner or electric heater
3 150 mL beakers
pair of gloves or tongs
1 gauze pad and tape

1 funnel
250 mL Erlenmeyer flask of a
    supersaturated hypo solution
1 test tube and stopper
1 10 mL graduated cylinder
1 test-tube rack

Note: These materials are listed by section of the lab, so some items repeat. Students will need a test-tube rack at more than one station, so it is listed twice.

The expected results and descriptions are summarized in the chart that follows. This lab is far superior to giving a lecture on how minerals become concentrated.

Concentrating Process	Observations	Short Description of Concentrating Process
Replacement	Day 1: Some brown (copper) material begins to collect on the side of the nail.	One mineral gradually takes for itself the place occupied by another. This is due to differences in chemical activity.
	Day 2: The blue solution is now a brownish color (rusty water) and a thick brown solid has collected on the nail.	
Immiscible Liquids	Day 1: The two solutions are mixed together and look as one. However, they begin to separate as time passes.	A concentration can occur as two materials that won't mix separate. This is because only one of the layers contains the valuable substance.
	Day 2: A clear solution is located on the top. A purple water solution is located on the bottom. This contains the mineral.	
Deposition from Lake Water and Seawater	Day 1: A clear salt solution with a large surface area is in the petri dish.	Precipitation of valuable material occurs after its concentration has been increased by evaporation.
	Day 2: Small crystals of salt are on the bottom of the dish and a little liquid also remains.	
Secondary Enrichment and Residual Concentration	The warm water dissolves and carries away the blue salts contained in mineral deposit #1. The salt ends up in the beaker and worthless material remains in the column.	Occurs when a valuable material is dissolved and removed from one location and redeposited in a concentrated state somewhere else, or a worthless material is dissolved and carried away, leaving behind a concentration of valuable ore.
Selective Crystallization	Day 1: Some crystals were beginning to form in the cool liquid.	As some solutions cool, some dissolved minerals may crystalize before others. This results in the separation of some substances from others and may lead to the concentration of a valuable mineral.
	Day 2: Crystals in the bottom of the test tube with clear liquid above them.	

This activity requires adequate preparation as well as time for discussion.

Tape gauze to the lower portion of the glass column provided (see drawing). Add mineral deposit #1 to the column until it is 2/3 full. Attach the column to a ringstand. Place a 500 mL beaker below the column and a funnel in the top of the column. Slowly pour hot water into the top of the column. Do this in three steps, adding 100 mL each time.

Provide each lab group or student with a copy of the illustration that follows or make a transparency and project the drawing on to the screen.

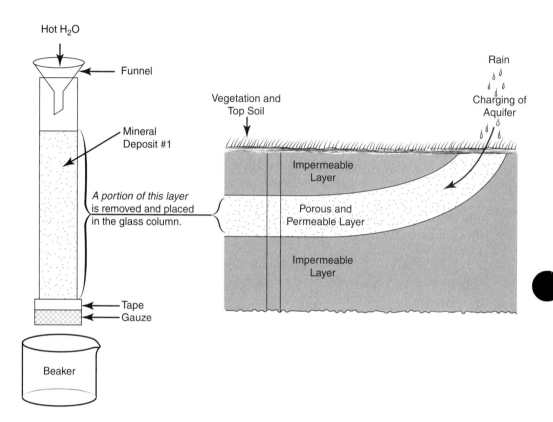

 4.5

Transparency 4.4

READING 4.9 ORE MINERALS AND PLATE TECTONICS

See *Student Edition*, p. 160.

ACTIVITY 4.9 GOOD AS GOLD

See *Student Edition*, p. 163.

ADVANCE PREPARATION _____

Before beginning this activity, do a quick demonstration that illustrates the concept nicely. Pour a slurry of playground sand into a tight-fitting glass jar. Shake and then set the jar down to let the sediment settle out. By the end of the class period, students should see how the denser minerals have settled on the bottom.

There are two essential points to this activity. First, mineral concentration can occur in familiar settings such as beaches or streams. Second, the activity can be fun and easily tied to a historical context that students will find a welcome break from previous labs. If possible, try scheduling a field trip to a local beach or stream to demonstrate how running water segregates minerals.

When you prepare the "gold ore," seed the 15–20 pounds of sand or gravel with three to five BBs per pan or student group.

SAMPLE ANSWERS TO QUESTIONS (PART B)

1. Slurry mixtures occur in streams or along beaches—wherever sediment is carried by running water.
2. Specific gravity or density.
3. No, because their specific gravities are nearly the same (see Figure 4.35).
4. Streamflow carrying gold-rich sediment. When the current slows down, sediment is dumped into sand or gravel bars along the inside curves of rivers or streams.
5. Magnetite, pyrite, copper, or platinum (any minerals with high specific gravity).
6. Sluice boxes are devices used to settle out materials by specific gravity.
7. Placer refers to gold deposits that form by the action of gravity and running water.
8. Check writing for appropriate use of concepts, grammar, and skill in integrating both historical and scientific concepts.

READING 4.10 EXPLORING FOR MINERALS TODAY

See *Student Edition*, p. 164.

READING 4.11 MINE IT, MILL IT, CONCENTRATE IT

See *Student Edition*, p. 167.

ACTIVITY 4.10 MILLING LAB

See *Student Edition*, p. 170.

 4.6, 4.7, 4.8

ADVANCE PREPARATION

You can obtain ore samples for this lab by contacting your Kendall/Hunt representative. If you have the time, you can make them yourself. Directions for making the ore samples follow. The percentages are by volume and are approximate and without packing.

Pour the components into a 100 mL-graduated cylinder as you make up the samples. That way the percentages become milliliters. After the cylinder is full, pour the crushed ore into a beaker and stir. Then divide it up five or more ways into small vials to be given to the students. The directions are for making four different ore samples, but the numbering scheme makes it appear you have eight different samples. Keep the students guessing!

This is one of the most popular labs in *Global Science*. Students enjoy coming up with their own ideas for milling and using the lab equipment. Some teachers give no hints at all and grade strictly on the end separation. That's the way it is in the real world. Others give a few hints such as:

❦ Your sample has more than three and less than eight different materials in it.

❦ Don't add water to your sample right away because that makes the separations more difficult.

Some teachers hold the students to their Day 1 plan; others allow them to make modifications. When a company sees a competitor doing something well, it will usually try to imitate it somehow.

Note that each sample contains a few things that are easy to separate out so each group has some success. Each sample also contains one or two items that are a real challenge to isolate. The lab can be run in two 40-minute class periods, but you *must* be organized!

A sample scheme for separating one of the crushed ore samples follows. Develop your own grading standards.

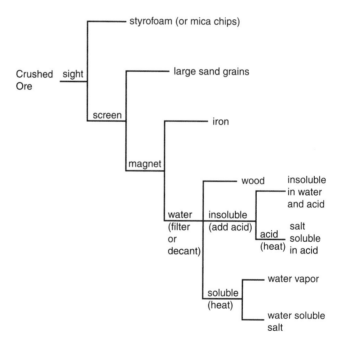

Ore Sample 1 and 5

1. Iron filings	(5%)
2. Table salt	(10%)
3. Sand	(65%)
4. Mica chips	(10%)
5. Wood shavings	(10%)

Ore Samples 2 and 6

1. Iron filings	(10%)
2. Sugar	(10%)
3. Sand	(65%)
4. Styrofoam balls	(5%)
5. Wood shavings	(10%)

Ore Samples 3 and 7

1. Sand   (65%)
2. Copper sulfate   (10%)
3. Calcium carbonate   (10%)
4. Iron filings   (5%)
5. Wood shavings   (10%)

Ore Samples 4 and 8

1. Iron filings   (5%)
2. Calcium or magnesium
   carbonate   (10%)
3. Sand   (65%)
4. Mica chips   (10%)
5. Sugar   (10%)

Make wood shavings by sharpening wooden dowels (from a hardware store or lumber company) or skewers (from the meat market) in a pencil sharpener. This way you get the wood without the graphite. The mica chips are made by taking larger sheets of mica and cutting them into small chips with a scissors. You can also obtain vermichlite from a garden store and break up the pieces. The styrofoam balls are the type used in bean bag chairs.

Tabulate the equipment items the students list on Day 1; assemble and place on a lab chart. You may wish to put out one magnet and filtering setup per group—even if all the groups didn't request them. This will save you valuable class time.

MATERIALS

safety goggles and lab apron
distilled water, large flask available for student use
vial of crushed ore
magnet
magnifying glass
dil HCl (1 vol. con. HCl to 6 vol. H_2O) or a 15% solution
dil NaOH (optional)
100 mL beakers and tongs to lift them (4/group)
50 mL beakers, for separated samples (5/group)
heaters (small electric hot plates or Bunsen burners)
tweezers
wire screen filters, different sizes (optional)
filtering apparatus (filter paper, funnel, ringstand, ring, and utility clamp)
stirring rod

OTHER MATERIALS THAT STUDENTS OCCASIONALLY REQUEST INCLUDE

copper wire	spoon	tin can lids	hammer
matches	knife	rubber tubing	petri dishes

READING 4.12 ALLOYS

See *Student Edition*, p. 172.

ACTIVITY 4.11 IMPORTANCE OF MINERALS REVISITED

See *Student Edition*, p. 173.

This activity revisits the role of minerals in society that students first read about in Reading 4.2. The information on the following chart comes from the *Global Science* student textbook and the *World Book Encyclopedia*. Students can also access on-line resources to add additional facts.

Academics may not consider obtaining information from an encyclopedia as research. However, the major encyclopedias usually have a whole section on each of the minerals listed on this chart. *Practically* everything around us that we use (except wood) contains one or more of these minerals. Most students know very little about them. A good deal of useful and interesting information can be obtained by reading these sections. Even if a student works rapidly, the time required to complete the table is at least 45 minutes.

Mineral or Resource Obtained from Minerals	Metal (M) or Nonmetal (N) (or source of)	Description or Special Properties	Principle Uses	Leading Suppliers*
1. Gypsum	N	A white, chalky mineral. Soft.	Filler in candy, paint. Plaster-board. Plaster of Paris.	U.S., Canada 34% imported.
2. Lead	M	Dense, bluish-gray, soft metal.	Storage batteries. Mfg. of paint, dye.	U.S., USSR, Australia 11% imported.
3. Salt	N	Tiny, cubelike crystals. Essen. for human life.	14,000 uses— seasoning & pres. food. Chem. mfg.	Ocean, seas, mines.
4. Sand	N	Loose grains of rocks & minerals.	Glass, sandpaper, concrete, mortar.	Beaches, river beds, dunes.
5. Potash	N	Normally found as a white, fine-grained salt.	Mainly used to make fertilizer. Also used in soaps, glass, ceramics.	Canada, Israel 72% imported.
6. Copper	M	Reddish-orange metal. Low-cost conductor of electricity.	Electricity, wire, pipes, pans, sheet. Alloys brass & bronze.	U.S., Canada, USSR, Chile 19% imported
7. Hematite	Source of M	Brick-red ore. Supplies most of world's iron.	From paperclips to autos, pipes, wire, rails.	USSR, Australia, Brazil 39% imported.
8. Granite	N	Hard, crystalline rock— mostly quartz & feldspar.	Bridges & buildings. Monuments.	Quarried in more than 30 states.
9. Sulfur	N	Yellow, soft, nonmetallic solid.	Converted to sulfuric acid for manufacturing fertilizer, explosives, insecticides.	U.S., Canada
10. Cement	N	Fine, gray powder. Mostly lime & silica.	Foundations & structures of buildings, roads.	U.S., Italy, China, Japan
11. Zinc	M	A bluish-white silvery metal.	Electric batteries, alloys (brass, bronze), galvanize.	Canada, Russia 62% imported.
12. Aluminum (from bauxite ore)	M	Lightweight, silvery metal. Easily formed.	Cans, foil, pans, boats, tanks, auto parts.	Australia, Guinea, Jamaica 93% imported.

* Includes % import reliance (if over 10%)

READING 4.13 MINERALS AND SOCIETY

See *Student Edition,* p. 175.

READING 4.14 ECONOMIC AND POLITICAL ISSUES

See *Student Edition,* p. 179.

ACTIVITY 4.12 MINERAL IMPORTS

See *Student Edition,* p. 179.

STRATEGIES AND PROCEDURES

The success of this activity hinges on students' successful interpretation of Figure 4.53. Each student or group of students will need a map of the world to record data on. Photocopy-ready maps of the world can be obtained from most social studies teachers.

On steps 1–6, students may respond as follows:

1. List should include names of the first fourteen minerals from Figure 4.53. All are 100% imported.
2. Encourage the use of atlases or globes to help students locate the less familiar countries.
3. List should include the remaining minerals from Figure 4.53.
4. Labeling developing [d] and developed countries [D] will require your assistance. Reiterate that developed nations are wealthier and consume more resources than developing countries, who are economically poorer. Make sure students see that the United States, Japan, and countries in western Europe are developed countries [D] that import many (or most) of their mineral resources. South Africa and former USSR republics are examples of developing countries [d] that export minerals for others to use.
5. Look for comprehension of the following points:
   - concept of imports and exports is used correctly (i.e., to see that consuming nations aren't always producing nations and vice versa);
   - ability to see the inherent economic dangers in total dependency on all minerals;
   - students' realization that no one country is completely self-sufficient; and
   - economic or political consequences of having too many or too few minerals.
6. Grade on technical points such as:
   - how frequently and appropriately new terms are used;
   - spelling, sentence structure, readability; and
   - neatness, legibility of maps, etc.

READING 4.15 MINING AND THE ENVIRONMENT

See *Student Edition,* p. 181.

READING 4.16 WISE USE OF MINERALS

See *Student Edition,* p. 183.

READING 4.17 WHERE DO WE MINE NEXT?

See *Student Edition,* p. 186.

ACTIVITY 4.13 MINERAL ISSUES

See *Student Edition,* p. 187.

STRATEGIES AND PROCEDURES

This activity ties together many of the mineral issues covered in this chapter. It can be as simple as a poster using colored markers and art and photos or as elaborate as an electronic presentation, such as a web page or video newscast. Regardless of the medium, encourage students to concentrate the content and illustrate their main points through pictures, graphs, bar charts, maps, or free-hand drawings.

It is important for students to understand that all of these issues are *real,* as they are the subjects of ongoing debate among consumers, people in government, and those in private industry. Point out that these issues have no "one solution" but rather have many sides to them—each of which is valid for the interest group that stands by a particular idea or policy.

As students work through these mineral issues, keep in mind some popular misconceptions:

- *Misconception:* New technology can eliminate mining. *Reality:* Mining will always be needed to supply raw materials.
- *Misconception:* Countries need to be self-sufficient in mineral and energy production. *Reality:* Given our current global market, self-sufficiency would lead to inefficient use of our resources.
- *Misconception:* Mines are always located in "out of the way" places. *Reality:* Mining can only take place where the needed resources exist.
- *Misconception:* Reclamation is voluntary or just ignored. *Reality:* Reclamation and other environmental safeguards are required in the United States and in other countries.
- *Misconception:* Aluminum is the only common metal to be recycled. *Reality:* See Figure 4.56 for other recycled metals in the U.S.

At the beginning of this activity, assign each student an issue. Encourage them to organize their information as shown in the chart that follows. As presentations are made, they can fill in the blanks for the other issues. The rubric can be used to grade presentations.

What Is the Issue?	Why an Issue?	Choices/Options	The Future
Imports/Exports			**Mineral Issues**
Minerals and the Environment			Names _____
Substitution			_____
Recycling			Headline (3) _____
Taxation			Why an Issue? (3) _____
Where Do We Mine Next?			Choices/Options (3) _____

Future/Challenge (3) _____

Presentation (3) _____
• Organization
• Delivery
• Listening

TOTAL (15) _____

As time allows, encourage outside reading and research to supplement readings from the chapter. Many of these issues are current events, so look for newspaper articles or TV shows to share with the class. This is a good source of homework or extra credit for students.

The grading rubric will assist in your assessment of students' progress for this activity.

Because this is the last activity in the chapter, you may want to reassess your students' MAQ from Activity 4.1. Have students redo the first activity (What is Your MAQ? Activity 4.1) and allow them to compare their MAQ scores. Ask them what insights and/or appreciation they have gained around their personal experience as consumers of mineral resources.

The following are possible "bullet" statements on each of the six issues.

IMPORTS/EXPORTS (ACTIVITY 4.12) _____

🌿 Importing "cheaper" minerals can result in the loss of jobs in the United States.

🌿 Importing important minerals from "unfriendly nations" can become a security risk.

🌿 Importing from countries with weak environmental standards results in damage to the global ecosystem.

MINING AND THE ENVIRONMENT (READING 4.15) _____

🌿 Mined land must be reclaimed to reduce the environmental impact.

🌿 Water pollution can be minimized if tailings are stabilized and effluent from mills cleaned and/or contained.

🌿 Lack of reclamation (causing dust) and pollution control at smelters can result in air pollution.

🌿 Reclamation and pollution control don't happen if these costs aren't included in the price of the mineral.

SUBSTITUTION (READING 4.16)

* Substitutes can be found for many minerals that are in short supply:
  — plastic pipe can substitute for metal pipe.
  — concrete/fiber siding can substitute for wood.
  — optical fibers can substitute for copper wire.
  — minerals with special properties, such as mercury, are hard to replace.

RECYCLING (READING 4.16)

* Recycling slows down the scattering of resources and helps prevent needless waste.
* Designing products for recycling maximizes the use of the materials they contain.

TAXATION (READING 4.16)

* Taxation can be used as a tool to increase resource conservation.
* If taxes are too high, they can put mines out of production and both jobs and tax revenues are lost.

WHERE DO WE MINE NEXT? (READING 4.17)

* Minerals are mined where they *are* located, not where we *want* them to be.
* No roads, exploration, or mining are allowed in wilderness areas.
* Wilderness areas are set aside because some ecosystems are valuable just as they are.
* Land designated as wilderness may contain an unknown wealth of minerals vital to our future.
* Mining does not have to result in permanent damage.

CHAPTER 4 SUMMARY

See *Student Edition,* p. 188.

BLM 4.8

Transparency 4.5

Name_____ Date _____

MULTIPLE CHOICE

1. _____ Mineral resources
   A. are always artificial.
   B. have no useful purpose in society.
   C. are used as raw materials for manufacturing.
   D. always come from living things.

2. _____ A naturally inorganic substance with a characteristic internal structure and set of chemical and physical properties is (a)
   A. matter.   C. stone.
   B. mineral.   D. rock.

3. _____ Which of the following cannot be a mineral?
   A. silver   C. fool's gold
   B. sugar   D. quartz

4. _____ Density is a measure of a mineral's relative
   A. strength.   C. luster.
   B. hardness.   D. mass or "heaviness."

5. _____ The number of different kinds of minerals presently known is approximately
   A. 2000.   C. 8.
   B. 20.   D. 95.

6. _____ Rocks that have been formed by solidification of hot mobile material called magma are classified as
   A. igneous.   C. sedimentary.
   B. metamorphic.   D. erosional.

7. _____ Layered textures in rocks suggest their origin is most likely
   A. only sedimentary.   C. sedimentary or metamorphic.
   B. only metamorphic.   D. sedimentary or igneous.

8. _____ Rocks that split into smaller fragments by the actions of wind, water, ice, and temperature change are examples of
   A. physical weathering.   C. chemical weathering.
   B. percolation.   D. biotic factors.

9. _____ The pink crystals in granite are
   A. quartz.   D. calcite.
   B. biotite.   E. feldspar.
   C. basalt.

10. _____ Rock identification is often difficult because
    A. crystals grow too close together.
    B. without a microscope, fine-grained specimens tend to look alike.
    C. the colors don't always match photos in books.
    D. rocks are always made of three or more different types of mineral.

11. _____ Marble effervesces (bubbles) with dilute HCl to indicate
   A. volcanic gases are being released.
   B. the acid frees up gases trapped in the rock.
   C. the acid opens the sinuses of tiny fossils.
   D. the rock contains the mineral calcite.

12. _____ Which is *not* true about Earth's crust?
   A. It is analogous to a hard boiled egg's outer shell.
   B. It is the least dense of all Earth's layers.
   C. It is the source of almost all mineral resources.
   D. It lies above the outer core and below the mantle.

13. _____ The overall global pattern of earthquakes and volcanoes
   A. is associated with active plate boundaries.
   B. is entirely random.
   C. changes with the seasons.
   D. is a sign of crustal stability.

14. _____ The plate tectonic theory seems to explain
   A. why continents fit together like the pieces of a jigsaw puzzle.
   B. why Earth's magnetic poles move about as time goes by.
   C. why earthquake belts, active volcano belts, and ocean trenches occur at nearly the same places on Earth.
   D. all of the above.

15. _____ Mid-oceanic ridges and seafloor spreading are most commonly associated with
   A. plate sliding.   C. plate creation.
   B. plate destruction.   D. plates and cups.

16. _____ Plate movement is explained using
   A. convection currents.   C. radiation waves.
   B. conduction patterns.   D. electromagnetic radiation.

17. _____ A mineral deposit is called an ore when
   A. it is found only in oceanic crust.
   B. magma hardens into crystalline rock.
   C. the mineral can be mined profitably.
   D. the mineral is no longer valuable.

18. _____ Earth's crust contains a high concentration of
   A. platinum.   C. zinc.
   B. silicon.   D. copper.

19. _____ Which of the following is *not* true. Gold, copper, and silver
   A. are all minerals.   C. are each alloys.
   B. all have metallic luster.   D. each exist as native elements.

20. _____ Gold deposits along streams and rivers become concentrated by
   A. selective crystallization.
   B. chemical replacement.
   C. recipitation after evaporation.
   D. mechanical separation.

21. _____ Understanding plate tectonics helps geoscientists locate mineral resources because
   A. earthquakes always reveal valuable minerals.
   B. patterns of mineralization often follow former plate boundaries.
   C. they can now drill through crustal plates to reach minerals in the mantle.
   D. "supercontinents" are the only places where new minerals form.

22. _____ Exploring for new minerals does *not* involve
    A. smelting.
    B. remote sensing.
    C. collecting plant specimens.
    D. magnetic surveys.
    E. seismic reflection.

MATCHING AND ADDITIONAL MULTIPLE CHOICE

Match the method of ore body formation on the left with the description on the right.

23. _____ replacement

A. Moving stream may carry worthless materials away, leaving behind a concentration of dense ore.

24. _____ immiscible liquid

B. Precipitation occurs after substances have been concentrated by evaporation.

25. _____ deposition from lake water and seawater

C. Occurs when a valuable material is dissolved and removed lake from one location and redeposited in a concentrated state somewhere else. Or worthless material is dissolved and carried away, leaving behind a concentration of valuable ore.

26. _____ secondary enrichment and residual concentration

D. Due to differences in chemical activity, one mineral gradually takes for itself the place occupied by another.

E. A concentration can occur as two materials that won't mix separate. This is because only one of the layers contains the valuable substance.

27. _____ Ore bodies are formed in all the following ways *except*
    A. the seafloor splits and separates; molten material from below moves into the void.
    B. mineral geologists hide valuable ore deep in the earth for prospectors to locate.
    C. dense crust slides under less dense crust and is melted to become new magma.
    D. particles erode from mountains and hills and separate into mineral concentrations because of their properties.

Match the statement on the right with the concept on the left.

28. _____ seafloor spreading

A. Wind, water, and gravity continually change Earth's surface.

29. _____ subduction

B. The action of the sun and wind on lakes and seas can concentrate minerals that eventually precipitate to the bottom.

30. _____ weathering

C. Convection currents from below cause Earth's crust to split and move apart.

31. _____ evaporite deposits

D. Plates often collide and one plate will slide under the other.

32. _____ A knowledge of ore body formation, combined with technical tools and luck are all part of
    A. mineral concentration.   C. exploration.
    B. smelting and refining.   D. land reclamation.

33. _____ The first step in milling is to crush the ore as finely as possible to
    A. bring the ore to a pure or fine state.
    B. separate the mineral from the gangue.
    C. minimize the quantity of tailings.
    D. alloy minerals that are present.
    E. separate the more dense minerals from the less dense minerals.

Match the following terms on the left with the definitions on the right.

34. _____ milling

    A. The worthless rocks or Earth's material that occurs with a mineral deposit.

35. _____ gangue

    B. The process of separating valuable minerals from the ore and waste rock they are associated with.

36. _____ tailings

    C. The residue that remains after a mineral has been separated from the worthless portion of an ore.

37. _____ flotation

    D. A general term that means the process by which a mineral concentrate is brought to a fine or pure state.

38. _____ refining

    E. Process of agitating a crushed ore slurry in a vessel with a detergent or foaming agent.

39. _____ All of the following statements are true *except*
    A. the properties of alloys are usually preferable to those of the pure metals.
    B. an alloy is the solid that results when two or more metals are melted together and then cooled.
    C. alloys have properties that are different from those of the metals from which they are made.
    D. alloys are usually more resistant to corrosion than the metals from which they come.
    E. metals can be alloyed with metals but not with nonmetals.

Match the mineral on the left with its category of use on the right.

40. _____ limestone   A. abrasives

41. _____ phosphate   B. paint pigments and fillers

42. _____ molybdenum   C. construction material

43. _____ sandstone   D. iron alloys

44. _____ clay   E. fertilizer

45. _____ Which of the following are *not* found inside our homes?
    A. ceramics   D. alloys
    B. metals   E. aggregates
    C. plastics

Match the mineral issue on the left with the related problem on the right.

46. _____ imports

    A. The natural tendency is for resources to become more scattered, but a conscientious effort can slow down this tendency.

47. _____ recycling

    B. The challenge is to keep the avenues of commerce open, trade equitably with our fellow humans, and not use supply withholding, political interference, economic blockades, and military power as threats.

48. _____ taxation

    C. The setting aside of land for its scenic beauty, ecological value, and future economic importance vs. present economic and political concerns.

49. _____ environmental impact

    D. People within a state bear many of the initial costs and negative impact impacts of mining, but the nation as a whole benefits from the success of the venture.

50. _____ wilderness classification

    E. Leaves scars on the landscape, contributes to air and water pollution, and in some cases, poses health risks. Can be helped through reclamation.

CHAPTER 4 ASSESSMENT

1.	C	26.	C
2.	B	27.	B
3.	B	28.	C
4.	D	29.	D
5.	A	30.	A
6.	A	31.	B
7.	C	32.	C
8.	A	33.	B
9.	E	34.	B
10.	C	35.	A
11.	D	36.	C
12.	D	37.	E
13.	A	38.	D
14.	D	39.	E
15.	C	40.	C
16.	A	41.	E
17.	C	42.	D
18.	B	43.	A
19.	C	44.	B
20.	D	45.	E
21.	B	46.	B
22.	A	47.	A
23.	D	48.	D
24.	E	49.	E
25.	B	50.	C

CHAPTER

5

GROWTH AND POPULATION

LEARNING OUTCOMES

The student will:

1. model exponential growth by manipulating materials and equipment and completing the activity "Modeling Exponential Growth." (C,P)

2. change variables and attempt to slow down and stop exponential growth by completing the activity "Modeling Exponential Growth." (C,P)

3. interpret population trends from graphs. (C)

4. calculate doubling time and percent annual growth in various situations by using the doubling time equation. (C)

5. give possible reasons for the rapid growth in human population. (C,A)

6. know the relationship between birth and death rates and population growth/decline. (C)

7. realize the problems brought about by exponential growth by observing a NASA photo of Earth. (A)

8. calculate what a billion is and relate that to human populations on Earth by completing the activity "Now What's a Billion?" (C,A,P)

9. construct population histograms and analyze them to obtain useful demographic information. (C,P)

10. state the factors that tend to limit the population size of various organisms. (C)

11. explain why the population of the United States will continue to grow for some time even if the average preference is for the two-child family. (C)

12. become aware of current demographic trends by filling out a survey and analyzing class-averaged results and related data by doing the activity "A Demographic Survey." (C,A,P)

13. use population histograms to explain some of the problems faced by a society that is undergoing growth reduction. (C,A)

14. know the economic and social factors that influence birth and death rates. (C)

15. explain the demographic transition concept using the graph for that phenomenon. (C)

16. recognize the demographic transition as a means of dealing with the human population problem. (A)

17. realize the economic implications of becoming a parent. (A)

18. recognize the responsibilities associated with raising children. (A)

KEY TERMS

RECOMMENDED BLACKLINE MASTERS

5.1   Modeling Exponential Growth

5.2   Modeling Graphing Summary

5.3   Characteristics of Exponential Growth

5.4   The Energy History of the United States

5.5   The Demographic Transition

5.6   Power of the Pyramids

The Recommended Blackline Masters listed above are supplemental to the activity/reading, and can be found on the *Teacher Resource CD*. Blackline Masters 5.7–5.11 are essential to teaching the activity/reading, and so are included in the *Teacher Guide* (pp. 127–131) as well as on the *Teacher Resource CD*.

ACTIVITIES FLOW CHART

CHAPTER 5: GROWTH AND POPULATION

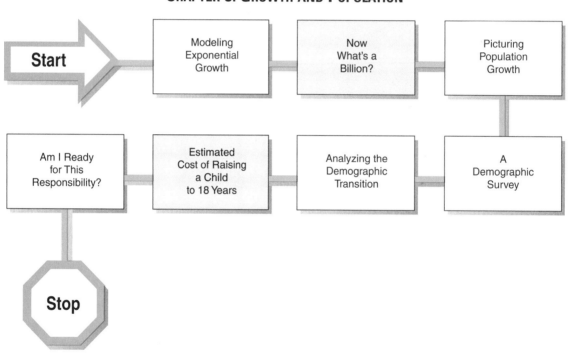

NOTE: Shaded items are lower priority.

TEACHING STRATEGIES AND ANSWERS FOR ACTIVITIES

CHAPTER OPENER, See *Student Edition*, p. 193

In the United States we enjoy a relatively low proportion of people to open land. We also have reached a near replacement rate of growth in our population. That situation is not uniform around the world, however. This photograph helps to engage students in thinking about the human population situation.

READING THE MATHEMATICS OF GROWTH

See *Student Edition*, p. 194.

ACTIVITY 5.1 MODELING EXPONENTIAL GROWTH

See *Student Edition*, p. 195.

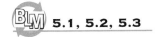
5.1, 5.2, 5.3

ADVANCE PREPARATION

You will need to collect about 250 dice or colored wooden cubes for this activity. You can make the dice yourself. Use a 3/4″-thick board of birch or maple that is 2 ft. × 7.5 ft. This will result in about 1400 3/4″ dice—enough for four groups of six to eight students, with some left over to compensate for loss. Before you cut the board, spray one side red and the other blue. After the board is cut, spray paint another side white by placing all the cubes very close together (no spaces between cubes). Dice also can be purchased by contacting your Kendall/Hunt representative.

Sort the dice into sets of 250 or 300 and place in large plastic containers.

STRATEGIES AND PROCEDURES

This activity provides a direct, hands-on experience for the students to help them visualize exponential growth. We begin this chapter with a concrete model, rather than a computer simulation, so students have something real to think about as they start reading and discussing the more abstract concepts related to exponential growth later in the chapter.

The first part of the lab takes about 25 minutes to build the population from 10 to 100 and only about 5 minutes to build it from 100 to 500. This result often surprises the students, which is one of the main goals of the activity.

The following sketches represent the results you can typically expect in this activity:

Students often have difficulty drawing the best fit line or a smooth curve through their data, especially with the graphs of growth rate vs. time and

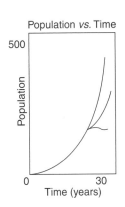
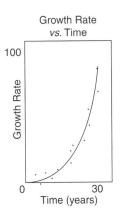
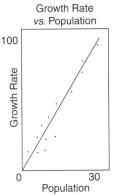
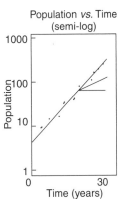
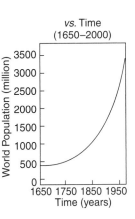

growth rate vs. population. You may want to team with a math teacher and co-ordinate how you guide students through this process.

One possible glitch in this activity is the statistical probability that about one group in 50 will start with so many deaths in its first few throws that its population never increases. This is analogous to an event such as a catastrophic disease or earthquake hitting a small population. The population is wiped out or stops growing. If you don't want to make this point, you can have the group start over.

To extend this activity, consider having the students plot a world population vs. time graph on semi-log paper. Alternatively, you could project this plot on a transparency. This technique helps answer the question, Is the rate of the world's population increasing or declining?

Many ninth-grade teachers only have their students plot graph one, four, and five. Graphs two and three represent more abstract ideas.

Students may reach the following conclusions:

- *Population vs. Time.* When population grows exponentially and unchecked, it grows slowly when the population is small and then rapidly increases once a significant population base is established.
- *Growth Rate vs. Time.* As the population increases, so does the growth rate. It appears that the growth rate also increases exponentially with time.
- *Growth Rate vs. Population.* Averaging out the randomness that is very pronounced when one deals with small numbers of objects, one can see that the best graph is a straight line that passes through the origin. Hence: Growth Rate $\propto$ Population.

In steps 4 and 5 of Part E, students may respond as follows:

4. Exponential growth plots as a straight line on semi-log paper. This technique, therefore, can serve as a test for exponential growth.
5. The world population increased slowly from 1650 to 1900, when technology and medicine were relatively undeveloped. After 1900, however, the curve shoots up rapidly. The world population currently increases more in a few decades than it did in a few centuries before 1900.

After you discuss the graphs and the conclusions for each, ask the students what they think can be done to slow or stop exponential growth. Typically, students will mention these six ideas:

- war;
- doing nothing and letting disease and starvation take their toll;
- providing birth control information and devices to help people in developing countries;
- use food as a weapon by withholding food exports from countries that do not encourage population control;
- help countries modernize (People are less likely to have large families if they know where their next meal is coming from and that they will be cared for in old age.);
- dictatorships that enforce birth control programs via governmental edict and action.

These are NOT all good ideas. They are what students suggest!

READING 5.1 THE NATURE OF EXPONENTIAL GROWTH

See *Student Edition,* p. 198.

SAMPLE ANSWERS TO QUESTIONS

1. r = 70/Td
2. 14 years
3. 10%
4. 6.4 years
5. r% ≃ 70/12.3 ≃ 5.69%
6. 4.7 years
7. Td = 70/%(agr)   70/Td = %(agr)   70/140 = 50%
8. Td = 70/%(agr)   Td = 70/1.7% =   41 years
9. Td = 70/%(agr)   Td = 70/2.4% =   29 years
10. Td = 70/%(agr)   70/Td = %(agr)   70/700 = .10%
11. The account will reach $2000 in 14 years. At age 28, the value of the account will be $8000. By age 70 the account will contain $512,000.

The population of the Palestinian Territory will double in only 20 years. With such little space and high unemployment, conflicts with Israel will probably increase.

READING 5.2 THE LIMITS OF EXPONENTIAL GROWTH

See *Student Edition,* p. 202.

ACTIVITY 5.2 NOW WHAT'S A BILLION?

See *Student Edition,* p. 204.

 5.4

STRATEGIES AND PROCEDURES

This activity is similar to Activity 5.1 in that it helps the students grasp an abstraction. For most of us, the reality of a billion is difficult to conceptualize. This activity provides one means of beginning to understand just how large that number is.

1. 50 × 80 = 4000 dots
2. 1,000,000/4000 = 250 pages
3. 250,000 pages
4. 1 inch
5. 1000 inches = 83.3 feet
6. 6.3 × 250,000 = 1,575,000 pages
7. 1,575,000 pages/250 pages per inch = 6,300 inches = 525 feet height of building = 525 ft/12 ft per story = 43.8 stories

READING THE GROWTH OF LIVING POPULATIONS

See *Student Edition,* p. 206.

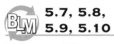

READING 5.3 THE GROWTH OF HUMAN POPULATION

See *Student Edition*, p. 206.

5.7, 5.8, 5.9, 5.10

Transparency 5.3

ACTIVITY 5.3 PICTURING POPULATION GROWTH

See *Student Edition,* p. 209.

ADVANCE PREPARATION

Make one copy of Student Worksheet 1 and 2 for each student (Blackline Masters 5.7 and 5.8).

Note: Answers to BLMs 5.7 and 5.8 are on page 136.

Make one copy of the two sheets of graph paper, male and female, (Blackline Masters 5.9 and 5.10) for every two students.

STRATEGIES AND PROCEDURES

In this activity students will examine population data broken down by country and sex. This breakdown will reveal some interesting patterns for discussion. You may want to assign part of the work for this activity as homework.

SAMPLE ANSWERS TO QUESTIONS

1. Males; more born to begin with, able to survive infancy better, selected for in some populations.
2. Females; longer life expectancy; less susceptible to life-shortening diseases; if they survive the childbearing years, then they live for a long time.
3. Student responses will vary, but most students will select Nigeria and India histograms because they are wide at the base and narrow at the top. A pyramid is the result of a high birthrate and a high death rate. A change in either of these rates will change the shape of the pyramids. If the birth and death rates stay the same, the pyramids should look the same in 25 years.
4. France has the slowest rate of growth. It is the most rectangular shaped, indicating even rates of birth and death. The histogram should look similar in the future or slightly inverted if the birthrate drops below the death rate.
5. People aged 35–39 and 40–44 make up the largest age groups in the United States. They belong to the group of people who were born between 1946 and 1964. Called "baby boomers," they were born shortly after World War II, when many husbands and wives were reunited, and the country experienced greater economic prosperity than it did during the years of the Great Depression and the war. Couples felt confident in their ability to support families, and the birth rate soared as a result.

   The concern is that when the larger group retires, much of their retirement income must come from pension and Social Security deductions from the paychecks of the younger group. The problem is that this group is smaller. Hence, they must pay more or the retirement checks will be less. This is not easy to resolve.

6. China has relatively constant percentages for all age groups under age 30. The rest of the age groups taper off in a pyramid shape. Strict birth control laws have helped change the shape of this pyramid.

7. The country with the highest percentage of people between the ages of 0 and 5 years is adding people at the fastest rate. Thus, the answer is Nigeria, where 17.1% of the population is in the 0–4 group.

8. The histogram shows that the Mexican population was growing rapidly until about 25 years of age, at which time the rate of growth slowed. If this trend continues unchanged, the Mexican "pyramid" will gradually become more rectangular.

POWER OF THE PYRAMIDS—SAMPLE PYRAMIDS

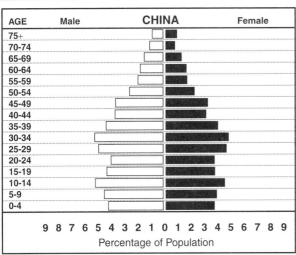

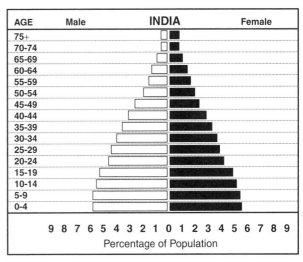

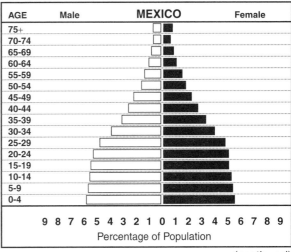

(continued)

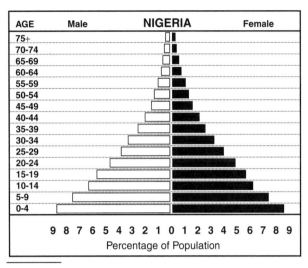

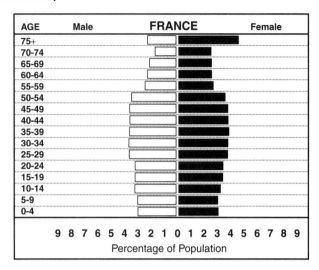

Reprinted with permission from Multiplying People, Dividing Resources: Global Math Activity, 2002. Activity used with permission of Population Connection, 1400 Sixteenth Street, NW, Suite 320, Washington, D.C. 20036.

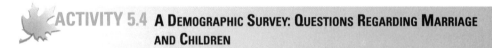

ACTIVITY 5.4 A DEMOGRAPHIC SURVEY: QUESTIONS REGARDING MARRIAGE AND CHILDREN

See *Student Edition,* p. 210.

ADVANCE PREPARATION

Decide how you will tabulate the data your students turn in. It is often simplest and most anonymous if the teacher tabulates the data from several sections of students.

Plan to save the data from this activity from year to year. The larger your sample size, the more meaningful your data are for drawing conclusions about your population.

STRATEGIES AND PROCEDURES

Tabulate data separately for males and females. Express as percentages. These U.S. averages may be helpful for comparison.

Percent of U.S. men and women age 18 and 19 in college or trade school:

1950	Men: 20.7%	Women: 15.9%
1986	Men: 40.1%	Women: 42.8%
1991	Men: 40.1%	Women: 47.8%
1998 (college only)	Men: 41.7%	Women: 51.3%

Median age of Americans at first marriage:

1900	Men: 25.9 years	Women: 21.9 years
1950*	Men: 22.8 years	Women: 20.3 years
1988	Men: 25.9 years	Women: 23.6 years
1991	Men: 26.3 years	Women: 24.1 years
1998	Men: 26.7 years	Women: 25.0 years
2000	Men 26.8 years	Women 25.1 years

Fertility rates for U.S. women:

1900	3.68 children	1991	2.07 children
1940	2.30 children	1999	2.00 children
1950*	3.09 children	2000	2.03 children
1986	1.84 children	2001	2.03 children

*The 1950s were the baby boom years of great prosperity.

Life expectancy for U.S. men and women:

1900	Men: 46.3 years	Women: 48.3 years
2003	Men: 74 years	Women: 80 years

Sources: Population Reference Bureau, Washington, D.C.; U.S. Census Bureau; and the Centers for Disease Control/National Center for Health Statistics.

In steps 7 and 8, students may respond as follows:

7. People in developed nations usually list the following as the advantages of having children:

   - Someone to share love and experiences with.
   - Children can carry on the family name (genes), traditions, and values, which makes the world a better place.
   - The pleasure of having children and watching and helping them grow.
   - Having children makes life more meaningful and complete.
   - Children are fun to be around and add happiness to life.

   People in poorer nations list the following as advantages of having children:

   - Someone to help in housework and family chores.
   - Companionship and avoidance of loneliness.
   - Happiness for the parent.
   - Help in old age.

8. People in developed nations usually list the following as the disadvantages of having children:

   - Children cost money.
   - The strain of the responsibility.
   - Loss of independence, privacy, and career.
   - Children take time.
   - Having to discipline and/or coping with negative influences (drugs, alcohol, etc.).
   - Potential disappointment (poor parent, poor grades, handicapped, crime, strain on marriage).

The results of Activity 5.4 can serve as a basis for understanding Activity 5.5.

READING 5.4 UNDERSTANDING POPULATION GROWTH

See *Student Edition*, p. 211.

READING 5.5 PROBLEMS RELATED TO GROWTH REDUCTION

See *Student Edition*, p. 213.

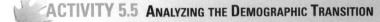

READING 5.6 THE DEMOGRAPHIC TRANSITION

See *Student Edition*, p. 214.

ACTIVITY 5.5 ANALYZING THE DEMOGRAPHIC TRANSITION

See *Student Edition*, p. 216.

ADVANCE PREPARATION

Make an overhead transparency of Figure 5.17. Post the World Population Data Sheet in your room. You may want to obtain several copies and place them in several locations in your classroom. The *World Population Data Sheet* can be purchased from Population Reference Bureau, 1875 Connecticut Ave., NW, Suite 520, Washington, DC 20009–5728 USA; (800) 877–9881, website: www.prb.org.

STRATEGIES AND PROCEDURES

If your students are proficient at analyzing graphs, you could assign this activity as homework and have a class discussion. If graph analysis is difficult for your students, consider a directed class discussion where you project the graph on an overhead and lead the students through the analysis. You could also have the students come to the overhead and lead different sections of the analysis.

1. Limited access to medical care results in more infant deaths; also, more deaths are due to disease and poor sanitation. People have more children to compensate for the high death rate and to ensure that someone from the next generation will be around to care for them in old age.
2. Natural causes maintained a balance in the size of the population. The birthrate was high, but an equally high death rate maintained a relatively constant-sized population.
3. Improved sanitation, availability of vaccinations, improved nutrition, safer childbirth, children survive infancy.
4. Women are better educated, families have access to family planning services, fewer children are needed to run the household, children live through infancy so families have fewer children, people marry later in life and have fewer years in which to produce children.
5. Students will collect data from the World Population Data Sheet to complete the chart in Figure 5.18.
6. In the section farthest to the right: "modern living in natural balance." Developed countries tend to have low or replacement birthrates. In other words, the birth and death rates are equal so the population size does not change over time.
7. In the middle section of the graph. For a while these countries will have high birthrates until people realize the consequences of a dropping death rate. When this economic and societal shift occurs, families start having fewer children and the birthrate drops.
8. The birth and death rates balance each other out and the population is stable.

9. If living standards are raised, then birth and death rates will balance out if current patterns can be extrapolated to all countries.

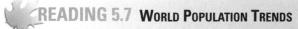

READING 5.7 World Population Trends

See *Student Edition,* p. 217.

READING Controlling Growth

See *Student Edition,* p. 219.

READING 5.8 Family Planning

See *Student Edition,* p. 219.

READING 5.9 The Case for Total Abstinence for Young People

See *Student Edition,* p. 220.

ACTIVITY 5.6 Estimated Cost of Raising a Child to 18 Years

See *Student Edition,* p. 222.

This is an excellent activity for students to complete at home with their parents or guardians. The activity may promote interesting family discussions. You may want to send a cover letter home explaining that the focus of the activity is to emphasize the large financial responsibility associated with child rearing, *not* to pry into family finances.

Item	Total ($)
1. Food	$150/month × 12 months/yr × 18 years = $32,400
2. Clothing	$100/month × 12 months/yr × 18 years = $21,600
3. Medical (incl. drugs)	$100/year (with good insurance) × 18 years = $1,800
4. School	$300/month × 18 months = $5,400
5. Housing	$300/month × 12 months/yr × 18 years = $64,800
6. Transportation	$50/month × 12 months/yr × 18 years = $10,800
7. Entertainment	$100 × 12 months/yr × 18 years = $21,600
8. Utilities	$25/month × 12 months/yr × 18 years = $5,400
9. Dental/Eyes	$40/year × 13 years = $520
10. Vacations	$2,500/year × 15 years = $37,500
11. Recreation	$500/year × 18 years = $9,000
12. Insurance	($300/month × 12 months/yr × 18 years) + ($100/month × 12 months/yr × 3 years) = $68,400
Total (before college)	$279,220
Modest college costs	$25,000/year × 4 years = $100,000
Total (after college)	$379,220

The following data represent reasonable numbers from 2000. There are a variety of ways to calculate these costs, so your students' responses could be very different from this sample.

The estimated costs for raising a child (for the first 17 years) in the United States as determined by the U.S. Department of Agriculture and reported in *Expenditures on Children by Families (1998)* are as follows:

For a child born in 1981:

Housing	$ 52,140.00
Food	27,450.00
Transportation	22,560.00
Clothing	10,920.00
Health Care	10,830.00
Child care/education	15,030.00
Miscellaneous (personal care, entertainment, books)	17,760.00
TOTAL:	$156,690.00*

* These figures assume a middle-income family, with average before-tax income of $47,900/yr. They do not include the cost of a college education.

 5.11

ACTIVITY 5.7 AM I READY FOR THIS RESPONSIBILITY?

See *Student Edition*, p. 224.

ADVANCE PREPARATION

Make one copy of Blackline Master 5.11 for each student.

STRATEGIES AND PROCEDURES

Distribute Blackline Master 5.11 to each student. After students have had time to reflect on their responses to the questions, conduct a class discussion by asking the students to share the aspects of being a parent that they are most looking forward to, those they most dread, and those they had never considered before completing this survey. During this discussion, keep the norms of your community in mind and reinforce ideas such as the importance of getting an education, being married, and being gainfully employed before considering having children.

READING 5.10 REDUCING PROBLEMS RELATED TO POPULATION GROWTH

See *Student Edition*, p. 225.

SPECIAL FOCUS TO HAVE OR HAVE NOT? THE QUESTION OF CHILDREN

See *Student Edition*, p. 225.

CHAPTER 5 SUMMARY

See *Student Edition*, p. 226.

Sample answers can be found on p. 136 of the *Teacher Guide*.

POPULATION IN THOUSANDS (2000)

Age Group	United States			Mexico			China		
	M	F	%	M	F	%	M	F	%
0–4	9,673	9,222		5,736	5,487		51,082	46,444	
5–9	10,378	9,900		5,624	5,391		54,187	49,274	
10–14	10,218	9,760		5,421	5,219		62,771	57,109	
15–19	9,819	9,386		5,212	5,050		51,262	47,605	
20–24	9,135	8,805		5,056	4,998		49,039	46,382	
25–29	9,182	8,970		4,627	4,751		60,593	57,479	
30–34	10,004	9,825		3,705	3,944		63,973	60,510	
35–39	11,364	11,123		3,019	3,244		52,476	49,964	
40–44	11,339	11,201		2,555	2,767		42,616	39,454	
45–49	9,995	10,071		2,086	2,260		43,093	40,851	
50–54	8,601	8,831		1,657	1,791		31,698	29,374	
55–59	6,567	6,900		1,330	1,459		23,865	22,040	
60–64	5,144	5,583		1,025	1,153		21,122	19,794	
65–69	4,371	5,006		788	918		17,571	17,356	
70–74	3,892	4,861		551	683		12,281	13,145	
75+	6,051	10,294		614	909		10,129	13,494	
Total	135,733	139,738		49,006	50,024		647,758	610,275	
Total	275,471			99,030			1,258,033		

Source: The World Bank, *2000 World Development Indicators CD-ROM* and U.S. Bureau of the Census, *International Database*.

Growth and Population   127

Sample answers can be found on p. 136 of the *Teacher Guide*.

POPULATION IN THOUSANDS (2000)

Age Group	France M	France %	France F	France %	Nigeria M	Nigeria %	Nigeria F	Nigeria %	India M	India %	India F	India %
0–4	1,835		1,745		10,900		10,755		59,045		55,521	
5–9	1,867		1,778		9,328		9,266		59,096		55,223	
10–14	1,968		1,884		7,827		7,815		56,744		52,730	
15–19	1,986		1,901		7,130		7,125		53,202		49,046	
20–24	1,996		1,918		5,903		6,012		46,466		42,717	
25–29	2,179		2,107		4,819		5,060		44,129		39,959	
30–34	2,179		2,146		3,937		4,112		40,224		36,499	
35–39	2,157		2,182		3,104		3,266		35,698		32,475	
40–44	2,127		2,163		2,501		2,651		30,957		28,158	
45–49	2,118		2,142		1,980		2,138		25,443		23,349	
50–54	2,028		2,030		1,585		1,744		20,062		19,318	
55–59	1,410		1,436		1,252		1,427		16,138		16,300	
60–64	1,311		936		936		1,113		13,121		13,725	
65–69	1,247		1,473		650		814		10,146		10,822	
70–74	1,065		1,416		406		541		6,958		7,589	
75+	1,415		2,691		322		489		6,896		8,168	
Total	28,889		30,431		62,580		64,330		524,325		491,598	
Total	59,320				126,910				1,015,923			

SOURCE: The World Bank, *2000 World Development Indicators CD-ROM.*

Country: _____

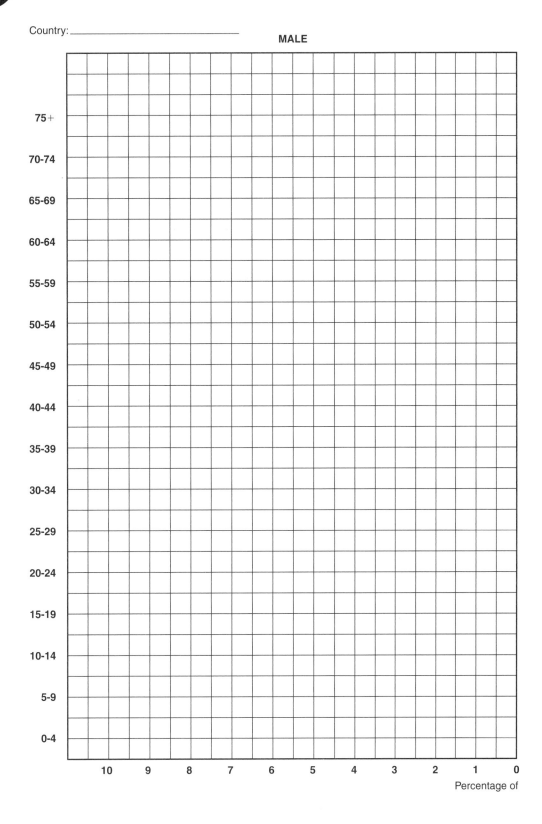

MALE

Growth and Population 129

Country: _____

FEMALE

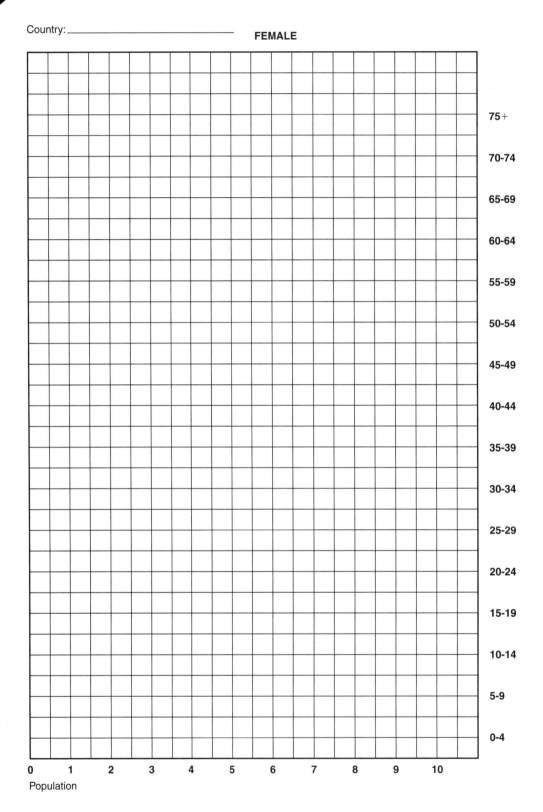

Population

BLACKLINE MASTER 5.11
AM I READY FOR THIS RESPONSIBILITY?

Am I Ready to Raise a Child?	Yes	I think so	I'm not sure	I think not	No
1. Do I communicate easily with others? Do I enjoy teaching others?					
2. Do I have enough love to give a child?					
3. Would I have the patience to raise a child? Can I tolerate noise and confusion? Can I deal with disrupted schedules?					
4. How do I handle anger? Would I hurt my child if I lost my temper?					
5. Do I know my own values and goals? Could I help my child develop constructive values?					
What Do I Expect to Gain from the Parenting Experience?					
6. Would I feel comfortable if my child had ideas different from mine? How different?					
7. Would I expect my child to make contributions I wish I had made in the world?					
8. Would I expect my child to keep me from being lonely in my old age? To take care of me? What if my child neglected me?					
9. Would I be prepared to let my child leave when he or she grows up?					
10. Do I need parenting to fulfill my role as a man or woman—to make my life more meaningful?					
Is My Lifestyle Conducive to Parenting?					
11. Am I financially able to support a child? (Am I prepared to spend $100 a week or a total of over $100,000 to raise a child to age 18? Can I afford this without the second income of my spouse if he or she chooses to remain at home?)					
12. Would I be willing to give up the freedom to do what I want, when I want?					
13. Would my partner and I be prepared to spend more time at home? Would we have enough time to spend with a child?					
14. Would I be willing to devote a great part of my life, at least 18 years, to being responsible for a child and spend my entire life being concerned about my child's welfare?					
15. Would I be prepared to be a single parent if my partner left or died?					

Name_____ Date_____

MULTIPLE CHOICE

1. _____ All of the following statements describe characteristics of exponential growth *except*
   A. exponential growth plots as a straight line on ordinary graph paper.
   B. exponential growth plots as a straight line on semi-log paper.
   C. exponential growth starts slowly, but is capable of generating large numbers very quickly.
   D. exponential growth is characterized by doubling in a fixed amount of time.

2. _____ A population tends to increase if the
   A. birthrate is high and death rate is high.
   B. birthrate is high and death rate is low.
   C. birthrate is low and death rate is low.
   D. birthrate is low and death rate is high.

3. _____ To achieve zero population growth, one *must*
   A. equate the birthrate to the death rate.
   B. provide birth control information to developing countries.
   C. use food as a political weapon.
   D. increase international warfare.
   E. redistribute the world's wealth.

4. _____ The major reason for the dramatic increase in the world's human population during the last 100 years is
   A. increasing birthrates.   D. increasing death rates.
   B. decreasing birthrates.   E. decreasing death rates.
   C. improved day care for children.

5. _____ The present world population is closest to
   A. 500 million.   D. 9 billion.
   B. 2 billion.   E. 20 billion.
   C. 6 billion.

6. _____ Which of the following is *not* a method of natural population control?
   A. voluntary sterilization   C. disease
   B. famine   D. death

7. _____ All of the following lower population growth rates *except*
   A. public health programs.   C. disease.
   B. birth control.   D. accidents.

8. _____ While retaining long life expectancy and low infant mortality rates, populations can be stabilized by achieving a
   A. lower birthrate.   C. lower death rate.
   B. higher birthrate.   D. higher death rate.

9. _____ All of the following contributed to the growth of human populations in the 1600s *except*
   A. increased standard of living.
   B. improved birth control practices.
   C. better understanding of the nature of disease.
   D. improved medical practices.
   E. efforts to eliminate premature deaths.

10. _____ As the rate of population growth declines
   A. all population-related problems decline.
   B. the percentage of young people increases.
   C. population histograms do not change.
   D. for a time, a small group of workers must support a large group of retired people.

11. _____ The demographic transition suggests that population growth in poorer nations is most likely to be reduced by
   A. aid, which helps raise their standard of living.
   B. doing nothing and letting nature take its course.
   C. sending them birth control devices.
   D. providing books and pamphlets on population issues.

SHORT ANSWER

The graph below summarizes the demographic transition:

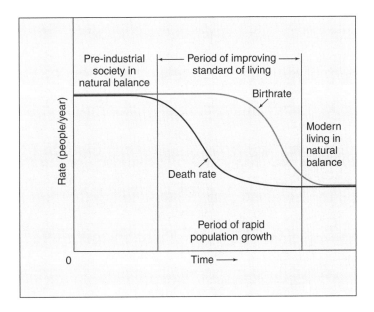

During the time period of increasing standard of living, the *birthrate* stays constant at first and then drops. Give three reasons why the birthrate declines.

12. _____

13. _____

14. _____

15.–16. The demographic transition suggests a way of dealing with the problem of rapid population growth in poorer nations. This solution is humane and dignified. Briefly describe what it is and why it should work.

_____

_____

_____

_____

ADDITIONAL MULTIPLE CHOICE

17. _____ When plotted on semi-log paper, quantities that grow exponentially give
   A. an exponential "J" curve.   C. a bell-shaped curve.
   B. a straight line.   D. an inverse curve.

Use the following equation to answer questions 18–22.

$$\text{Doubling time (years)} = \frac{70}{\text{\% annual growth rate}}$$

18. _____ If the percentage annual growth rate is 2%, what would be the doubling time?
   A. 20 years   C. 30 years
   B. 25 years   D. 35 years

19. _____ If the doubling time is 10 years, what would be the percentage annual growth rate?
   A. 5%   C. 9%
   B. 7%   D. 11%

20. _____ If the doubling time in years of a new energy source is five years, what is the percentage annual growth rate?
   A. 7%   C. 21%
   B. 14%   D. 28%

21. _____ If you invest $3000 in a new energy source that pays an annual interest rate of 14%, when will you have $6000?
   A. 1 year   C. 5 years
   B. 3 years   D. 7 years

22. _____ If a nonrenewable resource is consumed exponentially, the quantity of resource consumed in the next doubling will be
   A. the same as the quantity consumed in the previous doubling.
   B. four times as much as was consumed in the previous doubling.
   C. half as much as was consumed in the previous doubling.
   D. more than was consumed in all previous consumption.
   E. There is no way to predict something like that.

23. _____ The Limited Birth Control (LBC) program
   A. stopped the exponential growth.
   B. slowed down the exponential growth.
   C. had no effect on the exponential growth.
   D. had more impact than the ZPG plan.

24. _____ A population pyramid that tapers smoothly from a large base to a small top represents
   A. a rapidly expanding population.
   B. a declining population.
   C. an established and stable population.
   D. a clumped population.

25. _____ Even if all new couples prefer and have two-child families, zpg would not be achieved *immediately* in the United States and other developed nations because
   A. birth control practices are opposed by some powerful religious groups.
   B. some birth control methods are not too reliable.
   C. there is such a large percentage of young people in the population.
   D. our tax structure allows a family to claim an exemption for each child.

26. _____ Some demographers expect the world's population to stabilize around the 10 billion figure for all of the following reasons *except*
   A. the declining importance of children as part of the family labor force.
   B. the improved social status of women.
   C. the increased cost of raising and education children.
   D. decreased urbanization.
   E. rising educational attainment and improved employment patterns for women.

27. _____ Family planning is based on
   A. the desire of people to practice birth control.
   B. the availability of birth control information.
   C. the availability of a wide variety of birth control methods.
   D. all of the above.
   E. none of the above.

28. _____ Demographers study
   A. animal populations.
   B. plant populations.
   C. human populations.
   D. all kinds of populations.

29. _____ A main advantage of raising children in America is
   A. the care they have traditionally provided in old age.
   B. the opportunity for sharing love and experiences.
   C. the help they provide around the house.
   D. the additional income they contribute to the family budget.

30. _____ The Special Focus on having or not having children listed some *selfish* reasons for having children. Which of the following is *not* a selfish reason?
   A. Insurance for care in old age.
   B. To prove your responsibility to others.
   C. To find an extension of one's ego.
   D. The joy of sharing love with them.
   E. A hedge against regretting not having children.

SAMPLE ANSWERS FOR BLACKLINE MASTERS 5.7 AND 5.8

	POPULATION IN PERCENTAGES, BY AGE COHORT (2000)											
	United States		Mexico		China		France		Nigeria		India	
Age Group	M%	F%	M%	F%	M%	F%	M%	F%	M%	F%	M%	F%
0–4	3.5	3.3	5.8	5.5	4.0	3.7	3.1	2.9	8.6	8.5	5.8	5.5
5–9	3.8	3.6	5.7	5.4	4.3	3.9	3.1	3.0	7.4	7.3	5.8	5.4
10–14	3.7	3.5	5.5	5.3	5.0	4.5	3.3	3.2	6.2	6.2	5.6	5.2
15–19	3.6	3.4	5.3	5.1	4.1	3.8	3.3	3.2	5.6	5.6	5.2	4.8
20–24	3.3	3.2	5.1	5.0	3.9	3.7	3.4	3.2	4.7	4.7	4.6	4.2
25–29	3.3	3.3	4.7	4.8	4.8	4.6	3.7	3.6	3.8	4.0	4.3	3.9
30–34	3.6	3.6	3.7	4.0	5.1	4.8	3.7	3.6	3.1	3.2	4.0	3.6
35–39	4.1	4.0	3.0	3.3	4.2	4.0	3.6	3.7	2.4	2.6	3.5	3.2
40–44	4.1	4.1	2.6	2.8	3.4	3.1	3.6	3.6	2.0	2.1	3.0	2.8
45–49	3.6	3.7	2.1	2.3	3.4	3.2	3.6	3.6	1.6	1.7	2.5	2.3
50–54	3.1	3.2	1.7	1.8	2.5	2.3	3.4	3.4	1.2	1.4	2.0	1.9
55–59	2.4	2.5	1.3	1.5	1.9	1.7	2.4	2.4	1.0	1.1	1.6	1.6
60–64	1.9	2.0	1.0	1.2	1.7	1.6	2.2	2.4	0.7	0.9	1.3	1.4
65–69	1.6	1.8	0.8	0.9	1.4	1.4	2.1	2.5	0.5	0.6	1.0	1.1
70–74	1.4	1.8	0.6	0.7	1.0	1.0	1.8	2.4	0.3	0.4	0.7	0.7
75+	2.2	3.7	0.6	0.9	0.8	1.1	2.4	4.5	0.3	0.4	0.7	0.8
Total	49.2	50.7	49.5	50.5	51.5	48.4	48.7	51.2	49.4	50.7	51.6	48.4
Total	99.9*		100		99.9*		99.9*		100.1*		100	

*Due to rounding, totals don't add up to 100.

CHAPTER 5 ASSESSMENT

1. A
2. B
3. A
4. E
5. C
6. A
7. A
8. A
9. B
10. D
11. A
12. Cost of raising children increases. People know their babies will live.
13. Retirement plans become available.
14. New roles for women. Having families delayed.
15.–16. Modern nations need to help poorer nations raise their standard of living. This helps them get through the period of rapid population growth faster. Then, their birthrates drop for the reasons given in items 12–14.

17. B
18. D
19. B
20. B
21. C
22. D
23. B
24. A
25. C
26. D
27. D
28. C
29. B
30. D

SEEDS OF LIFE

LEARNING OUTCOMES

The student will:

1. examine the properties of life and use them to make **determinations** in the activity "Is It Alive?" (C)
2. know about the various kinds of cells and **manipulate** laboratory equipment to **observe** different cells and some cell behavior by doing the activity "Cells: A Quick Look." (C,P)
3. examine a variety of seeds and **know** that seeds store the genetic information they need to grow and reproduce by doing the activity "Characteristics of Seeds." (C,P)
4. place seeds under stress in a variety of ways to **determine** their ability to adapt by doing the activity "An Inquiry into Seed Adaptation" and pooling class results. (C,P)
5. appreciate the important role seeds play in agriculture, the human diet, and industry by analyzing Reading 6.3. (A)
6. examine the concept of diversity and the value of diversity in our seed supply by doing the activity "If You've Seen One Tomato Seed, You Haven't Seen 'Em All!" (C,P,A)
7. demonstrate the effects of natural selection in animal populations by **manipulating** materials and **completing** the activity "Competing to Survive, Surviving to Compete." (C,P)

8. be aware of what happens when a population, or some members of a population, are resistant to the effects of some environmental change by **completing** the activity "Competing to Survive, Surviving to Compete." (A)
9. recognize the conditions that can lead to extinction by **completing** the activity "Competing to Survive, Surviving to Compete." (A)
10. define the process of natural selection and **relate** it to agriculture. (C,A) See Reading 6.5.
11. examine the benefits and challenges related to the use of pesticides in agriculture by **manipulating** equipment and data by doing the activity "Pesticide Application." (C,P)
12. examine the various factors that have resulted in the tremendous amount of variety that exists in nature. (C) See Reading 6.6.
13. analyze various reasons for saving biological diversity and **classify** those reasons different ways by doing the activity "Why Preserve Biological Diversity?" (C,P)
14. evaluate various strategies for preserving genetic material and **compare** traditional biotechnology to genetic engineering by **analyzing** Reading 6.8 and answering the related questions. (C,A)

KEY TERMS

cell
seed
natural selection
extinction

integrated pest management (IPM)
biological control
pesticide
biomagnification

diversity
wilderness
seed bank
germplasm

biotechnology
hybrid
genetic engineering
endangered species

RECOMMENDED BLACKLINE MASTERS

6.1 Plant Biotechnology

The Recommended Blackline Master listed above is supplemental to the activity/reading, and can be found on the *Teacher Resource CD*. Blackline Masters 6.2-6.4 are essential to teaching the activity/reading, and so are included in the *Teacher Guide* (pp. 149-151) as well as on the *Teacher Resource CD*.

ACTIVITIES FLOW CHART

CHAPTER 6: SEEDS OF LIFE

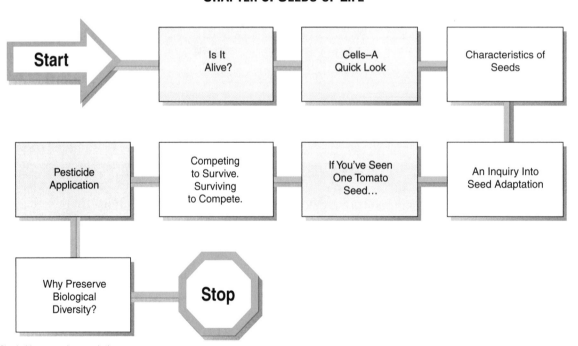

NOTE: Shaded items are lower priority.

TEACHING STRATEGIES AND ANSWERS FOR ACTIVITIES

READING 6.1 WHAT IS LIFE?

See *Student Edition*, p. 230.

ACTIVITY 6.1 Is It Alive?

See *Student Edition,* p. 230.

Teachers may set up as many lab stations as they see fit. The following are possibilities for lab stations:

Living: Plant (any kind or part of a plant), fur, shell, bones or skull, insects, wood, classroom pets (fish, frogs, turtles, hamsters, etc.), ocean sponge.

Non-living: Plastic objects, metal objects, rocks, crystals, glass of water, kitchen sponge, candle, ceramic objects (flower pot, figurines).

The following are sample answers for the earth:

Growth and repair—The ecosystems that make up the biosphere are continually growing and repairing themselves.

Reproduction—The organisms that make up the global ecosystems continually reproduce.

Change—The global ecosystems undergo continual change due to shifts in climate.

Movement—The materials within the global ecosystem undergo continuous movement.

Response—Ecological succession is a natural response to environmental change.

Death—Organisms are continually dying and regenerating in the biosphere.

From this viewpoint, one can argue that the earth, itself, is a living organism. In general, the objects can be divided into living, non-living, and once living.

SPECIAL FOCUS Levels of Organization of Life

See *Student Edition,* p. 232.

READING 6.2 Cells

See *Student Edition,* p. 233.

ACTIVITY 6.2 Cells: A Quick Look

See *Student Edition,* p. 234.

ADVANCE PREPARATION

Collect microscope and slide materials. In most schools, the microscopes, slides, forceps, and medicine droppers can be obtained from the biology teachers. You may also want to check to see if the biology teachers have any prepared slides that you can use. If this option is not available, then you can order basic cell kits by contacting your Kendall/Hunt representative.

Kit #1: Contains five prepared slides including human cheek cells, *Amphiuma* liver, cork, onion bulb epidermis, privet leaf and a study guide.

Kit #2: Contains materials to make your own slides (including slides, cover slips, and stains). It also includes two prepared slides and instructions.

Acquire the *Elodea* from a supply house or local pet store or raise them yourself. If you are planning to obtain the *Elodea* ahead of time, make sure the plant has plenty of light to ensure the maximum amount of photosynthesis. You will also need one small onion.

STRATEGIES AND PROCEDURES

This activity allows students to view two different types of cells: plant and animal. Students will have the opportunity to view prepared slides and make their own. Based on the number of microscopes available, keep the groups as small as possible so each student can view the slides adequately.

Students will struggle with finding the cells initially, especially if it is their first time using a microscope. They may need assistance at first, but once they know what to look for it will become easier for them.

CHEEK CELLS

When students obtain cheek cells, remind them to scrape *gently* and on the inside of their cheek. You may want to demonstrate this so students know exactly what to do. Additionally, methylene blue can be replaced with other stains such as crystal violet (included in the second kit listed). Remind students that any stain can permanently stain their clothing and to be very careful.

ONION CELLS

When students prepare slides for the onion, you may want to demonstrate how to obtain the "skin." It is important to keep the "skin" as flat as possible when transferring it to the slide. If time permits, you may want to have the students look at a piece of onion after adding saline solution and iodine to the slide. You can make your own saline solution by making a concentrated salt solution (~20%). Do this after they have already viewed the onion with just iodine.

Some questions that students may have include:

- What is the general shape of the cell? Brick; rectangular
- What has happened to the cells? Shrink; getting smaller
- Based on what you have seen, how would you compare the rigidity of the cell membrane to the cell wall? Cell membrane is not as rigid as cell wall.

Students may have difficulty seeing the chloroplasts move. Depending on how fresh the *Elodea* is will determine whether or not chloroplast movement can be detected. The chloroplasts themselves should look like small granules that are green. There are usually several chloroplasts inside each cell.

Students will need at least one full class period and possibly part of a second. You can determine how many slides students view according to your specific time requirements. You can choose to look at either the prepared slides only or the slides that the students make only. The prepared slides could also be set up as demonstration slides only.

SAMPLE ANSWERS TO QUESTIONS

1. They all have a nucleus; they all have a cell membrane; they are all microscopic.
2. Animal cells are more round in shape; plant cells are more rectangular or brick shaped.
3. Plant cells are more regular (uniform) in shape whereas animal cells are more irregular in shape. Plant cells are mostly green (due to chlorophyll; except the onion); animal cells have no chlorophyll and therefore, are never green.
4. The stain was used so that the cells could be viewed better. Without the stain, some of the cells would be very difficult, if not impossible, to see.

READING SEEDS FOR THOUGHT

See *Student Edition,* p. 236.

ACTIVITY 6.3 CHARACTERISTICS OF SEEDS

See *Student Edition,* p. 236.

ADVANCE PREPARATION

Collect an assortment of seeds and assemble them in small, plastic bags. Seeds fit nicely in the clear plastic holders sold at coin shops. You will need one set of seeds per pair of students.

STRATEGIES AND PROCEDURES

This short activity identifies students' prior knowledge about seeds. Encourage students to brainstorm freely. Eventually they will connect their seemingly random thoughts to the idea that there is a lot of genetic information stored inside each tiny seed.

In step 3, students may respond as follows:

1. Plants make them.
2. Seeds grow into plants.
3. Seeds can be small.

4. We can eat seeds.
5. Seeds are alive.
6. Seeds have many shapes.
7. Seeds come in many colors.
8. Seeds are found everywhere.
9. Seeds grow in soil.
10. Seeds need water to grow.
11. Seeds get carried around in many ways.
12. Seeds need light to grow.
13. Seeds can be stored.
14. Seeds can be frozen.
15. Seeds are at the bottom of the food chain.

In step 4, students may respond as follows:

🍁 Record its shape, size, and color(s), and go to the library and/or field guides and try to identify it.
🍁 Look for the seed in seed catalogs.
🍁 Bring it to a garden store (nursery) and ask an expert.
🍁 Open it to see what's inside.
🍁 Bring it to a university and ask a botanist.
🍁 Plant it and grow it to see what you get.

In step 7, students may respond as follows:

🍁 What kind of seed it is.
🍁 When it should germinate.
🍁 How to make roots, stems, and leaves.
🍁 How to make more seeds to grow more plants.
🍁 How best to adapt to stressful situations.
🍁 How to maximize photosynthesis.

ACTIVITY 6.4 AN INQUIRY INTO SEED ADAPTATION

See *Student Edition,* p. 236.

ADVANCE PREPARATION

Arrange for access to a microwave oven. Set up the materials for the activity.

STRATEGIES AND PROCEDURES

This activity is another opportunity for students to design and conduct an inquiry. Again, the simpler the question, the more possible it will be for the students to conduct their inquiries. In this activity most of the testable questions should be organized as comparisons (i.e., How does this unstressed seed sprout/grow in comparison to this stressed seed?).

As you guide students through their experimental designs, emphasize the need to control all the variables, except the one being tested.

In step 8, students may respond as follows:

8. a. Any change the students notice and can give evidence is reasonable.

    b. In general, positive changes are those that increase the rate of growth or the production or size of the tomatoes. The responses will vary depending on how long the students grow their seeds.

    c. Negative changes are those we find undesirable in terms of tomato size, color, production, or taste.

    d. If we can make changes that increase resistance to pests, drought, or other negative influences, then we can increase the production of a crop without exhausting the soil or otherwise influencing the ecosystem.

READING 6.3 THE IMPORTANCE OF SEEDS

See *Student Edition,* p. 237.

ACTIVITY 6.5 IF YOU'VE SEEN ONE TOMATO SEED, YOU HAVEN'T SEEN 'EM ALL!

See *Student Edition,* p. 239.

ADVANCE PREPARATION

Assemble the seed packages. The clear plastic holders sold at coin shops or something similar are a nice way to display the seeds. The color photographs of the nine tomato varieties and the plastic holders (packets) can be mounted on styrofoam sheets called display boards. These boards are sold at office supply or stationery stores and stores that sell art supplies. They can be cut with a razor blade to the desired size. You will have to purchase the seeds from a garden store or from a mail-order seed supplier.

STRATEGIES AND PROCEDURES

This activity uses tomato seeds to introduce the concept of genetic variation because there are so many varieties of tomatoes. Students should have fun trying to match the seeds and the varieties. The goal is not so much to be correct, but rather to develop an appreciation of the tremendous variety of genetic information contained in seemingly similar packages. The questions in step 4 are designed to start the students thinking about reasons for genetic variation. They will build on these general ideas in the next activity.

SAMPLE ANSWERS TO QUESTIONS

A. All the seeds are similar in size, shape, and color.

B. The seeds "know" which variety they are because this information is stored inside their genes.

C. They differ in average size, shape, color, taste, nutritional value, and ability to survive climate stress and insect attack.

D. Some varieties adapt to climate better than others. Some varieties resist insect attack better than others. Varieties vary in tastes that appeal to people. Varieties vary in their nutritional value.

E. Variety provides choice and choice takes time.

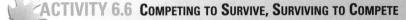

READING 6.4 NON-HUMAN ORGANISMS AND AGRICULTURE

See *Student Edition,* p. 240.

 6.2

ACTIVITY 6.6 COMPETING TO SURVIVE, SURVIVING TO COMPETE

See *Student Edition,* p. 241.

ADVANCE PREPARATION

Prepare one cup of a mixture of black-eyed peas and elbow macaroni for each group of four students. (You can modify the mixture based on materials that are easily available. Try to have two items with distinctly different shapes.)

Make one copy of Blackline Master 6.2 for each student or each group, depending on how you want the students to record data.

STRATEGIES AND PROCEDURES

Talk your students through the activity before they begin. You may also wish to have one practice round. When you begin, give students 1 minute to gather food. Watch that they are not cheating in how they use their traits. You can add the element of prediction to this activity by asking students what will happen in the next generation once they have collected some data.

In step 9, students may respond as follows:

9. a. Usually the spoon or pincher trait proves more adept at gathering food. The more food that is gathered, the greater the size of the next generation. Though greatly simplified, that is the basic principle at work in natural selection.

   b. Students should be able to justify their responses based on evidence.

   c. If it did not occur within the three generations, it is likely the knife trait will disappear in just one or two more generations.

   d. No. Some individuals use their traits more effectively than others.

   e. Yes. Some traits are less effective means of gathering. The general trends across all tables will be similar, if no one cheated.

   f. Answers will vary depending on how students used their traits.

READING 6.5 NATURAL SELECTION, PESTS, AND THE FOOD SUPPLY

See *Student Edition,* p. 242.

 6.3

ACTIVITY 6.7 PESTICIDE APPLICATION SIMULATION

See *Student Edition,* p. 245.

ADVANCE PREPARATION

Purchase white vinegar at the grocery store. Small plastic spray bottles that hold about 60 mL liquid can be purchased at many drug stores in the cosmetics section. The rest of the materials are found in most high school chemistry labs.

A producer calibrates his/her sprayer before applying pesticides so that they know the exact amount of material delivered to ensure safety and effectiveness. His/her goal is to deliver the active ingredient in an even, fine mist that covers the target but does not drip or run off of the target but not so fine that it evaporates or drifts away before reaching the target. Calibrate your sprayer by first examining your sprayer's spray pattern.

A. Place a full open sheet of newspaper on your lab table.
B. Put 10 mL of water in your spray bottle and practice spraying the area. Spray only enough material to create a circle.
C. Examine your spray pattern. Is it even? Does the nozzle clog? (Correct this problem before continuing.)
D. What is the optimum distance from the target (in this case the newspaper) to create a fine even mist that would not run off plants targeted.
E. How large a spray circle does this create?
F. How far from the surface of the newspaper are you holding the sprayer to create this optimum spray circle?
G. Now practice making a spray pattern for a full squeeze of the spray trigger. You may move from one side to the other (left to right) or arm extended and brought toward your body or any direction you feel comfortable with as long as the action can be used to create a stable spray pattern that will cover an area.
H. What size spray area is covered with one squeeze of the trigger?
I. Use this information in the next step.

SAMPLE RESULTS _____

White vinegar   pH = < 4
Distilled water   pH = 7
Vinicide   pH = ~3.5

Area of the table surface = 60 cm × 120 cm = 7200 cm^2
Acres of potato cropland = 7200

DETERMINATIONS _____

1. Concentration of the vinicide:

$$2 \text{ parts in } 1000 \text{ mL}$$
-or-
$$2000 \text{ ppm}$$

2. Dose of vinicide in 10 mL solution:

$$0.02 \text{ parts}$$

3. Vinicide per acre:

$$0.02 \text{ parts}/7200 \text{ acre} =$$
$$2.8 \times 10^{-6} \text{ parts/acre}$$

4. Parts (dose)/plant:

$$2.8 \times 10^{-6}/16,000 = 1.74 \times 10^{-10} \text{ parts/plant}$$

5. Parts (dose)/potato:

$$1.74 \times 10^{-10}/7 = 2.5 \times 10^{-11} \text{ parts}$$

1. The farmer buys pesticide, dilutes it to the desired concentration, places it in a sprayer, and applies it evenly across the field. This is what we did. Due to crudeness of equipment and inexperience, our spraying wasn't as even as the farmers. We were more like a home gardener.

2. This is where the materials are the most concentrated and when human error is most likely to enter. Proper and easy to understand labeling and cautions should lessen the danger. Commercial applicators must be trained.

3. Pesticide use can be reduced by:
   a. Developing and/or using more natural enemies of pests.
   b. Planting a greater diversity of crops.
   c. More *sparing* use of highly specific pesticides.
   d. Use of plant varieties that are resistant to certain pests.

4. Lack of safety is tied to the *dose* of a toxin received. The dose must be above a certain level to be harmful. The quantity *detected* may be way below the harmful threshold. If this is the case, the water is safe to drink.

An extension of this lab is to do Part B, which allows students to make a simulated toxicological determination. Part B is Blackline Master 6.3

1. $180 \text{ lb}/2.2 = 82 \text{ kg}$
2. $5 \times 10^{-9} \times 82 = 4.1 \times 10^{-7}$ parts/day
3. 4.1×10^{-7} parts$/2.5 \times 10^{-11}$ parts/potato $= 1.64 \times 10^4 = 16,400$ potatoes
4. Yes. Intake is such that no one will eat enough potatoes in any reasonable time period to ingest enough vinicide to cause any detectable health effects.
5. Potatoes/yr $= 50 \times 365.25 = 18,262.$

 READING 6.6 **WHY SO MUCH DIVERSITY?**
See *Student Edition*, p. 247.

 6.4    **READING 6.7** **THE IMPORTANCE OF DIVERSITY**
See *Student Edition*, p. 249.

READING 6.8 **HOW TO PRESERVE DIVERSITY**
See *Student Edition*, p. 250.

1. Large wilderness areas serve as *living banks* from which we can withdraw genetic materials when needed. It is becoming more and more difficult to set lands aside because of the growing human population. Demand for both space and the resources that may exist on/under these lands make it difficult to set more land aside.

2. Seeds (germplasm) can be dried, placed in cool or cold (cryogenic) storage, in vitro preserved, or stored in a partial vacuum.

3. *Biotechnology* involves selective breeding. Two parent plants are selected for their desirable traits and bred to produce offspring with specific desirable characteristics. When this is done, some less desirable traits often are transferred as well *Genetic engineering* allows for the transfer of very specific information so that only desired characteristics are passed.

4. Scientists can transfer very specific desirable traits to new plants. The seeds of these plants then contain these traits. Since the desired traits can be more carefully selected, the diversity of the seed supply can be both added to and enriched.

5. The economic justification is that seed banks are a form of *insurance* against devastating losses due to drought, insects, or disease. Seed banks provide the raw materials we can draw on to combat future human and economic disasters.

READING 6.9 PLANT BIOTECHNOLOGY AND AGRICULTURE

See *Student Edition,* p. 254.

Transparency 6.1

ACTIVITY 6.8 WHY PRESERVE BIOLOGICAL DIVERSITY?

See *Student Edition,* p. 258.

ADVANCE PREPARATION

This activity can first be done as a homework assignment and then used as a basis for class discussion. It could also be used with cooperative learning groups.

SAMPLE ANSWERS TO QUESTIONS

1. 3,4. 3—The tie between diversity and stability has been scientifically established. 4—Modern medicine has an economic payoff. In addition, the tie between the diversity stored in various plant material and modern medicines has a scientific basis.

2.
Type of Value	Reason Number
A. Ethical	1
B. Aesthetic	2
C. Economic	3, 4
D. Ecological	3, 4
E. Intellectual	4
F. Emotive	2
G. Religious	1
H. Recreational	2

CHAPTER 6 SUMMARY

See *Student Edition,* p. 259.

The following editorial may prove useful in your discussions of biotechnology and ethics in science.

We must fight biotech fears with facts

By John E. Foster

Six months ago, a poorly developed laboratory study raised the specter that pollen from genetically improved corn could adversely affect the Monarch butterfly population. Immediately there were two predictable reactions: Anti-technology activists called for a ban of the insect-protected corn and researchers called for more research.

At a recent science symposium in Chicago a great deal of new research was presented and the conclusion was obvious: The Monarch population is not at grave risk from genetically modified corn.

There was a great consistency in two key findings of the new research—there is not widespread exposure to the pollen, and where there is exposure, the concentration is rarely high enough to cause harm. Twenty researchers, mostly from universities, presented their findings. From various institutions and various regions, the conclusions were the same.

As the data began to mount, the anti-biotech activists in the room began to get edgy. Then they began to grasp at straws, insulting the researchers by insinuating that industry directed the work and nit-picking that the research hadn't answered every question that might ever be asked.

As researchers too often do, we retreated into our listening mode, absorbing their insults and agreeing that there were areas that could be explored further. There are always areas that can be researched further. But at that very moment, we should have hammered them with the facts that had clarified the Monarch issue.

Silence is not golden when being silent distorts the picture. And the picture is this: The new research was good. It was consistent. It was conducted in actual field situations, and it showed clearly that there is not widespread and significant risk to Monarch butterfly populations.

But there is something about the academic mind. We are always open to the possibility that there might be some new finding that will disprove what has been learned to date. We always feel vulnerable if all possibilities, no matter how remote, have not been researched. So we say things like: "More research is needed. There are still some areas we could explore.

The possibility of a meteorite falling into a cornfield and dispersing the pollen is something that we can't rule out."

And when scientists say such things, we distort the picture. It makes us look as if we are not sure about our findings. In matters of public policy, the public is poorly served when we do not speak out. The public, regulators and lawmakers look to us to put the fact-twisters into perspective. When we don't speak up, facts stay twisted.

We are well past the time when scientists can deliver facts and retreat to their laboratories. We live in the day of the sound bite. Unless we are willing to reinforce our research with passion, we will be handing the future to activist organizations that too often distort science and exploit uncertainty to advance their agenda.

Look how activists exploited that one little laboratory study last spring. Monarch larvae in a cage were fed milkweed dusted with genetically altered corn pollen. About 40 percent of them died. Never mind that the researcher did not know what dose he had applied or whether it had any relevance to field situations.

This one study was able to catalyze the activist community, create a media focus on biotechnology, result in European bans on genetically altered corn and lead to heightened public concern. Biotechnology, which has tremendous potential benefits, has been sidetracked.

Now the facts are in. Many reputable researchers working independently of each other reached the same conclusions. The questions people wanted answered have been answered. But activists are not satisfied. So they'll talk about data gaps and continue to stir up concern.

As scientists, we must speak out against this continual distortion or we will soon be at the point where the public has no faith in science at all.

John E. Foster is professor of entomology at the University of Nebraska-Lincoln. He was one of the lead scientists who presented research data at the recent Monarch butterfly symposium.

SOURCE: *Denver Rocky Mountain News*, Sunday, Jan. 23, 2000.

BLACKLINE MASTER 6.2 DATA TABLES: COMPETING TO SURVIVE, SURVIVING TO COMPETE

FOOD UNITS ACQUIRED					
GENERATIONS	Knife	Fork	Spoon	Pincher	Total
0					
1					
2					
3					

INDIVIDUALS					
GENERATIONS	Knife	Fork	Spoon	Pincher	Total
0	25	25	25	25	100
1					
2					
3					
4					

SURVIVAL POTENTIAL					
GENERATIONS	Knife	Fork	Spoon	Pincher	Total
1					
2					
3					
4					

Name _____ Date _____ Period _____

PART B: TOXICOLOGY

In Part A of this activity, you prepared a simulated fungicide sold under the commercial name *vinicide*.
In the blanks below, record the information you determined about this spray:

1. Concentration of the prepared spray solution = _____ ppm.
2. Parts of vinicide applied per acre = _____ parts/acre.
3. Parts (dose) received by each potato PLANT = _____ parts/plant.
4. Average dose per potato = _____ parts/potato.

You may assume that scientific research has shown that a threshold exists for the human intake of vinicide. Below this level, no health effects occur. That level is 0.0000005 parts/adult individual. Health effects above the threshold include dizziness, drowsiness, hives, wheezing, and fatigue.

You may assume the Environmental Protection Agency has set an acceptable intake of vinicide of 5×10^{-9} parts per kilogram of body weight per day.

To understand this standard, do the following:

1. Determine your mass in kilograms. Conversion Factor: 1 kg = 2.2 pounds

   My mass in kilograms = _____ kg

2. Determine how many parts of vinicide you may ingest/day. This is your acceptable intake:

   Acceptable intake = _____ parts/day

3. How many potatoes would you have to eat to ingest your acceptable dose of vinicide?

   _____ potatoes

4. Based on your calculations, is it safe for humans to eat french fries made from potatoes that have been sprayed with vinicide (as you simulated in Part A)?

   _____

   _____

5. If one ate 50 potatoes/day, how many potatoes would one eat in a year?

   _____

1. *All* life has a right to exist. Ethics should extend beyond *Homo Sapiens*.

2. The variety of nature adds to the enjoyment and meaning of life.

3. Variety adds to the diversity of ecosystems, and diversity means stability to our life-support system.

4. Every different organism is a genetic marvel that may some day be valuable to us or other species.

---

*There are millions of organisms/species in nature that help us in countless ways most of us have no knowledge or appreciation of. The least we can do is allow them to exist!

Name_____ Date_____

MULTIPLE CHOICE

1. _____ Living things are able to do all of the following *except*
   A. repair damaged parts.
   B. reproduce themselves.
   C. respond to their surroundings.
   D. grow larger from the outside.
   E. die and decompose.

2. _____ The animals cells viewed in class had all of the following characteristics *except*
   A. rectangular shape.
   B. cell membrane.
   C. nucleus.
   D. a curved surface.
   E. organelles.

3. _____ Which piece of information do seeds NOT store for future use?
   A. What kind of seed it is.
   B. The exact location of where it was planted.
   C. How to make roots, stems, and leaves.
   D. How to make more seeds to make more plants.
   E. How to maximize photosynthesis.

4. _____ Of the following, which BEST describes what a seed is?
   A. A small leaf.
   B. A special type of virus.
   C. A reproductive structure that contains a plant embryo and stored food.
   D. A piece of stem that can grow into a plant.
   E. The part of a plant that photosynthesizes.

5. _____ All of the following are products that come from seeds *except*
   A. coffee.
   B. vegetable oil.
   C. mustard.
   D. peanut butter.
   E. nail.

6. _____ Advantages of having a variety of tomatoes include all of the following *except*
   A. some varieties are more resistant to drought.
   B. some varieties resist insect attack better than others.
   C. varieties vary in tastes that appeal to different people.
   D. varieties provide choice and choice takes time.
   E. varieties vary in their nutritional value.

7. _____ Which of the following is NOT part of the natural selection process?
   A. Variation within a population.
   B. The fittest have a survival advantage.
   C. Desirable traits are passed on to new genes.
   D. Competition over time can lead to extinction.
   E. Weak traits can band together to survive anyway.

8. _____ Extinction is the term used when all members of a species
   A. disappear in a locality.
   B. die out.
   C. live in zoos.
   D. are threatened with habitat loss.
   E. many members disappear in a locality.

9. _____ Insects adapt readily to environmental change because
   A. they are widespread.
   B. they are numerous.
   C. they contain great variability across species.
   D. they reproduce rapidly.
   E. all of these are reasons.

10. _____ Monocultures involve
    A. small plots of land.
    B. the growing of one kind of crop in a large area.
    C. genetically engineered crops.
    D. setting aside land as wilderness.
    E. saving seeds for future generations.

11. _____ Integrated Pest Management (IPM) involves all of the following *except*
    A. use of natural enemies.
    B. greater diversity of crops.
    C. application of highly specific chemicals.
    D. use of intense plowing to increase yields.
    E. use of pest-resistant plants.

12. _____ A pesticide that kills spiders is called a(n)
    A. fungicide.
    B. arachnicide.
    C. herbicide.
    D. insecticide.
    E. rodenticide.

13. _____ Even though the fittest survive, nature is very diverse because
    A. there can be many niches in a small area.
    B. populations became separated when the earth's plates separated.
    C. warm climates can support a greater variety of species.
    D. organisms can gain benefit from one another (symbiosis).
    E. all of the above.

14. _____ Which of the following is a scientific reason for preserving biological diversity?
    A. All life has a right to exist.
    B. Variety adds enjoyment to life.
    C. Diversity brings stability to the biosphere.
    D. Diversity has economic payoffs.
    E. None of the above are scientific reasons.

15. _____ Setting land aside to preserve diversity is an example of
    A. wilderness preservation.
    B. seed banks.
    C. cryopreservation.
    D. biotechnology.
    E. genetic engineering.

SHORT ANSWER

16. What is natural selection? How does it relate to agriculture?

17. How do seed banks preserve seeds for future generations?

18. How does genetic engineering differ from traditional biotechnology?

CHAPTER 6 ASSESSMENT

1. D
2. A
3. B
4. C
5. E
6. D
7. E
8. B
9. E
10. B
11. D
12. B
13. E
14. C
15. A

16. Natural selection is a process by which certain genetic characteristics are eliminated from the gene pool of a population. Over long periods of time, this may result in changes in that population. Natural selection relates to sustainable agriculture in terms of crop species that can withstand certain pests or environmental conditions and, conversely, pests that are immune to certain pesticides.

17. Seeds (germplasm) can be dried, placed in cool or cold (cryogenic) storage, in vitro preserved, or stored in a partial vacuum.

18. *Biotechnology* involves selective breeding. Two parent plants are selected for their desirable traits and bred to produce offspring with specific desirable characteristics. When this is done, some less desirable traits often are transferred as well. *Genetic engineering* allows for the transfer of very specific information so that only desired characteristics are passed.

AGRICULTURE AND NUTRITION

LEARNING OUTCOMES

The student will:

1. know that much of agriculture purposely keeps a field in the early stage of ecological succession. (C)
2. observe and **analyze** soil samples by **manipulating** materials and equipment and **completing** the activity "What's in That Dirt?" (C,P)
3. identify the characteristics of soil and **relate** those to agriculture. (C)
4. list several soil conservation practices and **explain** how each works. (C)
5. calculate the number of Calories he or she needs per day based on age, sex, size, and daily activities by **completing** the activity "How Much Food Energy Do I Need?" (C)
6. compare the number of Calories he or she needs per day to his or her average daily diet by **completing** the activity "How Much Food Energy Do I Need?" (C)
7. calculate the amount of land it takes to raise the food he or she eats and **compare** that number to the amount of arable land available per person on Earth. (C,A)
8. evaluate his or her average diet with reference to the Food Guide Pyramid. (C)

9. evaluate the nutritional value of various seeds by **completing** the activity "Connecting Seeds and Human Nutrition." (C,P)
10. know that seeds, when properly selected, can form the basis of a healthy diet. (C)
11. connect lab data on seeds to the position of grains, fruits, & vegetables on the Food Guide Pyramid. (C)
12. know that seeds can be altered to our benefit by **completing** the activity "Seeds for the Future." (C)
13. evaluate the problem of human hunger by **analyzing** a variety of data from selected countries in the activity "The Politics of Hunger." (C,A)
14. create a model of an oak forest and **calculate** the average annual food production of the forest by **completing** the activity "How Many Squirrels Can an Oak Forest Support?" (C,P)
15. calculate the carrying capacity of squirrels in an oak forest by **manipulating** materials and **completing** the activity "How Many Squirrels Can an Oak Forest Support?" (C,P)
16. identify factors that might increase or decrease the carrying capacity of squirrels in an

oak forest and **compare** the carrying capacity of forests of different species of oak trees by **completing** the activity "How Many Squirrels Can an Oak Forest Support?" (C)

17. know what carrying capacity is and what its **relevance** is to humans. (C,A)

18. articulate a point of view about the carrying capacity of Earth for humans. (A)

19. identify some of the strategies farmers are using to make agriculture a sustainable endeavor. (C)

KEY TERMS

soil	clay	terrace	vitamins
soil profile	texture	windbreak	basil energy requirement (BER)
horizon	loam	nutrition	starch
humus	soil erosion	nutrient	lipids
porosity	soil conservation	metabolism	sugar
sand	tillage	proteins	carrying capacity
silt	no-till	carbohydrates	vegetarian

RECOMMENDED BLACKLINE MASTERS

7.1 Composition (by Volume) of Loamy Soil

7.2 Map of the World—Countries Sized by Population

7.3 Politics of Hunger Poster

7.4 Idealized Approach to Carrying Capacity

7.5 Vegy vs. Cafeteria Diet

The Recommended Blackline Masters listed above are supplemental to the activity/reading, and can be found on the *Teacher Resource CD*.

ACTIVITIES FLOW CHART

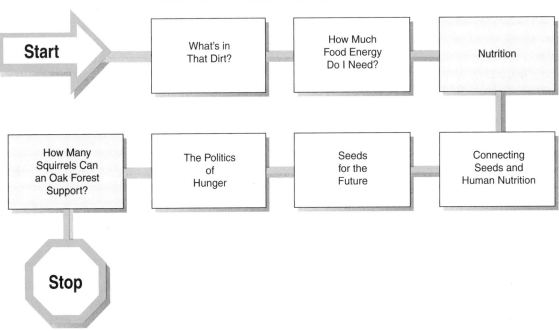

CHAPTER 7: AGRICULTURE AND NUTRITION

NOTE: Shaded items are lower priority.

TEACHING STRATEGIES AND ANSWERS FOR ACTIVITIES

READING THE ESSENCE OF AGRICULTURE

See *Student Edition,* p. 262.

READING 7.1 THE STRATEGY OF AGRICULTURE

See *Student Edition,* p. 262.

QUESTIONS

Q. What is the challenge of agriculture?

A. The challenge is to feed the world and preserve our biosphere.

Q. Why is farming an efficient way to grow crops?

A. When crops are planted on open land with plenty of water, fertilizer and sunlight, biomass increases the fastest.

READING SOIL: LINKING THE NONLIVING TO THE LIVING

See *Student Edition,* p. 264.

READING 7.2 INTRODUCTION TO SOILS

See *Student Edition,* p. 265.

QUESTIONS

Q. What is soil?

A. Soil is a mixture of minerals, organic matter, water, and air. It has a definite structure and composition.

ACTIVITY 7.1 WHAT'S IN THAT DIRT?

See *Student Edition,* p. 265.

 7.1

ADVANCE PREPARATION

Collect a variety of soil samples or ask students to bring in their own samples.

Familiarize yourself with the details of the soil testing kit you use. The student directions were written to accommodate a variety of kits. We tested the activity using the Rapitest® soil test kit available by contacting your Kendall/Hunt representative. Other kits are available in home and garden stores. The Rapitest kit is packaged so that the testing chemicals are contained neatly in capsules. There is a device for each test that has compartments to hold the test solution for comparison to the color scale. It is simple to use.

STRATEGIES AND PROCEDURES

This activity will extend over several days. You will probably need two days to review the testing procedures and then let the students conduct their tests. After all the data are collected, lead students through a discussion of the data so they can learn how to compare, contrast, and draw generalizations based on the evidence they have.

For step 9, divide the class into expert groups. Each student will become an expert on either pH, nitrogen, phosphorus, or potash. You could add more experts, if you want to get more technical with this activity. Students should be able to describe what the nutrient does for plants, the consequences of too little or too much and how the level can be adjusted.

SPECIAL FOCUS SOIL CONSERVATION

See *Student Edition,* p. 272.

READING NUTRITION: NURTURING LIFE

See *Student Edition,* p. 275.

READING 7.3 PLANT NUTRITION

See *Student Edition,* p. 275.

READING 7.4 ANIMAL NUTRITION

See *Student Edition,* p. 277.

ACTIVITY 7.2 HOW MUCH FOOD ENERGY DO I NEED?

See *Student Edition,* p. 278.

ADVANCE PREPARATION

This is another activity that adapts well to using computer technology. There are a variety of software programs focusing on diet and nutrition that will calculate Calorie needs. Also, there are websites that have built-in calculators. Several options are cited in the references and margin notes. A simplified version of this activity can be found on the *Teacher Resource CD.*

STRATEGIES AND PROCEDURES

This lab enables students to obtain a rough estimate of the number of Calories they need per day based on their age, sex, size, and activities. They then compare their need to their average daily Caloric intake. From this personal perspective, the lab finishes by connecting personal Calorie intake to land use.

PART 1

Caloric need depends on both metabolism and physical activity. The metabolism of the body relates to the total of all the chemical reactions in all the cells in the body. This is related to food consumption. Since essentially all of the energy released from food eventually becomes heat, the heat output of the body is used to measure one's metabolic rate. The basal metabolic rate is the amount of energy one requires just to stay alive. It can be measured directly using a human calorimeter, which measures the heat output of the body under basal conditions. It can be determined indirectly by measuring the amount of oxygen burned by the body in a given period of time. Since the equipment used in both of these techniques is too expensive for most high school labs, we use a different method in this lab.

Experimental studies have shown that the basal metabolic rate varies from one normal person to another approximately in proportion to body surface area (not in proportion to weight). By determining one's height and weight, one can determine his or her surface area from a graph. Then the basal metabolism can be read from a graph using age and sex. The figure obtained is an average determination for most people. If someone has a thyroid problem or is going through an abnormal growth spurt, the figures from the graph will be inaccurate.

Researchers have determined that the oxygen consumption and heat output of an individual rises upon eating, even if one remains at rest. This elevation in metabolic rate over the basal rate is called the specific dynamic action of foods. It is compensated for in the lab by adding an extra 10% to the basal energy requirement.

Emphasize to your students that they must be realistic in listing their average daily routines; otherwise they will get meaningless results. Also, the Caloric intake must be from an average day.

These sample average data may be helpful for examining students' work:

Characteristic	Girls (range)	Boys (range)	Units
height	175–155	190–170	cm
weight	66–46	90–55	kg
surface area	1.8–1.4	2.2–1.6	m^2
BMR	36–39	39–42	$Cal/m^2/hr$
BER	70–50	85–65	Cal/hr
dynamic BER	75–55	95–70	Cal/hr
d.d Ber	1800–1300	2300–1700	Cal/day

PART 2

How many Calories of food a student consumes in a day requires the student to record all food items consumed in a day and an estimate of the quantity of each item. The Caloric Counter included in the Appendices of the student textbook and package labeling should enable each student to determine his or her daily total.

Apples: In 1998 in Washington State,

95×10^6 boxes harvested from 2.2×10^5 acres.
Each box weighs 42 pounds.
There are about 100 apples/box.

Source: Washington Apple Commission

Orange Juice: In 1997 in Florida,

6.09×10^5 acres produced 244×10^6 boxes.
97% was for processed → juice!
On average, you get 6¼ gallons OJ/box.
1 gallon = 128 oz.

Source: Florida Agricultural Statistical Service

Corn Flakes: 1998 U.S. field corn production,

9.76×10^9 bushels from 72.6×10^6 acres.
1 bushel gives 38 12 oz. boxes corn flakes.
Note: Corn flakes made from #2 yellow dent field corn.

Sources: USDA, Kelloggs, Cereal Qual Lab-TX A&M

Wheat Flour:

In 1998, U.S. average wheat harvest was 43.2
bushels/acre.
You can get 560 hamburger buns/bushel.
1 bushel = 60 pounds.
1 bun contains 29 grams of flour.

Sources: USDA, Kansas Wheat Commission

Hamburger:

Mature beef steers weigh ~ 1200 lbs. and live 1.5–2
years.
Average diet of a beef steer:
 25 lbs./day corn silage
 14 lbs./day corn
 0.5 lbs./day soybean meal
Average production of diet items:
 silage = 16 tons/acre
 corn = 4.0 tons/acre
 soybeans = 1.17 tons/acre
Assume the weight of beef, bone, and organs
average out.

Sources: USDA, Natl. Cattlemen's Beef Assn.

Potatoes: In 1994 in Idaho,

13.8×10^9 pounds harvested from 4.08×10^5 acres.
1 pound = 454 grams.

Source: Potato Growers of Idaho

Sugar: In 1996 in Florida,

6.4×10^4 acres produced 2.8×10^6 tons sugar cane.
About 1 ton sugar cane produces 220 lbs. raw sugar.
1 pound (lb.) = 454 grams.

Source: Sugar Cane Growers Coop. of Florida.

Ketchup: In 1997 in California,

9,349,600 tons of tomatoes from 2.6×10^5 acres.
24 tomatoes (4.26 lbs.) give 14 oz. ketchup.
Note: California produces over 90% of U.S. processed
tomatoes each year.

Sources: California Tomato Growers, Heinz

Chicken: You can make 55 nuggets from

1 chicken (7.2 lbs. live).
The grain-to-chicken conversion is 2:1.
To simplify, assume all the grain is corn.
U.S. corn production is 134 bushels/acre at
56 lbs./bushel.

Sources: USDA, Tyson

Daily Products:

It takes ~ 3.0 acres to produce the silage, hay, and
grain a dairy cow consumes/year.
The average dairy cow weighs 1450 lbs. and produces
16,900 lbs. milk/year.
1 gallon milk weighs 8.6 pounds.
1 gallon = 128 oz.
On the average, "raw milk" is made into various
grades of milk (29.5%); butter (6.2%); cheese (46.2%);
frozen milk products (7.4%); powdered milk (3.8%);
other (6.9%).

Sources: American Dairy Assn., Wisconsin Farm
Bureau

PART 3

The total number of Calories consumed (as listed in Figure 7.25) is 3089. To obtain the yearly equivalent, multiply each number in the second column by 365. To obtain the number of acres, multiply the amount eaten in a year by the related conversion factor. The total amount of land used to provide the diet in Figure 7.25 is 0.2792, or about 0.28 acres.

In steps 19 and 20, students may respond as follows:

19. The land used to provide a fairly typical American teenage diet is represented by the size of an average lot in suburban America.
20. Area of Earth's surface = 197,000,000 mi^2 amount of arable land = 5,920,000 m^2 or 3,790,000,000 acres. Arable land per person = 0.63 acres-person (assumes 6 billion people).

Ask students if the following is a way to estimate the carrying capacity of Earth if all food was raised like that in America:

$$\frac{.28 \text{ acres/person}}{6.0 \text{ billion}} = \frac{.63 \text{ acres/person}}{x}$$

$$x = 13.5 \text{ billion}$$

This should lead to a lively discussion. The extrapolation is huge!

 **ACTIVITY 7.3 NUTRITION**

See *Student Edition,* p. 284.

Transparency 7.1

Evaluate students on how well they organize their data; the method they develop to analyze their diet, in terms of the recommendations in the Food Guide Pyramid; and the quality of the conclusion they draw. This activity is very individualized and open-ended.

ACTIVITY 7.4 CONNECTING SEEDS AND HUMAN NUTRITION

See *Student Edition,* p. 285.

ADVANCE PREPARATION

Obtain a variety of large seeds. It is best to get foods that are seeds we eat than to use dried seeds from packets. The food is moist, which allows the chemicals in the detecting solutions to get at the nutrients. Recommended are:

* seeds high in carbohydrates (starch): lima beans and other large beans
* seeds high in lipids: sunflower seeds
* seeds high in sugar: sweet corn
* seeds high in protein: soybeans

Lima beans, soybeans, green beans, and corn are available both fresh and quick frozen at large grocery stores. The same is true for corn. Raw sunflower seeds are available unsalted and are already removed from the shell.

Detecting stains can be obtained by contacting your Kendall/Hunt representative.

Make sure students read the WARNINGS regarding the chemicals and wear their safety goggles. The reason students are told not to place the seeds in their mouth is because they are never to taste chemicals in the lab. Also, seeds used commercially in agriculture may have pesticides added. Do NOT use such seeds.

The following chart shows *average* seed content (% dry weight) as obtained using high-tech analyzing equipment. The numbers don't total 100% because fiber is not included in the chart.

Seed	Starch	Sugar	Protein	Fat
Sweet Corn	60	13	11	3
Lima Bean	50	5	21	1
Soybean	19	8	46	24
Raw Sunflower	7	3	23	50

SOURCES: USDA/ARS, United Soybean Board, National Sunflower Association.

RESULTS

The initial tests with the potato, turkey, honey, and butter enable students to view positive test results.

All the seeds should test positive for starch and protein. Since sugars are only present in small amounts, except for sweet corn, the indicator should only show small amounts present. The Sudan III will most likely be red around the edge (seed coat) and at the embryo except for the sunflower where it most likely will be pink or red all over.

SAMPLE ANSWERS TO QUESTIONS

1. All the seeds tested are nutritious. The most nutritious are probably bean and soybean.
2. Beans and soybeans are rich in carbohydrates (starch and sugar) and protein. *Notes:* The protein in sweet corn is of a lower quality than in beans and soybeans. Sunflower seeds are rich in nutrients, but it is difficult to consume them in quantity.
3. Sugar mainly comes from sugar cane and sugar beets. The stalk of the sugar cane plant and the fleshy root of the sugar beet contain high concentrations of sugar. Cornstarch can also be processed as a sweetener (syrup).
4. Grains (in cereal); corn directly (or corn in margarine, syrup, snacks, and cornmeal, which is in tortillas, tamalies, and corn bread); wheat, which is in flour; meat (livestock and chicken feed are mainly grains); mixed nuts (eaten directly or contained in cookies, candy bars, pastry goods); coconut; apples-pears-peaches-watermelon, etc. (all directly related to seeds).
5. a. We like the taste of seeds and seed products.
   b. Seeds and seed products are readily available.
   c. Seeds and seed products are nutritious and recommended to us.
   d. Compared to the cost of meat, seed products are less expensive.
6. Most people on Earth receive the bulk of their Calories and nutrients from seeds and seed products. A well selected variety can provide all essential nutrients. *Note:* Too heavy a dependence on a limited supply can cause problems. The protein in corn does not provide all the amino acids to meet human requirements.

7. The Food Guide Pyramid was designed by the USDA to help people make daily choices for better health. It shows the recommended daily portions from the five major food groups.

8. Nutritionists have determined that a healthy diet is rich in carbohydrates and protein and low in fats, oils, and sweets. Seeds and seed products meet this standard, and hence they are emphasized.

9. Student answers will vary. Grade on depth of their analysis.

EXTENSION

Soybeans are used to make high protein animal feed, vegetable oil, tofu, soy flour, baby food, imitation meat products, snacks, adhesive tape, various drugs, and explosives.

READING THE CHALLENGE OF AGRICULTURE: FEEDING THE WORLD AND SAVING DIVERSITY

See *Student Edition,* p. 287.

ACTIVITY 7.5 SEEDS FOR THE FUTURE

See *Student Edition,* p. 288.

ADVANCE PREPARATION

Consider inviting guest speakers to your class to highlight careers in agronomy, agriculture, and genetic engineering.

STRATEGIES AND PROCEDURES

This is a role-playing activity. Students will get to know one method of preparing seeds for the future well and learn about two other strategies from their peers. Consider setting up panels of "experts" to answer the questions in the student textbook. The students in the audience can keep track of the responses as a means of gathering information about the ideas they did not study.

SAMPLE ANSWER TO PROCEDURE QUESTIONS

A. Seed banks enable us to store genetic characteristics for future times when the problems of drought, new diseases, and insect pests may overwhelm traditional varieties of plants.

B. Genetic engineering techniques may soon enable scientists to quickly design plant varieties that resist drought, diseases, and insect pests more effectively than those developed using traditional plant biotechnology.

C. Plant scientists may develop plants that transpire less water & hence require less water. They may develop crops, that can tolerate brackish or saline water and therefore grow on poorer soils. They may also develop crops that fertilize themselves and therefore require less fertilizer.

ACTIVITY 7.6 THE POLITICS OF HUNGER

See *Student Edition*, p. 289.

ADVANCE PREPARATION

Assign countries to students so that about one-fourth of the class has a country from each of these categories: very well fed, well fed, poorly fed, nearly starving. This information is found in Figures 7.30 and 7.31. Each student needs a copy of Figure 7.33 with enough rows to accommodate all the countries reported on. As students give their reports, fill in the chart. After all students have reported, analyze the data to identify patterns and trends.

The best references for doing this activity are:

1. The World Population Data Sheet from the Population Reference Bureau.
2. The Chart of Literacy Rates for Selected Countries - which a good librarian can help you find.
3. The Map of paved roads as a share of total roads from the World Bank Atlas.

STRATEGIES AND PROCEDURES

At the present time, people who are well fed live in countries where the population is well educated, the economy is strong, the government is democratic, and there is a good infrastructure for moving goods around. Populations are also stable. People who are poorly fed or nearly starving live in countries with rapidly growing populations, low literacy rates, poor infrastructure, and poor economies. The government is usually a dictatorship, anarchy, or involved in a civil war.

Note: In poor nations, the form of government is usually *not* what is listed in an encyclopedia or atlas. The form of government is best determined by learning about current events in that country.

It appears that at the present time hunger is more related to politics and our ability to move food around than it is to our ability to actually raise food.

Types of Governments:

- *Communism.* A system of government in which the state government controls the means of production and a single, often authoritarian party holds power with the intention of establishing a higher social order in which all goods are shared equally among the people.
- *Constitutional Monarchy.* A monarchy in which the powers of the ruler are limited to those granted under the nation's constitution and laws.
- *Democracy.* Government by the people, exercised either directly or through elected representatives. Usually ruled by majority.
- *Dictatorship.* A ruler with absolute power and supreme jurisdiction over the government and state.
- *Federal Republic.* A system of government in which a union of states-provinces recognizes the power of a central or national government. The states, however, retain many powers of government. In addition, the supreme power of the states and nation lies in the people's ability to elect

representatives who are responsible to the people. The government usually contains a legislature and a president.

* *Monarchy.* Government or state ruled solely by an absolute ruler or monarch (king, queen).
* *Parliamentary State.* Government ruled by a national representative legislative body having supreme power over the nation.
* *Republic.* Supreme power of the state lies in the people's ability to elect representatives who are responsible to the people. The government usually contains a legislature and a president.
* *Socialist Republic.* A system of government where the state controls many of the factors of production (industry) and the means of distribution (transportation).
* *Anarchy.* A state (condition) of society without government or law. The absence of governmental control.

READING 7.5 THE CONCEPT OF CARRYING CAPACITY

See *Student Edition*, p. 292.

 7.4

ACTIVITY 7.7 HOW MANY SQUIRRELS CAN AN OAK FOREST SUPPORT?

See *Student Edition*, p. 293.

ADVANCE PREPARATION

If possible, arrange to conduct this activity in a real oak forest.

Prepare the colored circles and work boards ahead of time. You will need 10 circles each of the following diameters for each team: 25, 30, 35, 40, 45, 50, 55, 60, 65 mm. (Scale: 1 mm = 1 cm.) Cut the circles out of brown, red, white, black, and orange paper. Each team needs a work board about 0.5 meters square of poster board or cardboard (size is not critical, but all boards should be the same).

These materials can be used repeatedly with different classes if students do not draw on them.

STRATEGIES AND PROCEDURES

Encourage students to be creative, but realistic as they design their forest in steps 1–4.

Wait until all students have finished those steps before moving on to step 5. Students make their own data table.

The following example may be helpful for assisting students as they work on their calculations:

Suppose students use eight white oaks with a diameter of 30 cm. The mass of acorns produced by one tree of this species and size is 1.6 kg. Multiplied by eight trees, this results in a total of 12.8 kg of acorns per year. To convert mass to kilocalories:

$$12.8 \text{ kg} \times (4.5 \times 10^3 \text{ kcal/kg}) = 5.7 \times 10^4 \text{ kcal}$$

To calculate the carrying capacity:

$$(5.7 \times 10^4 \text{ kcal})/(137 \text{ kcal/squirrel/day} \times 365 \text{ days}) =$$
$$1.1 \text{ squirrels/day for 365 days}$$

In step 7, students may respond as follows:

7. a. Answers will vary depending on how students designed their forests. More trees means a greater carrying capacity. Certain species are more productive.
   b. Because it is the energy in the acorns, not the mass, that determines how many squirrels will be kept alive.
   c. The capacity is probably less because our calculations do not take into account a loss of acorns due to rotting or other animals eating them.
   d. Usually the carrying capacity is greater with a few larger trees because they produce so many more acorns. For example, a white oak of 50 cm produces five times as many acorns as a white oak half the diameter.
   e. The carrying capacity for squirrels would be reduced.
   f. Students may make a variety of connections, but they should make the general connection that there are a variety of factors working together to determine carrying capacity.

7.5

READING 7.6 HOW MANY PEOPLE CAN THE EARTH SUPPORT?

See *Student Edition*, p. 295.

QUESTIONS

Q. Why is Dewit's estimate so high and Hulett's estimate so low?

A. If one assumes everything that grows can eventually end up as food for people and that there are ample water, minerals, and sunlight to grow things, huge quantities of food can be produced. If everyone is a vegetarian, the world can feed lots of people; hence, Dewit's large number. On the otherhand, Hulett assumes everyone eats like Americans whose average diet contains considerable meat. He also computed carrying capacity numbers based on American per capita use of various raw materials. Since America leads the world in raw material consumption his carrying capacity numbers are low.

Note on the carrying capacity estimate tied to Activity 7.2, Part 3.

This determination is shown in the *Teacher Guide* Section for Activity 7.2. It is totally unrealistic, based on odd assumptions—but that's the point. A good discussion based on the equation used could be very useful.

Q. How can agriculture be even more efficient?
   1. Soil erosion can be reduced using any combination of the six methods described in the Special Focus.
   2. Diversity can be increased through expanded seed storage, setting more land aside as wilderness (living seed banks), and advances in

genetic engineering.

3. Energy efficiency can be increased using high tech equipment to pinpoint where fertilizer should be placed, no-till decreases plowing, and new equipment/materials combine steps. Example: some seeds contain pesticides. This eliminates the need to spray.

Q. What are the pros and cons of a vegetarian diet?

A. P—A vegetarian diet is high in grains, fruits, and vegetables. It is close to what the Food Guide Pyramid recommends.

C—Vegetarians must work to get the proper mixture of proteins. Meat eaters don't have that problem. Some vegetarians won't drink milk. That creates other problems, such as lack of vitamin B_{12}.

Q. Can you argue for or against the vegetarian diet?

A. Student answers will be all over the place. Grade on depth of thought and quality of *evidence*. The purpose of the question is to get them to think and seek out information, not to take a position on the subject.

CHAPTER 7 SUMMARY

See *Student Edition,* p. 298.

CHAPTER 7 ASSESSMENT

Name_____   Date_____

MULTIPLE CHOICE

1. _____ Soil is a natural mixture of all of the following *except*
   A. minerals.
   B. water.
   C. stones.
   D. air.
   E. organic matter.

2. _____ Which layer of soil is of most value because it supports agricultural crops?
   A. C-horizon
   B. A-horizon
   C. O-horizon
   D. B-horizon

3. _____ All of the following can cause soil erosion *except*
   A. wood gathering.
   B. overgrazing.
   C. clearing for construction.
   D. straight row plowing.
   E. planting windbreaks.

4. _____ Which soil conservation practice minimizes cultivation and leaves crop residues on the surface throughout the year?
   A. Terraces
   B. Strip cropping
   C. Grass waterways
   D. Field windbreaks
   E. Conservation tillage

5. _____ A farm field is kept in the early stage of succession for all of the following reasons *except*
   A. most crops do best in the shade.
   B. photosynthesis mainly goes to plant growth.
   C. water and nutrients can easily be supplied.
   D. sunlight can readily get to the plants.

6. _____ Which one of the following are organic molecules needed by higher animals to perform specific biological functions (e.g., blood clotting)?
   A. water
   B. proteins
   C. vitamins
   D. carbohydrates
   E. fats

7. _____ The number of Calories you need each day is based on your
   A. age.
   B. sex.
   C. size.
   D. activities.
   E. all of these are factors.

8. _____ A person's surface area is most closely related to
   A. age.
   B. heat loss.
   C. sex.
   D. activity level.

9. _____ The Food Guide Pyramid is
   A. a strategy used by early Egyptians to plan diets.
   B. a device developed by the USDA to help people make food choices.
   C. a device used by vegetarians to plan diets.
   D. a strategy developed by General Mills to get people to eat more breakfast cereal.

10. _____ Seeds can be an excellent source of all of the following *except*
   A. carbohydrates.
   B. protein.
   C. starch.
   D. sugar.
   E. fat.

11. _____ The major reason so many people on Earth go hungry is
   A. poor distribution of food due to political conflict.
   B. lack of meat in developing countries.
   C. the earth's inability to grow enough food.
   D. low literacy means people can't plan good diets.

12. _____ Which statement about the earth's carrying capacity for humans is *not true?*
   A. As the standard of living goes up, the carrying capacity goes down.
   B. The earth can support more vegetarians than meat eaters.
   C. There is no one single number for the earth's carrying capacity.
   D. Scientists have accurately determined that the earth's carrying capacity is well over 100 billion.

SHORT ANSWER

Respond in a few sentences to questions 13-17.

13. Describe three characteristics of soil that indicate it is good for agriculture.

14. Design an experiment to test for the "best" bean seed. Include in your explanation a clear, testable question, a definition for "best," and a description of your experimental controls.

15. What do you consider are the four most important points about good nutrition?

16. Why should we be concerned about Earth's carrying capacity?

17. Choose one view of the carrying capacity of Earth in terms of how many people it can support, and explain why you think it is a valid view.

Agriculture and Nutrition

CHAPTER 7 ASSESSMENT

1. C
2. B
3. E
4. E
5. A
6. C
7. E
8. B
9. B
10. D
11. A
12. D

13. Good agricultural soil contains organic material; drains well; has a pH between 6 and 8; and has reasonable amounts of potash, phosphorus, and nitrogen.

14. A good experimental design will compare bean seeds for a desirable characteristic such as protein, carbohydrate, or lipid content. Students' experiments should fall logically from their definition of "best."

15. It is difficult to reduce good nutrition to four key points, but students might select from these ideas:
    - Limit the intake of fats, oils, and sweets.
    - Eat a variety of foods.
    - Increase the amount of vegetables, fruits, and grain products you eat.
    - Use salt and other sodium products in moderation.
    - The less processed a food product is, the greater the nutritional value per Calorie.
    - Eat meat, poultry, fish, and eggs in moderation.

16. Attending to Earth's carrying capacity gives a perspective for understanding how to take care of Earth and manage our resource use.

17. Students can argue any of the perspectives about carrying capacity as long as they do so logically.

CHAPTER 8

ENERGY TODAY

LEARNING OUTCOMES

The student will:

1. draw pie graphs using raw data and analyze them by completing the activity "Where Do We Get Our Energy?" (C,P)
2. realize that 85% of all commercial energy used by the United States comes from fossil fuels. (A)
3. list the three major energy-consuming sectors of our economy. (C)
4. analyze a graph of historical energy use, determine why that use changes, and speculate on future changes by completing the activity "An Energy History of the U.S." (C,A)
5. state two reasons why early Americans converted from wood to coal. (C)
6. calculate the energy content of a fossil fuel by manipulating materials and equipment and completing the activity "Counting Calories … The Energy Content of a Fuel." (C,P)
7. compare his or her energy content calculation with a table of average energy contents by observing a table and writing a response. (C,P)
8. answer questions about energy use in the United States by observing a graph of U.S. energy consumption from 1875 to 1980 and completing the activity "Unquenchable Energy Thirst." (C,A)
9. realize the United States and North America consume a large portion of the energy in the world and recognize energy consumption in other countries is growing rapidly. (C,A)
10. state how oil deposits originated. (C)
11. name the layers of sediment in which petroleum is formed. (C)
12. draw and label different types of petroleum traps and use the concepts of porosity and permeability. (P,C)
13. state the products that result when oil is burned by writing a chemical equation. (C)
14. list five common products made from petroleum. (C)
15. explain why natural gas is, in some ways, a better fuel than oil. (C)
16. name the products that result when natural gas is burned by writing an equation. (C)
17. assemble a simple distillation apparatus and use it to separate a solution for the purpose of analyzing the distillation process. (C,P)
18. identify two reasons why coal is ranked third behind oil and gas. (C)

19. realize that there is a renewed interest in coal. (A)
20. explain how coal was originally formed. (C)
21. examine and categorize samples of the main types of coal and correlate the information gained with maps, charts, and diagrams by completing the activity "Coal." (C,P)
22. compare coal from the eastern United States with coal from the western United States by completing the activity "Coal." (C)
23. name a major use for each of the four types of coal. (C)
24. list and distinguish among the types of coal mining. (C)

25. manipulate materials and equipment to gain a basic understanding of what happens in an electrical generator unit by completing the activity "How Electricity Is Generated." (C,P)
26. explain how electrical generating plants function by writing a response and drawing picture. (C,P)
27. explain how hydropower generates electrical energy. (C)
28. define thermal pollution and relate it to electric power generation. (C)

KEY TERMS

residential	source bed	anaerobic	turbine
commercial	geologist	room-and-pillar mining	generator
industry	attitude	continuous miner	armature
coal	structural trap	longwall mining	unit-train
energy content	anticline	surface mining	cooling tower
fossil fuel	fault	overburden	voltage
crude oil	salt dome	open pit mining	transformer
petroleum	strata	hydropower	resistance
organic	stratigraphic trap	circuit	electric power transmission
hydrocarbon	distillation	galvanometer	watt-hour meter
natural gas	peat	solenoid	thermal pollution
reservoir	lignite	magnetic field	cooling pond
porous	subbituminous	electromagnetic induction (EMI)	cooling system
permeable	bituminous	current	
impermeable	anthracite		

RECOMMENDED BLACKLINE MASTERS

8.1   Energy History of the United States
8.2   Combustion (Burning) Equations
8.3   Distillation Lab
8.4   Typical Fractionating Tower
8.5   Magnet and Coil
8.6   Coal-Fired Generating Plant

The Recommended Blackline Masters listed above are supplemental to the activity/reading and can be found on the *Teacher Resource CD.*

CHAPTER 8: ENERGY TODAY

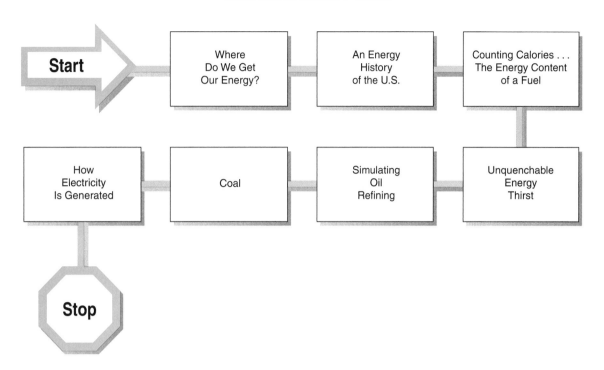

Start → Where Do We Get Our Energy? → An Energy History of the U.S. → Counting Calories . . . The Energy Content of a Fuel

How Electricity Is Generated — Coal — Simulating Oil Refining — Unquenchable Energy Thirst

Stop

 TEACHING STRATEGIES AND ANSWERS FOR ACTIVITIES

READING ENERGY FOR THE GLOBAL ECONOMY

See *Student Edition,* p. 302.

ACTIVITY 8.1 WHERE DO WE GET OUR ENERGY?

See *Student Edition,* p. 302.

ADVANCE PREPARATION

Each student will need one protractor, one drawing compass, and a calculator.

STRATEGIES AND PROCEDURES

The key to student success is using the conversion factor.

In step 2, students may respond as follows:

2. a. Oil, natural gas, coal.
   b. They are all Fossil Fuels and obtained from Earth's crust.
   c. 96.9 Q/376 Q × 100% = 26%. The United States, with 4.6% of the world's people, consumes 26% of the commercial energy supply.

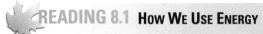

READING 8.1 **HOW WE USE ENERGY**

See *Student Edition*, p. 303.

8.1

Transparency 8.1

ACTIVITY 8.2 **AN ENERGY HISTORY OF THE U.S.**

See *Student Edition*, p. 304.

1. Wood to coal, about 1870–1900; coal to oil and gas, about 1920–1960; oil and gas to a mix of sources, about 1990–?

2. We switched from *wood to coal* because coal has a higher energy content than wood. It takes less volume to haul a ton of coal than a ton of wood. Railroads became an important means for hauling economic goods and people. Trees began to disappear around major American cities.

   We switched from *coal to oil and gas* because gasoline is a more versatile fuel than coal. It burns cleaner and waste disposal is less significant. The mass-produced automobile became significant. It is much easier to run an automobile on a liquid than on a solid fuel. Natural gas became a relatively clean fuel for heating homes

   We are switching *away from the use of oil* in some cases because our domestic supplies seem to be running low, cleaner methods have been developed for burning coal, nuclear energy is used for electric power generation, and solar options are beginning to be used.

3. Accept thoughtful responses. This question is a good introduction to the topics in Chapters 9–12. No one knows, with certainty, what lies ahead in the next 50 years.

READING 8.2 **HISTORICAL ENERGY USE**

See *Student Edition*, p. 305.

ACTIVITY 8.3 **COUNTING CALORIES . . . THE ENERGY CONTENT OF A FUEL**

See *Student Edition*, p. 306.

ADVANCE PREPARATION

Allow sufficient time to make and gather the materials for this activity; you will need more than an afternoon after school. Large juice cans make excellent chimneys. You will need a "church key" to make the holes near the bottom. Some teachers start a month ahead and offer extra credit for the cans. Others have the staff at the lunchroom or local restaurants or friends save them. Collect the cardboard frozen juice cans (with metal base) in a similar manner. Candles can be obtained locally.

For the chimney, use a large can (1.36 liters) opened at both ends; punch several holes in the side of the can near the bottom for ventilation. The calorimeter is a cardboard frozen juice can (16 fl oz = 473 mL). Cardboard absorbs and transfers heat to a much lesser degree than metal. Since heat lost to space is so much greater than that absorbed by the juice can (the juice can is only about 10% of the mass of the water plus can), no correction is made for this problem.

STRATEGIES AND PROCEDURES

WARNING

Safety is an important issue. Students will be working around an open flame. Make sure safety procedures are covered and followed carefully. Candles may seem innocent, but we are all responsible for students' safety.

Start with water somewhat below room temperature to minimize radiation gains and losses. The major portion of this activity takes one 40–50-minute class period.

SAMPLE ANSWERS TO QUESTIONS

1. Students will obtain answers that are about half the accepted value for the energy content of paraffin wax.

2. Our apparatus was not a closed system. Approximately 50% of the heat was lost as it escaped around the sides of the calorimeter. It either warmed the metal chimney or it rose into space. A small amount of heat was absorbed by the cardboard juice can and was not accounted for.

3. Because the energy content of coal is almost three times that of wood, coal proved to be a much more efficient energy source for running trains and making steel. For example, while it could use charcoal, the Bessemer process of steelmaking was more effectively fed by coal-derived coke. Also, the steam locomotive, which ran on steel rails, functioned more efficiently with coal. Energy content is one of several reasons. The forests near the industrial centers were being depleted. There was a growing scarcity of wood.

4. a. This kind of information is helpful in planning diets.

   b. Without knowing energy content, we have no common denominator for comparing and relating fuels. It is difficult to relate barrels of oil to cubic feet of gas and to tons of coal. With the common denominator that the energy content concept provides, we can make meaningful comparisons and plan for the future.

   c. A knowledge of the energy content of the fuel consumed by a machine is necessary to determine the efficiency of that machine. This type of knowledge is essential if we are to make the most efficient use of our fuels.

READING 8.3 AMERICA'S ENERGY TRANSITIONS

See *Student Edition,* p. 309.

ACTIVITY 8.4 UNQUENCHABLE ENERGY THIRST

See *Student Edition,* p. 310.

The graph for this activity (Figure 8.10) ends at 1980 on purpose so that students can more easily learn about problems related to growth. If possible, provide photocopies of the graph. Students can then draw lines on the graph to estimate their data more accurately.

1. Wood; coal; oil and gas.
2. Imports.
3. (a.) exponential growth curve
4. The economic depression.
5. 18 to 20 years.
6. 30 years.
7. 25 years.
8. $D.T._{ave.} = 20 + 30 + 25/3 = 25$ years.
9. $25 = 70/X, X = 70/25 = 2.8\%$.
10. 3 doublings → 80 to 160 to 320 to 640Q. Won't fit on the graph.
11. No, Earth's resources are finite. Reward thoughtful responses.

 READING **Fossil Fuels**

See *Student Edition*, p. 311.

 8.2 READING 8.4 **Oil**

See *Student Edition*, p. 311.

Demonstrate an aquifer with the following. Fill a glass or beaker close to the top with sand. Fill a second identical glass or beaker to the same level with water. To most students, it will look as if the glass of sand can't hold anything more. Pour the water into the sand. You should be able to pour about two-thirds of the water into the sand without an overflow. This action shows that the sand layer is *porous*. Now tilt the glass of sand (plus water); the water will run out. This shows that the sand layer is *permeable*. Relate this demonstration to pumping crude oil out of an oil and gas trap.

 8.2 READING 8.5 **Natural Gas**

See *Student Edition*, p. 317.

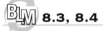 **8.3, 8.4** ACTIVITY 8.5 **Simulating Oil Refining—The Distillation Process**

See *Student Edition*, p. 318.

ADVANCE PREPARATION

 Your main concern in this activity probably will be in making the rubber stopper/glass connector unit. Preassemble these units because of the liability and safety issues related to students working with glass tubing and one-hole stoppers.

The clear plastic tubing can be aquarium tubing obtained by contacting your Kendall/Hunt representative or from a pet shop. If the glass connector does not fit snugly into the clear plastic tubing, build up its diameter slightly by wrapping tape around it.

Make the simulated crude oil as follows:

Add 4 cups of sugar per gallon of hot water. Stir and add food coloring to obtain the desired color. To color the simulated crude oil brown, use 7 drops red plus 6 drops yellow plus 2 drops green.

If you wish to make a smaller quantity, see these conversions:

$$1 \text{ liter} = 1.06 \text{ quarts}$$
$$\text{so, } 1000 \text{ mL} = 1.06 \text{ quarts}$$
$$\text{or, } 946 \text{ mL} = 1.00 \text{ quarts}$$
$$\text{so, } 3784 \text{ mL} = 1 \text{ U.S. gallon}$$

Thus, you may *add 1 cup sugar per 946 mL hot water.* Stir and adjust to proper color with food coloring. Cherry Coke may be substituted for simcrude.

STRATEGIES AND PROCEDURES

WARNING

Students will be working around open flames. Take proper precautions. Remember liability! This activity should fit nicely into a 45–55-minute lab period with ample time for prelab and cleanup. Make sure each student records a hypothesis. Student drawings should look something like this:

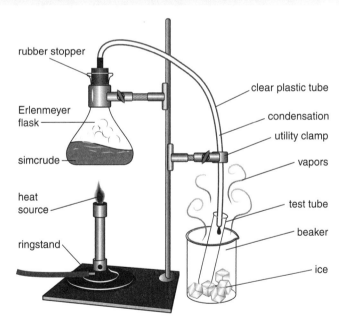

Evaluate observations on thoroughness and accuracy. Students should explain why their hypothesis was correct or incorrect. They also need to explain what happened and why. The simulated crude oil becomes a darker brown because clear vapors leave the flask, condense, and are then collected as a clear liquid in the test tube.

1. Although similar to the apparatus used in this activity, the distillation apparatus shown in Figure 8.19 is more efficient because the transfer tube is cooled. It also contains a thermometer for obtaining the temperature of the hot vapors.

2. This option is available to students who wish to learn more about the process of oil refining.

ACTIVITY 8.6 COAL

See *Student Edition*, p. 321.

ADVANCE PREPARATION _____

The coal samples can be purchased by contacting your Kendall/Hunt representative. If you have the time, your local utility may help you gather some of the samples.

Some teachers place the samples into labeled baby food jars and glue them shut. The samples are easy to see through the clear glass and they last a long time if the jars are sealed.

STRATEGIES AND PROCEDURES _____

Have students complete their observations first. Good descriptions are a must. Students are then directed to the related reading and matching exercises.

SAMPLE ANSWERS TO MATCHING _____

Descriptions

Peat: brown, dry, decayed plant matter
Lignite: dull, black, soft, crumbly
Bituminous: shiny, black, somewhat hard, breaks easily
Anthracite: hard, shiny black rock; breaks into small, layered pieces

Matching

Set 1					Set 2	
1. B	3. C	5. A	7. B	9. B	1. F	3 F
2. E	4. D	6. E	8. D	10. E	2. G	4 G

 8.2

READING 8.6 COAL

See *Student Edition*, p. 322.

READING ELECTRICAL ENERGY

See *Student Edition*, p. 331.

READING 8.7 HYDROPOWER

See *Student Edition*, p. 331.

ACTIVITY 8.7 How Electricity Is Generated

See *Student Edition,* p. 333.

 8.5, 8.6

Transparency 8.2

ADVANCE PREPARATION

It will take some time to assemble the equipment. First, check with the physics teacher to see what is available. Most of the items, including inexpensive meters and a hand-crank generator, can be obtained by contacting your Kendall/Hunt representative. If you attempt to make some of the components, the wire in the coils *must* be insulated. Once assembled, practice the lab *before* students do it so you know what to expect.

STRATEGIES AND PROCEDURES

This activity helps students realize that at the electric power company, the pressure behind a dam, the burning of coal or nuclear fuels, and the focusing of sunlight all serve to accomplish the same thing. The turbine must rotate to produce motion between a coil of wire and the magnet in a generating unit.

Directions/Answers to Items

1. Initial setup upon success.
2. The circuit that lights the bulb is shown here:
3. The compass needle turns and points in a direction perpendicular to the coil.
4. The compass needle points in the opposite direction.
5. The compass needle moves.
6. Electric current.
7. Electricity; more current.
8. Rapid movement produces more current than very slow movement.
9. Energy.
10. Magnet and a coil of wire.
11. Complete; motion.
12. Motion between a magnet and a coil of wire.

A more sophisticated answer to step 12 is that **electromagnetic induction** is the production of electric current in a closed circuit caused by a change in the magnetic field that passes through that circuit.

READING 8.8 Electric Power Generation

See *Student Edition,* p. 337.

 8.6

Transparency 8.2

READING 8.9 Thermal Pollution

See *Student Edition,* p. 342.

CHAPTER 8 Summary

See *Student Edition,* p. 345.

Name_____ Date_____

MULTIPLE CHOICE

1. _____ At the present time, which one of the following provides the greatest amount of energy for powering the U.S. economy?
   A. natural gas
   B. oil
   C. solar
   D. coal
   E. nuclear

2. _____ Which of the following is *not* a renewable resource used by early humans?
   A. burned kerosene
   B. burned wood
   C. flowing water
   D. food from plants and animals

3. _____ In 1875, the principal energy source in the United States was
   A. solar satellites.
   B. wood.
   C. nuclear.
   D. oil.
   E. oil shale.

4. _____ Which one of the following statements about energy transitions is correct?
   A. The United States has switched from wood to oil.
   B. The United States has switched from oil to coal.
   C. The United States has switched from nuclear to solar.
   D. The United States has switched from wood to coal.

5. _____ The energy content of a fuel is the
   A. number of kWh in the fuel.
   B. amount of energy in a kilogram of fuel.
   C. amount of energy in the fuel.
   D. number of calories in a square centimeter of fuel.

6. _____ Until 1979, total U.S. energy demand was
   A. increasing linearly.
   B. increasing exponentially.
   C. static (not changing).
   D. decreasing at about 5% annually.
   E. none of these.

7. _____ U.S. energy consumption grew at approximately 3% per year from 1875 to 1975. If U.S. energy consumption continued to increase at about 3% a year from 1975 to 2075
   A. we should have little trouble satisfying our needs.
   B. our oil reserves will most likely provide the bulk of that energy.
   C. imported oil will most likely provide the bulk of that energy.
   D. it is highly unlikely we could satisfy those needs using the fuels we rely on today.

8. _____ Office buildings are part of the
    A. residential sector.
    B. commercial sector.
    C. industrial sector.
    D. transportation sector.

9. _____ All of the following are true about oil as an energy source for the United States, *except*
    A. oil is derived from the remains of prehistoric marine organisms.
    B. oil is trapped underground in a variety of geologic formations.
    C. oil is very plentiful and domestic supplies should last for centuries.
    D. oil is easily stored, transported, and consumed.
    E. oil is used for such things as wax, lubricant, asphalt, and jet fuel.

10. _____ Oil and gas are trapped under the ground in a variety of ways. Four of the most common types of traps are shown below. Which is a stratigraphic trap?

    A   B   C   D

11. _____ In what kind of geologic formations are oil deposits most likely to develop?
    A. sedimentary deposits in seas
    B. sedimentary deposits on land
    C. metamorphic deposits in seas
    D. metamorphic deposits on land

12. _____ What do we call layers of sediment in which petroleum formed?
    A. reservoir beds
    B. water beds
    C. source beds
    D. sedimentary beds

13. _____ Which of the following are possible *waste* products given off from petroleum combustion?
    A. soot and sulfur gases
    B. carbon dioxide and fly ash
    C. water and carbon dioxide
    D. carbon monoxide and nitrogen oxides

14. _____ What reactant is left out of the following chemical reaction for natural gas combustion?

NATURAL GAS $\rightarrow$ CARBON DIOXIDE + WATER + HEAT

    A. wastes
    B. oxygen
    C. coal
    D. nothing

15. _____ Why must coal have been formed in stagnant waters?
    A. Plants contain no oil or fat.
    B. Decomposition is more complete in stagnant conditions.
    C. Bacteria could not work to complete their action under these conditions.
    D. Running water would have decreased decomposition of plant material.

16. _____ Which fuel burns cleanest?
     A. natural gas
     B. coal
     C. oil
     D. wood
     E. tar

17. _____ Of all the energy sources we presently rely on, this source has, by far, the largest reserves for future use.
     A. oil
     B. nuclear
     C. coal
     D. natural gas
     E. hydropower

18. _____ The products of coal combustion make coal look like a poor fuel. Why are we returning to coal as a significant source of energy?
     A. We have a lot of coal.
     B. We are running out of petroleum.
     C. Coal decreases our need for foreign oil.
     D. All of the above.

19. _____ A type of low-grade coal that is only 70% carbon would be
     A. peat.
     B. lignite.
     C. bituminous.
     D. anthracite.

20. _____ Because of its wide availability around the country and its energy content, this type of coal is most often burned at electric power generation plants in the United States.
     A. peat
     B. lignite
     C. bituminous
     D. anthracite

21. _____ This type of coal is very hard, high grade, and has a very high carbon content.
     A. anthracite
     B. lignite
     C. subbituminous
     D. peat

22. _____ Which of the following is a very low-grade coal that is rich in volatiles and is good feedstock for coal gasification?
     A. peat
     B. lignite
     C. bituminous
     D. anthracite

23. _____ Which of the following is a high-grade coal that is hard to ignite, but once lit burns with almost no smoke?
     A. peat
     B. lignite
     C. bituminous
     D. anthracite

24. _____ If coal is ranked in terms of its energy (content) density from lowest to highest, the correct sequence is
   A. lignite, peat, anthracite, bituminous.
   B. bituminous, anthracite, peat, lignite.
   C. anthracite, bituminous, peat, lignite.
   D. peat, lignite, bituminous, anthracite.
   E. bituminous, peat, lignite, anthracite.

25. _____ Which of the following is a brownish-black organic material that is used to build up garden soil?
   A. peat
   B. lignite
   C. bituminous
   D. anthracite

26. _____ Which of the following types of coal is found mostly in eastern Pennsylvania?
   A. peat
   B. lignite
   C. bituminous
   D. anthracite

27. _____ Why is surface mining a problem?
   A. Irrigation is needed to reclaim the land.
   B. It removes good topsoil from productive use.
   C. It creates erosional problems.
   D. All of the above.

28. _____ Identify the type of coal mining where a cutter (shearer) is pulled back and forth across a mine face. The loosened coal drops onto a conveyor. As the mining machine cuts its way into the seam, hydraulic jacks automatically push steel roof supports forward. The roof behind is allowed to fall.
   A. surface
   B. conventional
   C. continuous
   D. longwall

29. _____ All of the following are methods of underground coal mining *except*
   A. room-and-pillar mining.
   B. conventional mining.
   C. continuous mining.
   D. surface mining.

30. _____ The cheapest way to mine coal is
   A. longwall mining.
   B. surface mining.
   C. room-and-pillar mining.
   D. continuous mining.

31. _____ How has underground mining improved?
   A. It is safer.
   B. We have achieved greater production with machines.
   C. The percentage recovery has increased.
   D. All of the above.

32. _____ All of the following are characteristics of eastern coal (as opposed to western coal) *except*
    A. higher in sulfur content.
    B. less expensive.
    C. buried deeper.
    D. more unionized.

33. _____ Which statement is *not* true about hydropower?
    A. The energy is supplied by dammed water.
    B. The northwest portion of the United States had been developed almost to its capacity.
    C. In the United States, hydropower is expected to expand greatly in the years ahead.
    D. Hydropower is used almost entirely for generating electricity.

34. _____ The kilowatt-hour is a unit of
    A. mechanical energy.   D. thermal energy.
    B. heat.   E. none of these.
    C. electrical energy.

35. _____ Cooling towers cool the water that comes off the
    A. generator.   D. coal silo.
    B. turbine.   E. pulverizer.
    C. boiler.

36. _____ At an electric power plant, electricity is produced in the
    A. turbine.   C. generator.
    B. condenser.   D. percipitator.

37. _____ To produce electric current without a battery, both a coil of wire and _____ are required.
    A. bulb   D. switch
    B. tinker toy   E. magnet
    C. resistor

38. _____ To produce electric current, the circuit must be complete and there must be _____ between the two items listed in question 37.
    A. attraction   D. contact
    B. repulsion   E. lubrication
    C. motion

39. _____ Electric generating plants *always* produce a certain amount of
    A. nuclear wastes.   C. thermal pollution.
    B. smoke particles.   D. sulfur gases.

40. _____ The practice of dumping waste heat into nearby lakes, rivers, or bays results in
    A. increased metabolic rates in fish.   D. dissolved oxygen loss.
    B. thermal pollution.   E. all of these are problems.
    C. lowered populations of desirable
       fish.

Chapter 8 Assessment

1. B
2. A
3. B
4. D
5. B
6. B
7. D
8. B
9. C
10. C
11. A
12. C
13. D
14. B
15. C
16. A
17. C
18. D
19. B
20. C
21. A
22. B
23. D
24. D
25. A
26. D
27. D
28. D
29. D
30. B
31. D
32. B
33. C
34. C
35. B
36. C
37. E
38. C
39. C
40. E

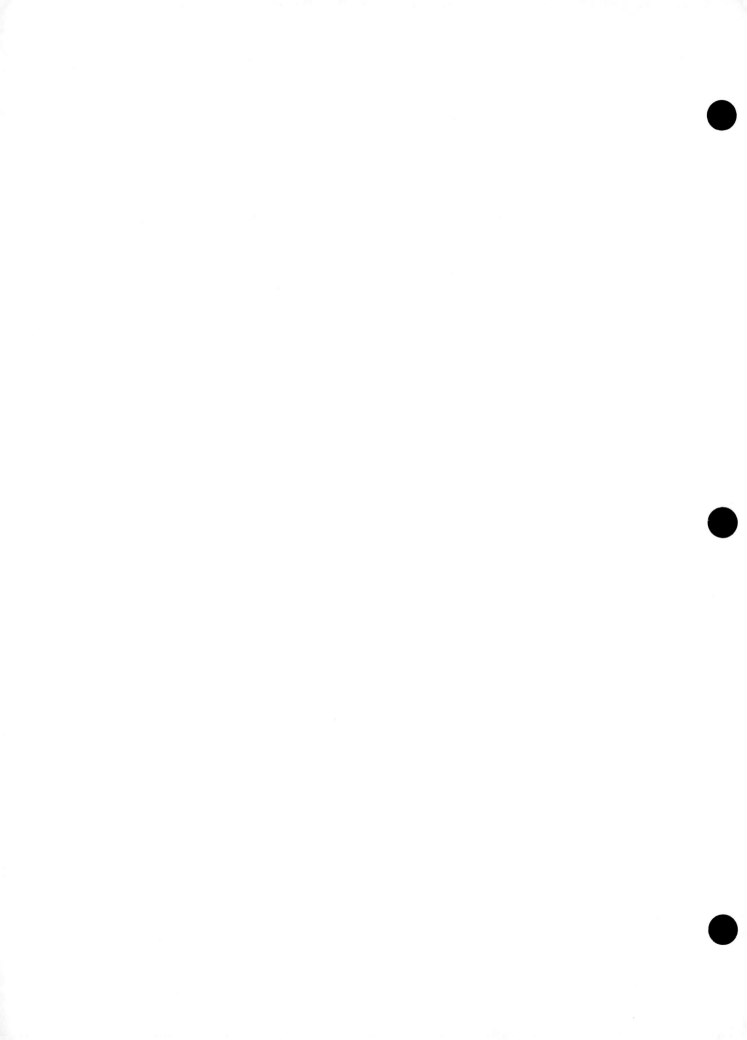

NONRENEWABLE RESOURCE DEPLETION

LEARNING OUTCOMES

The student will:

1. model the depletion of a nonrenewable resource by manipulating materials and equipment and completing the activity "Resource Depletion." (C,P)

2. graph the results obtained from the activity "Resource Depletion" by plotting the data and formulating conclusions. (C,P)

3. compare his or her graph of U.S. petroleum production to the graph by M. King Hubbert and draw conclusions by completing the activity "Applying a Model to a Real World Situation." (C)

4. explain why the physical process of looking for more crude oil will probably not be sufficient for the future. (C)

5. state another name for the graph of a production cycle of a finite resource and identify what the area under a production cycle graph represents. (C)

6. explain how a lack of domestic supplies of fuel can be compensated for with imported supplies. (C)

7. speculate about what actions the nation might take as a response to its lack of domestic supplies. (C)

8. distinguish between resources and reserves. (C)

9. realize that estimating the size of a resource before significant production and time data are available is a difficult task by completing the activity "The Problem of Estimating the Size of a Resource." (A)

10. graph the quantity of energy available from the remaining U.S. reserves of nonrenewable energy sources and compare these to estimated requirements for the next 20 years. (C,P)

11. realize that supplying national energy requirements using domestic reserves of nonrenewable resources is becoming a major problem. (A)

12. speculate about why, at the present, the nuclear option is not being pursued in the United States. (C)

13. calculate the lifetimes of some of our nonrenewable reserves based on several assumptions and speculate on the value of the answers obtained. (C)

14. compare the static reserve index, the exponential reserve index, and the way things really are. (C)

KEY TERMS

RECOMMENDED BLACKLINE MASTERS

The Recommended Blackline Masters listed above are supplemental to the activity/reading, and can be found on the *Teacher Resource CD.*

ACTIVITIES FLOW CHART

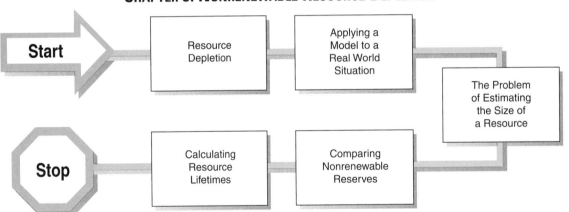

CHAPTER 9: NONRENEWABLE RESOURCE DEPLETION

TEACHING STRATEGIES AND ANSWERS FOR ACTIVITIES

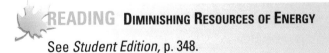

READING **DIMINISHING RESOURCES OF ENERGY**

See *Student Edition*, p. 348.

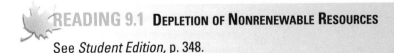

READING 9.1 **DEPLETION OF NONRENEWABLE RESOURCES**

See *Student Edition*, p. 348.

An understanding of resource depletion curves is crucial to an appreciation of our nonrenewable resource situation. This activity provides the basic tools for developing that understanding.

MATERIALS (FOR EACH LAB GROUP)

1 resource depletion box
4 plastic cups (ore cars)
800 plastic beads
dried feed corn (see Adv. Prep.)
1 stopwatch or wall clock
2 sheets of graph paper

ADVANCE PREPARATION

The equipment can be obtained by contacting your Kendall/Hunt representative. Each activity station consists of a plastic refrigerator box (about shoe box size), 800 plastic beads, and enough dried feed corn to fill 90% of the box. Dried feed corn can be obtained by the sack at any agricultural feed store. Plastic cups (ore cars) can be purchased at the grocery store in picnic and party supplies. Plastic beads are sold at craft stores.

To set up the activity, fill the "Earth boxes" to the 90% level with dried corn. Mix 800 beads into the corn and you are ready.

STRATEGIES AND PROCEDURES

Rules

Before beginning the simulation, go over these rules carefully with your students.

1. A large company = an executive + a miner.
2. A small, independent operator = 1 person.
3. Plastic cup = an ore car.
4. Beads = nuggets; corn = gangue (Earth material).
5. 15 seconds = 1 year of mining.
6. A minimum production is necessary to stay in business (9 to 12 nuggets/ year). The teacher decides. The exact number is not known by the companies until *after* each year of mining. This is the way it is for real companies. Economic conditions change weekly, monthly, and yearly—not comfortable, but reality!
7. The EPA can assess an environmental damage tax.
8. Yearly production is reported to the government.
9. *No* gross "strip" mining is allowed! Mining is done with *one* hand and nuggets must be removed with a *pinching* action between the thumb and index finger.

10. Ore is processed at the company mill, which involves separating the mineral (nuggets) from the gangue (corn). The nuggets are nonrenewable and remain at the mill site. The tailings (corn) are returned to the earth box each year.
11. New developers enter the business when existing companies make profits.
12. Companies are not added when profits become marginal.

Assumptions

🍁 The earth and its resources are finite.

🍁 Production and consumption of the nonrenewable resource (nuggets) will grow exponentially until economics and depletion prevent such growth.

Classroom Management

You are in charge of the simulation. You must maintain *firm* control. Your role is best played by standing on a chair in the middle of the room. Give instructions with a firm voice and keep track of *everything*. When you say STOP MINING, you mean *stop*. At the end of each round, have each company report production figures to you. Relay these figures to government officials who record them on the chart. You can either record class-averaged data on the board (transparency), or you can record the data for one table as a representative set and have the other tables do their own. One person at each table should record results. The rest can place their supplies on the floor so the table isn't too crowded.

Each company needs to choose a mill site somewhere in the room where it can go to process its production after each year. The number of beads (the production) is reported to the government. The beads then remain *at the mill*. The corn (gangue) is returned to the earth. That's what companies do with their tailings!

Classroom Setup

Each Earth box can represent 4 to 8 students depending on company size (see Rules). A class of 27–30 might be set up as follows: 3 boxes × 8 students = 24 + EPA + 2 data tabulators (at overhead and/or board) = 27. Also, a recorder/mathematician can be assigned to each of the three tables. This now totals 30.

The room arrangement for a class of 27–30 might look like this:

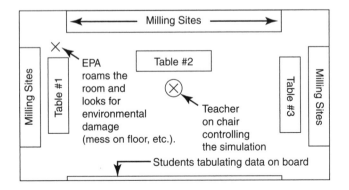

Each table has 8 students (4 companies) seated around it. If you have 30 students, add a recorder at each table.

When you become comfortable with this activity, you can run through the completed production cycle in a 45-minute class period. If you need more time, you can conduct prelab activities the day before. You will need to start when the bell rings. If you do it right, your students will rate this as one of the highlights of the year.

SAMPLE ANSWERS TO GRAPHS

Students' results should approximate these theoretical curves:

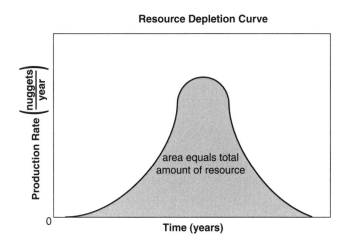

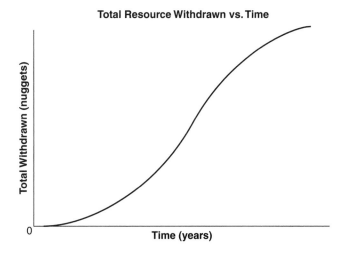

Abnormalities in the curves should not be ignored. Peaks can represent large new discoveries or lax mining laws; dips can represent economic recessions.

Since both graphs represent the same situation, some students may have difficulty writing a different conclusion for each graph. You might ask them to write one conclusion that summarizes both graphs. If your students have difficulty getting started, you can give them the beginning of these four statements and have the students complete them.

1. In the beginning, production was low because *there were few developers and there was little competition for the resource.*

2. Production grew rapidly because *profits were made, the number of developers increased, and so did the competition.*

3. Production peaked because *the resource is finite and it became harder to locate.*

   Note: Harder to locate means more time looking, which means less time extracting.

4. Production then fell rapidly because *the demand for the resource remained high even though the resource was getting harder to find.*

If you have advanced students, and they can write a separate conclusion for the second graph, it should read something like this:

Total Resource Withdrawn vs. *Time.* The total quantity of resources withdrawn grows slowly at first due to limited demand and few developers. However, as profits are made and more developers enter the business, competition increases and the quantity extracted increases rapidly. But, since the resource is finite, it becomes harder to locate. Nuggets are withdrawn more slowly. Finally, if development continues, the graph slowly approaches the total number of nuggets in the box.

Lab Extension

Help your better students see that each box on their graph represents a certain number of nuggets. The number depends on the scale chosen for the graph. Have students total the number of boxes and fractions of boxes under their graph. Those who work carefully will obtain a good answer. The number of boxes multiplied by the number of nuggets per box equals the number of nuggets. The number of nuggets calculated should be close to the number of nuggets approached by the *Total Resource Withdrawn* vs. *Time* graph. This number, in turn, should be very close to the number of nuggets in the earth box. Note: This shows the power of mathematics and graphing and what good engineers can do. Don't let the opportunity to point this out slip away. In summary, the area under a resource depletion graph represents the total amount of the resource.

 9.4
Transparency 9.1

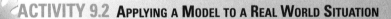

ACTIVITY 9.2 APPLYING A MODEL TO A REAL WORLD SITUATION

See *Student Edition,* p. 351.

This activity allows students to relate the model of Activity 9.1 to the actual extraction of crude oil from the 48 contiguous states. This enables them to evaluate the strengths and weaknesses of the modeling process.

STRATEGIES AND PROCEDURES

This is a good time to improve students' ability to choose scale, plot, and label graphs, plus extrapolate forward and backward.
Similarities:

🍁 Both graphs represent the extraction of a finite resource from a finite region.

- Both graphs are bell shaped.
- The area under both graphs represents the total quantity of the resource.

Differences:

- The bead graph is a simulation; the Hubbert graph is real.
- The Hubbert graph shows a true response to economic conditions. The simulation cannot accurately mirror all of those conditions.
- The bead graph plunges because the resource runs out. The real world graph can plunge for a variety of reasons.

Point out that the dashed portion of the graph is the extrapolation (guess).

SAMPLE ANSWERS TO QUESTIONS

1. Our activity graph is similar to the shape of M. King Hubbert's graph. Hubbert's graph is very close to what actually happened.
2. Hubbert predicted in the 1960s that U.S. petroleum production would peak about 1970. It peaked in 1970.
3. Hubbert predicted that 90% of U.S. petroleum supplies would be used up near the year 2000.
4. Even though domestic supplies are low, we are still driving because we are getting oil from Alaska and importing it from other countries. Also, on the average, vehicles are more efficient than they used to be.
5. The cost of labor in foreign countries is less than the cost of labor in the United States. Also, the costs of transporting crude oil must not be too high.
6. We can keep our military strong so that oil suppliers can't hold us hostage, or we can develop and expand new fuels for cars. We can also work on the vehicle efficiency challenge.
7. A curve may plunge because consumers prefer a substitute resource or because economic conditions or government regulations cause developers not to mine (or to mine less).

READING 9.2 RESOURCES AND RESERVES

See *Student Edition*, p. 354.

 9.5

Transparency 9.2

READING 9.3 ESTIMATING THE SIZE OF RESOURCES

See *Student Edition*, p. 355.

ACTIVITY 9.3 THE PROBLEM OF ESTIMATING THE SIZE OF A RESOURCE

See *Student Edition*, p. 355.

SAMPLE ANSWERS TO QUESTIONS

1. No. Students likely did not think about how many nuggets were in the box.

2. No. Students likely were not concerned about the total number of nuggets. It seemed that there were lots of them.

3. The number is usually around the fifth to seventh year. It depends on the size of the box, the number of nuggets, and how aggressive the students are.

4. No. Students likely were not worried about running out or how many nuggets there were.

5. Students became aware of the fact that they were running out of nuggets when the nuggets became much harder to find. This began when approximately 75% of them had been extracted.

6. The nuggets became much harder to find.

7. Production peaks when approximately half of all the nuggets are withdrawn. Take the number withdrawn when production peaked and multiply by two (2). The answer should be close to the number of nuggets in the box.

8. Students could block out a small section of the box (like drilling a core sample), withdraw it, and count the number of nuggets it contains. Then they can multiply that number of nuggets by the number of those sections in the entire box. *Note:* This technique could be demonstrated to the entire class.

9. The estimate could be very reliable or it could be way off. It depends on how representative the cross section is of the entire box.

 READING **How Much Do We Have?**

See *Student Edition,* p. 357.

 READING 9.4 **Nonrenewable Resources**

See *Student Edition,* p. 358.

 9.6 ACTIVITY 9.4 **Comparing Nonrenewable Reserves**

See *Student Edition,* p. 363.

Students should get these results:

Source	Quads
Crude oil	122
Natural gas	222
Coal	11,309
Uranium oxide	17.5
Syncrude	414

U.S. Requirement (2000–2020) = 100 × 20 = 2000 Q

The bar graph obtained should be:

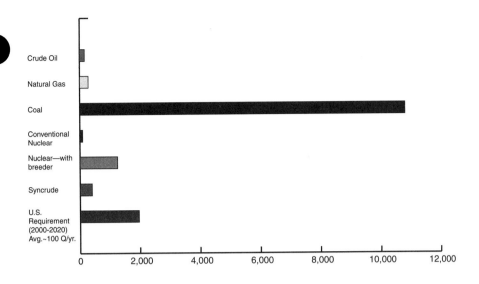

Note: This bar graph is Figure 12.26 in the *Student Edition*.

SAMPLE ANSWERS TO ANALYSIS QUESTIONS

1. The United States imports most of the crude oil it uses because our domestic reserves are small compared to our energy requirements. Even our remaining resources are small compared to our requirements.
2. Conventional nuclear power can supply very little energy when compared to our total requirements.
3. The nuclear breeder option could become a major player in our energy picture—if we choose to use it.
4. We don't have breeder reactors because the U.S. public as a whole has serious concerns about the nuclear option. We can't agree on what to do with the wastes from our conventional nuclear reactors. What would we do with 60–100 times more of it?
5. We don't use more coal because:

   🍁 Coal is a solid and cannot be easily used to heat homes or run vehicles.
   🍁 Coal doesn't burn as clean as oil and natural gas. It takes expensive technology to remove the pollutants.
   🍁 Coal must be mined—surface and/or underground.
   Note: Many Americans have negative feelings about mining even though they drive cars, fly in airplanes, and use a host of products that have their origins in mining.
   🍁 Coal can be changed to both a liquid and gaseous fuel, but we are not set up to do those conversions on a large scale.

6. The problems and related opposition to the development of synfuels are similar to those listed in question 5.
7. Our nation is powered primarily with hydrocarbons (crude oil and natural gas). Our reserves of these fuels are small relative to our energy requirements. We have not faced up to this situation very well. Some students may

state that the desert kingdoms of the Middle East have large reserves of these fuels, which has created a difficult economic and political situation.

READING HOW LONG WILL OUR RESERVES LAST?

See *Student Edition,* p. 366.

READING 9.5 THE STATIC LIFETIME

See *Student Edition,* p. 366.

ACTIVITY 9.5 CALCULATING RESOURCE LIFETIMES

See *Student Edition,* p. 367.

SAMPLE ANSWERS TO PROBLEMS _____

1. a. 600 cans /75 cans/day = 8 days.
    b. No. More baked beans will be brought in from the grocer's warehouse. The warehouse will be resupplied by the canner. The canner buys from growers.
    c. The cans of baked beans in the store are much like reserves. The quantities are well known, along with the economic details. The situation with regard to baked beans at the other locations is more like that of resources. Part of it is certain, part less certain, part quite uncertain. We do not know how many beans will be grown and harvested next year because of uncertainties with regard to weather conditions, economics, and labor/technology variables.

2. Static lifetime = 22×10^9 bbls/2.139×10^9 bbls/yr = 10.3 years.

3. Static lifetime = 501×10^9 tons/1.121×10^9 tons per year = 447 years.

4. Static lifetime = $1,000 \times 10^9$ bbls/22×10^9 bbls per year = 45.5 years.

5. Years added = 400×10^9/22×10^9 bbls per yr = 18.2 years. This adds about 18 to 20 years to the supply.

6. The major problem is that these calculations are based on proven reserves. As time goes by, more resources are discovered and thus move into the reserve category. Hence, the reserve almost always lasts longer than the time span calculated. The use rate also changes depending on economic/political conditions. Thus, these calculations simply give us a glimpse as to what will happen. That glimpse can, however, be useful.

    The least accurate calculation is the 447-year lifetime for coal. It is difficult to predict what will happen in the next 20 years. We have little idea about the status of coal 500 years from now. All that we can say for sure is that we have lots of coal. It is hard to say which answer is most accurate. They all will be wrong to some degree.

7. Calculations such as these are planning tools. They are not the only tools. However, the information they provide is of value if it is used wisely with other knowledge of our energy situation.

Extra Lifetime Problems

1. If coal production in the United States were to double to 750 million tons per year, how long would a 500 billion ton coal reserve last?
   Answer: Static lifetime = 500×10^9 tons $/750 \times 10^6$ tons/yr = 667 years.

2. The quantity of energy used by the U.S. economy in 1997 was approximately 90×10^{15} Btu (90 Quads). Coal has an energy content of approximately 2.62×10^7 Btu/ton.
   a. If it were possible to power the entire United States on coal alone, how many tons of coal would this require each year?
   Answer: No. tons = 90×10^{15} Btu$/2.62 \times 10^7$ Btu/ton = 3.435×10^9 tons/yr.
   b. At a yearly consumption rate equal to what you calculated in part a, how long would a 500 billion ton coal reserve last?
   Answer: Lifetime = 500×10^9 tons $/ 3.435 \times 10^9$ tons per year = 146 years.

3. Why are the assumptions of problem 2 highly unlikely to happen?
   Answer: Environmental concerns related to air quality, acid rain, land use, and global climate change would most likely prevent coal development to this extent. Also, coal is a solid, and most homes are heated with a gas. Also, almost all vehicles are powered by liquid fuels. It is possible to gasify and liquefy coal into fuels, but these technologies have not been expanded as yet to produce fuels in these quantities.

4. Crude oil reserves in the Middle East are estimated to be about 450 billion barrels. Countries in that region have been holding their total production to approximately 7 billion barrels per year. At that production rate, how long will reserves in the Middle East last?
   Answer: Lifetime = 450×10^9 bbls$/7 \times 10^9$ bbls/yr = 64 years.

5. Crude oil reserves controlled by the United Kingdom (UK) and Norway are estimated to be 24 billion barrels. This oil is being produced at about 1.5 billion barrels per year. At that production rate, how long will those reserves last?
   Answer: Lifetime = 24×10^9 bbls$/1.5 \times 10^9$ bbls/yr = 16 years.

6. On a global scale, the largest remaining crude oil reserves are located in the Middle East. What political and economic problems might occur in the near future?
   Answer: Because the rest of the world is dependent on oil and gas as major energy sources, and because little is being done either to improve efficiency of use (over what it is now) or to switch to other sources, the scenarios are interesting. Some involve military action, while others envision different sources and conservation strategies. There will most likely be major battles over these strategies. Much is at stake economically, politically, and morally.

READING 9.6 THE EXPONENTIAL LIFETIME

See *Student Edition*, p. 367.

🍂 In the real world, we don't consume resources at an ever-increasing rate until the day they run out. Why? Explain your answer.

Answer: As resources become harder to find and extract, their value increases and prices rise. Rising prices lowers demand. They also create interest in the development of substitutes for the resource and/or alternative ways of doing things. As they say: Necessity is the mother of invention. All these factors lower the demand for the resource. Hence, we go through a production cycle as discussed at the beginning of this chapter.

READING 9.7 THE WAY THINGS ARE

See *Student Edition,* p. 368.

Transparency 9.3

What might the buffalo in Figure 9.23 represent?
Answer: The buffalo may represent crude oil or any other nonrenewable resource. We can put money into exploration and development for a time and increase supply. However, if the resource is near the end of the depletion curve, money and equipment won't produce more and more resources forever. It is then time to move in a new direction.

Explain why this cartoon may not relate to Earth's mineral situation.
Answer: Buffalo still exist and their numbers are increasing because the meat has become a desirable food product. Also, since necessity is the mother of invention, scarcity of a resource stimulates the search for substitutes.

READING REDUCING PROBLEMS RELATED TO RESOURCE DEPLETION

See *Student Edition,* p. 371.

BLM 9.7

Transparency 9.4

CHAPTER 9 SUMMARY

See *Student Edition,* p. 372.

Name_____ Date_____

MULTIPLE CHOICE

1. _____ What is the focus of this chapter?
    A. Continuous resources will run out in the future.
    B. Reserves of crude oil and natural gas will eventually be depleted.
    C. People are using too many hair dryers.
    D. The supply of crude oil and natural gas appears to be infinite.
    E. All of the above.

2. _____ Which of the following is *not* a nonrenewable resource?
    A. coal
    B. solar energy
    C. natural gas
    D. nuclear power
    E. crude oil

3. _____ The resource depletion activity is based on two assumptions. They are that
    A. resources are finite and consumption grows exponentially as long as possible.
    B. resources are infinite and consumption grows exponentially as long as possible.
    C. resources are finite and consumption grows slowly at a constant rate.
    D. resources are infinite and consumption grows slowly at a constant rate.
    E. resources are finite and consumption remains fixed or constant.

4. _____ When plotted on regular graph paper, the rate of production *vs.* time graph for a
    nonrenewable resource has the shape of
    A. a straight line.   D. a reciprocal curve.

    B. a sigmoid "S" curve.   E. a bell-shaped curve.

    C. an exponential "J" curve.

5. _____ A resource depletion curve represents
    A. loss of renewable resources.
    B. only the exponential growth of a nonrenewable resource.
    C. the production cycle of a resource.
    D. only 90% of the total amount of a resource that can be extracted.
    E. CD sales in Canada.

6. _____ In the resource depletion activity
    A. corn is returned to the earth and beads are kept at the mill.
    B. beads represent a valuable mineral and corn represents nonvaluable material.
    C. companies compete for a finite resource.
    D. a minimum production (profit) is necessary to remain in business.
    E. all of the above are true.

7. _____ When a finite resource is consumed, the historical depletion pattern is most accurately described by which of the following statements:
   A. The resource is consumed at a constant rate until the day it is totally gone.
   B. Consumption starts slowly, increases exponentially for a time, peaks, and then decreases rapidly as it becomes more scarce.
   C. No pattern has been found that accurately describes the depletion.
   D. The resource is consumed exponentially until the day it is totally gone.
   E. The resource is consumed exponentially until we are rescued by outside intervention.

8. _____ The area under a resource depletion curve for a nonrenewable resource is equal to
   A. its doubling time.
   B. peak-year production.
   C. average production rate.
   D. the total amount of that resource.
   E. paint production in China.

9. _____ The assumptions made in the resource depletion activity
   A. determined the activity's outcome.
   B. had little influence on the activity's outcome.
   C. were incorrect and should not have been made.
   D. have no place in the science process.
   E. illustrate the attitude of skepticism.

10. _____ Crude oil production peaked in the United States in
   A. 1950.
   B. 1970.
   C. 1980.
   D. 1990.
   E. production has yet to peak.

11. _____ When did or will world crude oil production peak (according to Hubbert)?
   A. 1940
   B. 1980
   C. 1990
   D. 2010
   E. 2100

12. _____ The actual graph of U.S. crude oil production *vs.* time for the continental 48 states has the approximate shape of
   A. a straight line.
   B. a rectangle.
   C. an exponential "J" curve.
   D. an elongated "S" curve.
   E. a bell-shaped curve.

13. _____ Resource reserves are
   A. identified resources.
   B. undiscovered resources.
   C. both identified and undiscovered resources.
   D. neither identified nor undiscovered resources.
   E. all of the above.

14. _____ According to your textbook, U.S. reserves of this fuel are larger than the reserves of all others listed.
   A. natural gas
   B. oil shale
   C. nuclear (uranium)
   D. crude oil
   E. coal

15. _____ Which of the following can change the rate of resource use?
   A. economics
   B. technology
   C. world politics
   D. weather conditions
   E. All of these can.

16. _____ What determines the lifetime of a resource?
   A. How much we have and how fast we are using the resource.
   B. How fast we use the resource at a constant rate.
   C. How fast we use the resource at an increasing consumption rate.
   D. Resources don't run out.
   E. None of the above.

17. _____ The "lifetime" of the proven reserves of a substance, determined by dividing an estimate of the proven reserves by a constant level of production, is the
   A. static lifetime.
   B. exponential lifetime.
   C. index of leading economic indicators.
   D. doubling time.
   E. a bell-shaped curve.

18. _____ T_s represents the static lifetime, T_e the exponential lifetime, and T_{rw} the real world lifetime. Which of the following correctly shows the relationship between these three quantities? (< means "less than")
   A. $T_s < T_e < T_{rw}$
   B. $T_{rw} < T_e < T_s$
   C. $T_e < T_{rw} < T_s$
   D. $T_{rw} < T_s < T_e$
   E. $T_s < T_{rw} < T_e$

19. _____ At the present time, the United States has a reserve of about 500 billion tons of coal that can be mined economically using existing technology. If this coal is mined at the rate of 900 million tons per year, how long will the coal last?
   A. 556 years
   B. 100 years
   C. 180 years
   D. 140 years
   E. 400 years

   Note: 10^3 = thousand; 10^6 = million; 10^9 = billion.

20. _____ M. King Hubbert predicted that 90% of America's crude oil from the continental 48 states would be consumed by the year
   A. 1990.
   B. 2000.
   C. 2025.
   D. 2050.
   E. 2100.

21. _____ Oil shale is a sedimentary rock that contains a solid organic substance called
   A. granite.
   B. obsidian.
   C. leverite.
   D. kerogen.
   E. roadabya.

22. _____ Global supplies of some metals could become depleted because
   A. industrialization has caused the destruction of a significant portion of the inventory of several metals.
   B. the large American and European space programs have ejected large quantities of several metals from our planet.
   C. we mine resources where they are concentrated, but through use they become diluted, spread out, and lost economically.
   D. the Hunt family is hoarding valuable metals in hidden warehouses in Texas.
   E. all of the above.

23. _____ In terms of the energy that can be obtained,
   A. conventional nuclear reactors can provide for most of the U.S. energy needs at least through the year 2020.
   B. little additional energy can be obtained by developing the breeder reactor.
   C. it makes little sense to use nuclear power without developing the breeder reactor.
   D. syncrude seems to offer the most energy for powering our nation.
   E. all of the above are true.

24. _____ The oil that can be obtained from both oil shale and tar sands is
   A. much different than natural crude oil.
   B. a good substitute for natural crude oil.
   C. superior to natural crude oil.
   D. all of the above.
   E. none of the above.

25. _____ Which of the following are *true?*
   A. The Quad is a very large unit of energy.
   B. One Quad equals one quadrillion Btus.
   C. A Quad of energy can power the U.S. economy for about 4.0 days.
   D. The word Quad is derived from the word quadrillion.
   E. All of the above are true.

SHORT ANSWER

26. Explain why a calculated resource lifetime that is relatively short may not be cause for panic.

CHAPTER 9 ASSESSMENT

1. B
2. B
3. A
4. E
5. C
6. E
7. B
8. D
9. A
10. B
11. D
12. E
13. A
14. E
15. E
16. A
17. A
18. C
19. A
20. B
21. D
22. C
23. C
24. B
25. E

26. A short lifetime usually means geologists will be looking hard for those resources that might now become reserves. A rise in price will also move some resources into the reserve category. New reserves mean the resource will last longer. Also, scientists and engineers will be looking for substitutes. If a superior substitute is found, the old resource may not even be missed.

NUCLEAR ENERGY

The student will:

1. **observe** evidence for the idea that matter is composed of small building blocks called atoms by **manipulating** materials and equipment and **completing** the activity "Atoms and Molecules." (C,P)

2. **list** the parts of the atom and **state** the electric charge on each part. (C)

3. **calculate** the number of protons, electrons, and neutrons for various elements by **using** a periodic table and definitions and **completing** the activity "Working with Atomic Symbols." (C)

4. **observe** evidence of nuclear radiation by **manipulating** materials and equipment and **completing** the activity "Observations in a Cloud Chamber." (C,P)

5. **observe** evidence of background radiation by **manipulating** materials and equipment and **completing** the activity "Observations in a Cloud Chamber." (C,P)

6. **state** why nuclei can be radioactive. (C)

7. **list** and **distinguish** among modes of radioactive decay. (C)

8. **learn** to **write** nuclear equations by **completing** the activity "Writing Nuclear Equations." (C)

9. **calculate** the half-life of a radioactive sample by **manipulating** materials and equipment and **graphing** experimental results from the activity "Half-Life Investigation." (C,P)

10. **define** half-life. (C)

11. **realize** the problem of radioactive waste disposal by **completing** and discussing the activity "Half-Life Investigation." (A)

12. **simulate** and **construct** a three member radioactive decay chain by **manipulating** materials and equipment and **completing** the activity "Simulating a Radioactive Decay Chain." (C,P)

13. **recognize** some of the current problems related to the use of nuclear power by **writing** responses to questions from the activity "Simulating a Radioactive Decay Chain." (A)

14. **distinguish** between fission and fusion. (C)

15. **explain** what happens in a chain reaction. (C)

16. **list** and **distinguish** among the three fissionable isotopes. (C)

17. **state** why uranium must be enriched before it can be used. (C)

18. list and explain the steps of the nuclear fuel cycle by doing the activity "The Nuclear Fuel Cycle." (C)

19. list and explain the five main components of a nuclear reactor and/or design a nuclear reactor on paper and explain the function of the major components. (C)

20. design and construct a simulated cask for transporting radioactive waste and test it under a variety of conditions. (C,P)

21. list the advantages and disadvantages of using nuclear power. (A)

22. realize how radiation can affect biological organisms. (A)

23. know the units that are used to measure radiation. (C)

24. calculate his or her personal radiation dose and determine its meaning by completing the activity "Calculate Your Personal Radiation Dose." (C)

25. realize that radiation has properties that provide benefits to humans. (A)

26. realize that the breeder option can greatly increase the amount of energy available to us but there are serious implications to moving in this direction. (A)

27. name the fusion reaction that is easiest to make work. (C)

28. describe the one main conceptual difference in operation among the major methods of producing controlled nuclear fusion reactions. (C)

29. realize that the future of nuclear power is uncertain. (A)

KEY TERMS

atom	beta particle	uranium enrichment	control rod
molecule	gamma ray	gaseous diffusion	radiation
element	half life	fuel fabrication	ionizing radiation
periodic table	cloud chamber	radioactive waste	ion
nucleus	nuclear energy	nuclear waste	chromosome
nucleon	fission fragments	spent fuel	mutation
proton	fissionable isotope	high-level waste	cosmic radiation
neutron	uranium	transuranic waste	bleeder reactor
electron	thorium	low-level waste	magnetic confinement
atomic number	plutonium	uranium mill tailings	fusion
mass number	chain reaction	nuclear reaction	laser fusion
isotope	deuterium	nuclear reactor	plasma
radioactive	tritium	moderator	
alpha particle	nuclear fuel cycle	critical mass	

RECOMMENDED BLACKLINE MASTERS

10.1   Atoms and Molecules

10.2   Big Ideas about Atoms

10.3   Periodic Table of the Elements

10.4   Cloud Chamber Operation

10.5   Decay of a Radioactive Sample

10.6   A Typical Fission Reaction

10.7   Chain Reaction

10.8   Nuclear Power Plant Schematic

10.9   The Nuclear Fuel Cycle

10.10   Nuclear Fusion

The Recommended Blackline Masters listed above are supplemental to the activity/reading, and can be found on the *Teacher Resource CD*.

CHAPTER 10: NUCLEAR ENERGY

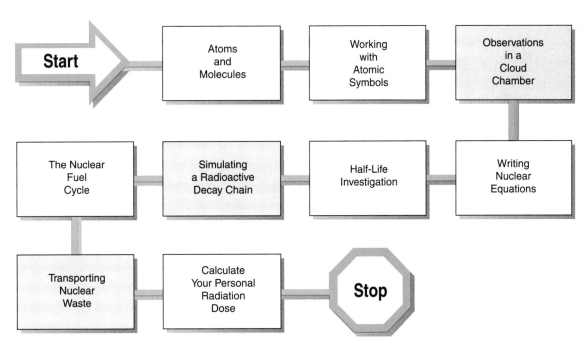

NOTE: Shaded items are lower priority.

 TEACHING STRATEGIES AND ANSWERS FOR ACTIVITIES

READING THE CONCEPT OF THE ATOM

See *Student Edition,* p. 376.

ACTIVITY 10.1 ATOMS AND MOLECULES

See *Student Edition,* p. 376.

 10.1

ADVANCE PREPARATION

Make the 0.3M $CuSO_4$ solution by weighing out 74.9 grams of $CuSO_4 \cdot 5H_2O$ crystals and adding distilled water until the total volume of solution is 1 liter. Purchase uncoated iron nails at a hardware store.

SAMPLE ANSWERS TO QUESTIONS

Day 1

5. a. A colorless, clear liquid.
   b. Light blue crystals.
   c. A clear blue solution.

d. Thin, gray metallic cylinder.

6. Student answers will vary. Many will guess (hypothesize) that the nail will dissolve in the copper sulfate solution or that the nail will rust.

7. New penny: shiny, copper colored. Old penny: dull, brownish color.

8. Nail in water: nothing observable happens; the nail gets wet. Nail in $CuSO_4$ solution: a thin copper-colored coating forms on the side of the nail.

10. A periodic table lists and groups all known elements.

11. Copper, sulfur, oxygen, iron.

13. Yes. The rearrangement in this activity was predictable and the same (reliable) in all beakers.

Day 2

1. Thick, dark brown materials collected on the nail and the blue solution turned clear to slightly bluish green. The nail in the water rusted a little and the water became slightly orange.

2. The nail that was placed in the $CuSO_4$ solution feels rough and a little thinner than it was yesterday. The nail placed in the water feels smooth and the same thickness as before.

SAMPLE ANSWERS TO END OF LAB QUESTIONS

1. Copper, sulfur, oxygen.

2. The copper sulfate solution is blue because Cu^{+2} particles, which are blue, are scattered throughout the water solution.

3. The blue Cu^{+2} particles leave the solution and become solid copper, which is dark brown.

4. The nail becomes a little thinner because some of the iron dissolved and went into solution.

5. Student answers will vary. Evaluate their degree of understanding about what happened in this experiment.

6. Copper left the solution as Cu^{+2} (blue) and became a solid on the nail. Some iron left the nail and is now in the solution.

7. Copper has gone from a blue particle in the solution to a dark brown solid.

8. a. Hopefully, your students will prefer the scientific explanation.

   b. By assuming materials around us are made of small particles and assigning certain properties to these particles, we can explain what happened in this experiment. We could explain what happened by assuming that the nail made the solution sick and that the solution vomited dark brown stuff on the nail. Scientists don't accept this type of explanation nor do most other people.

   c. Scientists believe in atoms because that belief enables them to explain what goes on around us in a consistent way and to develop products that modern societies find useful.

READING ENERGY FROM ATOMS

See *Student Edition,* p. 378.

See *Student Edition*, p. 379.

 **10.2, 10.3**

Transparency 10.1, 10.2

ACTIVITY 10.2 **WORKING WITH ATOMIC SYMBOLS**

See *Student Edition*, p. 382.

Gold	Copper	Beryllium	Mercury
$^{197}_{79}$Au	$^{63}_{29}$Cu	$^{9}_{4}$Be	$^{201}_{80}$Hg
79 protons	29 protons	4 protons	80 protons
118 neutrons	34 neutrons	5 neutrons	121 neutrons
Platinum	Radon	Silver	Lead
$^{195}_{78}$Pt	$^{222}_{86}$Rn	$^{108}_{61}$Ag	$^{212}_{82}$Pb
Strontium	Xenon	Thorium	Uranium
$^{90}_{38}$Sr	$^{131}_{54}$Xe	$^{232}_{90}$Th	$^{238}_{92}$U
Boron	Uranium	Plutonium	Neptunium
$^{11}_{5}$B	$^{233}_{92}$U	$^{244}_{94}$Pu	$^{237}_{93}$Np

READING 10.2 **RADIOACTIVITY**

See *Student Edition*, p. 383.

 **10.5**

ACTIVITY 10.3 **OBSERVATIONS IN A CLOUD CHAMBER**

See *Student Edition*, p. 385.

 10.4

Note: If you choose not to do this cloud chamber activity, we recommend that you at least obtain some type of Geiger counter and use it to demonstrate background radiation, radiation emitted from one or more sources, the decrease of radiation with distance from a source, and the shielding effect of various materials. You can obtain Geiger counters by contacting your Kendall/Hunt representative.

Cloud chambers give the students a chance to see evidence for nuclear radiation. This activity should be the first thing you do in the section on nuclear energy. After seeing the tracks, students will know what you are talking about when you discuss nuclear equations, ionizing radiation, and radioactive decay.

ADVANCE PREPARATION

A variety of diffusion cloud chambers are sold by scientific supply houses. The chambers can also be made by using plastic refrigerator jars and a small piece of a numeral off an old luminous dial clock face. However, the proper type of refrigerator jar may take some time to locate, there is some danger in cutting up luminous clock numerals, and the resulting cloud chamber can be purchased for a relatively small expense. You can obtain cloud chambers for classroom use by contacting your Kendall/Hunt representative. These chambers come with a radiation source.

Dry ice can often be obtained from a dairy, or look under "Dry Ice" in the Yellow Pages of the telephone directory. A 5-pound slab of dry ice will keep a chamber operating all day (8:00 A.M.–4:00 P.M.), provided the dry ice is covered with rags or paper. Insulate the dry ice from the tabletop by placing it on several thicknesses of newspaper. A 1-inch-thick slab of dry ice should keep a chamber operating for an hour or more. A dry ice machine can be ordered by calling your Kendall/Hunt representative.

Directions for an inexpensive way to operate cloud chambers follow. Obtain a slab of styrofoam about 1 inch thick. Cut out squares of styrofoam that are larger than the base of the cloud chamber.

cloud chamber base

Put on a pair of gloves. Heat the bottom of an empty tuna fish can with a Bunsen burner. Melt a depression into the styrofoam by pressing the hot can into the styrofoam square. DON'T BREATHE ANY FUMES!

Put some chunks of dry ice into a canvas money bag (obtained from a bank). Strike the closed bag many times with the side of a common hammer until the bag contains dry ice snow (no lumps). Pour some snow into the depression in the styrofoam and level the surface. Press the base of the alcohol-soaked cloud chamber into the depression that contains the snow. The cloud chamber should work well. This technique allows you to operate 10 cloud chambers for the same cost of operating one (using the other method).

STRATEGIES AND PROCEDURES

Keep these ideas in mind:

- Rubbing the top of the chamber with a dry cloth changes the apparent number and the quality of the tracks. Tracks not originating from the ore sample may be due to invisible specks of radioactive material contaminating the bottom of the chamber. It is also possible they come from natural radioactive atoms in the plastic. There is always a slight possibility of that. They may also originate with radon gas atoms that are always present in small abundance in the air.
- Stray tracks that do not originate from the ore sample may also be from cosmic rays. Cosmic rays are usually very faint and for the most part scatter strongly. However, a few cosmic ray tracks will be very straight and will pass completely across the chamber.
- Almost all tracks seen are α tracks. β tracks are thin, crooked (squiggly), and farther from the source. Because they are so faint, few (if any) students will notice them.

Charge (e)	Rest Mass (amu)	Relative Specific Ionization of Air	Range in Air	Method of Interacting with Matter	Effective Shielding Materials	Typical Energies (Mev)	Velocities (%C)
α +2	4	2500	Few inches	Ionizing collisions	Paper, dead skin	4–10	4.7–7.3%
β −1	1/1837	100	Several feet	Ionizing collisions	Plastic, glass, aluminum	0.025–3.15	25–99%
γ 0	0	1	Indefinite	1. Photoelectric 2. Compton scattering 3. Pair production	Lead, concrete, water	0.04–3.2	All at C. C is the speed of light.

This chart is a handy reference for the three most common nuclear radiations. Gammas don't produce enough ionization to be seen readily in a cloud chamber.

SAMPLE ANSWERS TO OBSERVATIONS

1. The tracks are produced at random.
2. The tracks move straight out from the ore sample and are quite thick.
3. The tracks move outward from the ore sample.
4. 1″ to 1½″.
5. The radioactive sample emits a great deal of radiation. Normally, this radiation is invisible.

ACTIVITY 10.4 WRITING NUCLEAR EQUATIONS

See *Student Edition*, p. 387.

1. $_{84}^{218}\text{Po}$
2. $_{83}^{214}\text{Bi}$
3. $_{6}^{12}\text{C}$
4. $_{36}^{95}\text{Kr}$
5. $_{8}^{17}\text{O}$
6. $_{93}^{237}\text{Np}$
7. $_{11}^{23}\text{Na}$
8. $_{59}^{144}\text{Pr}$
9. $_{83}^{209}\text{Bi}$
10. $_{0}^{0}\gamma$
11. $_{36}^{94}\text{Kr}$
12. $_{50}^{135}\text{Sn}$
13. $_{0}^{1}\text{n}$
14. $_{25}^{55}\text{Mn}$
15. $_{28}^{65}\text{Ni}$

ACTIVITY 10.5 HALF-LIFE INVESTIGATION

See *Student Edition*, p. 388.

 10.5

ADVANCE PREPARATION

This half-life activity replaces the former half-life lab because of cost. This investigation can be done using the dice from the exponential growth activity. Hence, it costs practically nothing. With good organization, the data can be obtained and graphs set up in one 45-minute lab period. You will need regular graph paper and two-cycle semi-log paper.

1. An exponential decay curve.
2. A downward-sloping straight line (on the average).

SAMPLE ANSWERS TO QUESTIONS _____

1. Four throws.
2. A radioactive sample theoretically never completely decays. Half is always left.
3. In several months, most of the short half-life radioactive materials will have decayed through several half-lives. The resulting radioactivity of the fuel rods will be down to a level low enough so they can legally and safely be shipped to an authorized storage facility.

 10.6

Transparency 10.3

READING 10.3 SOURCES OF NUCLEAR ENERGY

See *Student Edition,* p. 389.

 10.7

Transparency 10.4

READING 10.4 FISSIONABLE ISOTOPES

See *Student Edition,* p. 391.

READING 10.5 FUSION FUELS

See *Student Edition,* p. 392.

READING USING NUCLEAR FUELS

See *Student Edition,* p. 392.

ACTIVITY 10.6 SIMULATING A RADIOACTIVE DECAY CHAIN

See *Student Edition,* p. 393.

ADVANCE PREPARATION _____

Use dice from the exponential growth modeling activity. Because icosahedrons are difficult to obtain, you can use multifaceted beads by contacting your Kendall/Hunt representative. These beads are also available at craft stores. A bead with *two small* sides marked gives almost the same results as the icosahedrons with one side marked. Marks made with a Sharpie pen are permanent.

This graph summarizes the results of this activity.

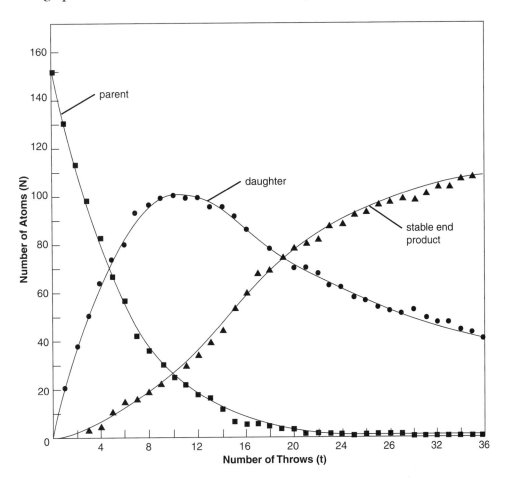

1. The graph represents a three member radioactive decay chain. As time goes on, the radioactive sample (ore) that contains the parent materials contains varying amounts of daughter and stable end product.
2. A direct analogy exists between what the simulated sample does and what real world parent-daughter-stable end product samples do.

1. The U-238 and the U-235 decay series are as follows:

Uranium-238 Series:

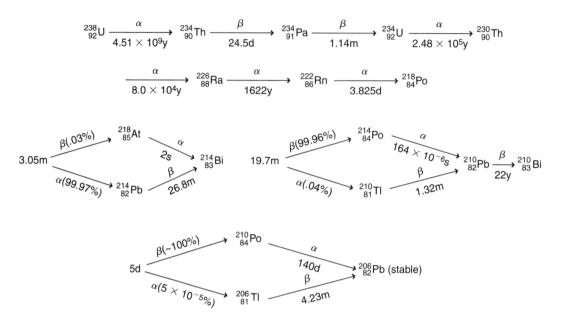

Uranium-235 Series:

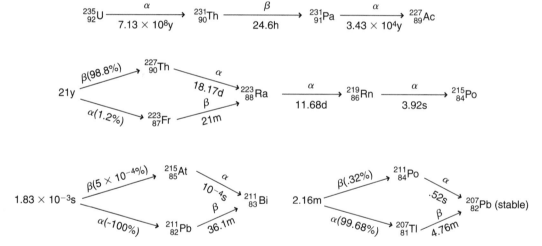

2. The concentration of radon gas in the air in and around the uranium mine is much higher than at other locations on Earth. This means that uranium miners will breathe in more radon gas atoms than the general public. Some of these atoms will deposit in their lungs and represent potential sites for future cancers.

3. The tailings contain varying amounts of all the daughter products of uranium. These atoms are radioactive.

4. The tailings are radioactive because of the daughter products they contain. One of these is radon gas. Breathing this gas increases one's chances for getting lung cancer. The residents have taken (and are taking) action to force the federal government to remove the tailings from around the foundations of buildings.

ACTIVITY 10.7 THE NUCLEAR FUEL CYCLE

See *Student Edition,* p. 394.

 10.9

See *Student Edition,* p. 394.

ADVANCE PREPARATION

If students keep portfolios, the nuclear fuel cycles fit nicely on 11″ × 17″ sheets of blank paper. They can be folded in half and placed in a student's portfolio. You need scissors and tape, glue, or rubber cement. Provide colored pencils so students who finish early can add color. This activity usually takes 40–50 minutes.

RESULTS

Student cycles should look similar to Blackline Master 10.9.

The chart on p. 216 summarizes how four countries dispose of their nuclear waste.

READING 10.6 THE NUCLEAR FUEL CYCLE—A CLOSER LOOK

See *Student Edition,* p. 396.

10.9

ACTIVITY 10.8 TRANSPORTING NUCLEAR WASTE: AN ENGINEERING DESIGN PROJECT

See *Student Edition,* p. 401.

ADVANCE PREPARATION

Obtain the required quantities of the following materials:

student instructions
two 2-liter soda bottles per student/group
scissors
rulers
markers
variety of stuffing/packing materials
strong tape
raw eggs to represent radioactive waste
roof, ladder, or high place from which an adult can drop the containers
gamma radiation source and Geiger counter (optional)

STRATEGIES AND PROCEDURES

Methods for Testing

- ❋ *Drop test.* Drop casks (by an adult) from a roof, ladder, window, or other high place so that the egg cask lands on a hard or solid surface (e.g., concrete, plywood).
- ❋ *Shaft test.* Attach a shaft of the listed dimensions to a piece of wood to support the shaft upright (with strong glue or screws), and drop the bottle onto the shaft so that the bottle will fall 3 feet before hitting the shaft.

Where/How Four Countries Propose to Dispose of Their High-Level Radioactive Waste

Country	% Electricity from Nuclear[1]	Proposed High-Level Radioactive Waste Disposal Method	Proposed Sites for Disposal of High-Level Radioactive Waste	Comments: In summary, "temporary" surface storage of high-level radioactive waste will continue for decades
France	75%	Deep geological storage (reversible) or burial (irreversible) in clay and/or granite formations	Underground "study lab" in clay formation at Bure in Meuse/Haute-Marne in east, 15 granite sites in northwest and west France under initial consideration	In 2006, Bure study results will be presented to the French Parliament for a decision on whether to proceed with disposal site. Aquifers above and below site. Geophysical[2] evidence clay may not be water tight. Regional residents in opposition. Such opposition stopped site searches in 1980s–90s.
Great Britain	27%	Reversible or irreversible geologic disposal in one or more of multiple rock types	Dozens of sites in England, Wales, and Scotland were identified in the 1970s–80s as suitable. Sellafield, Cumbria (northwest England on Irish Sea near the Lake District) is primary candidate site	Late 1970s–early 80s site search and proposed test shaft/underground lab at Sellafield stopped by social/political resistance. UK government report in 2006 will announce long-term strategy. It may take decades or a century to implement proposal[3].
Germany	30%	Deep geological disposal in salt, granite, siltstone, or other rock type providing longest possible isolation	All regions in Germany shall be considered	Proposed underground "study lab" in salt formations at Gorleben, Lower Saxony (near Elbe River in north central Germany) currently stalled due to large scale protests. "The aim is to have an operable repository as of 2030, approximately."
Japan	30%	Burial in "deep, stable strata"	Construction began on "Underground Research Labs" at Mizunami (Tono, central Japan) and Horonobe (Hokkeido, northern island) in 2001 and 2002, respectively	Although the Japanese government plans to name "volunteer" candidate sites in 2004, technical difficulties with geologic disposal, and safety scandals that have rocked the Japanese nuclear industry could cause delays. "The Japanese government plans to initiate operation of such a final disposal facility between the 2030s and 2040s."

Nuclear Information and Resource Service, www.nirs.org

Notes:

[1] U.S. Nuclear Regulatory Commission Information Digest 2001 Edition, NUREG - 1350, Vol. 13, p. 31.

[2] April 2001 discovery of high concentrations of radon gas above faults just several kilometers from Bure.

[3] The January 30, 2003 UK Parliament's *Hansard* quoted Margaret Beckett, UK Secretary of Environment, Food, and Rural Affairs as saying "… it will probably take billions of pounds and about a hundred years to deal with the issue. . ."

Sources Used/References/Websites:

World Information Service on Energy, www.antenna.nl/wise/

Agence national pour la gestion de dechets radioactifs, ANDRA (France's National Agency for Radioactive Waste Management), www.andra.fr

"Nuclear France: materials and sites," Yggdrasil Institute, www.francenuc.org/en_sites/lorr_bure_e.htm

Greenpeace UK, www.greenpeace.org.uk

UK Department of Environment, Food, and Rural Affairs, www.defra.gov.uk/environment/radioactivity

German Committee on a Site Selection Procedure for Repository Sites, www.akend.de/englisch/faq.index_1024.htm

Gorleben International Peace Team, www.gipt.de

Citizens' Nuclear Information Center, Tokyo, http://cnic.jp/english/topics/waste/takagi.html

Japan Nuclear Fuel Limited, www.jnfl.co.jp/english/outline/004.html

Japan Nuclear Cycle Development Institute, www.jnc.co.jp/jncweb/02r_d/02index.html

◈ *Side impact test.* Fill a 12-oz. plastic drink bottle with sand so that it weighs 1 pound. Attach a string to the bottle and the other end of the string to the top center of a doorframe (use strong tape or other similar material). Place the egg cask bottle directly underneath the string so that the hanging bottle touches the side of the egg cask. Pull the hanging bottle so that it is suspended at an angle of approximately 45°, then release the hanging bottle and have it collide with the cask.

After testing, open each cask to determine whether it protected its contents.

◈ *Optional radiation test.* Place the gamma radiation source inside the cask and use the Geiger counter to measure the counts of radiation released per minute before and after testing. Make sure to keep the Geiger counter the same distance from the cask and in the same position during both tests. Judge the effectiveness of the cask by determining whether the radiation increased after subjecting the cask to the stress of testing.

Questions and Extensions

◈ Have students report on the strengths and weaknesses of their designs. What could be improved in future attempts?

◈ When a cask fails to contain its contents, must all waste and contaminated material be cleaned up? How? By whom? What safety measures should be considered?

◈ What should ultimately be done with waste and contamination?

◈ Discuss the concept of reducing hazardous waste at its source (producing less to start with). How would changes in manufacturing/industrial methods affect the consumer of goods? Would our lifestyles have to change?

READING 10.7 **NUCLEAR POWER PLANTS**

See *Student Edition,* p. 403.

 10.8

Transparency 10.5

READING 10.8 **THE PROS AND CONS OF NUCLEAR POWER**

See *Student Edition,* p. 408.

READING 10.9 **BIOLOGICAL EFFECTS OF RADIATION**

See *Student Edition,* p. 409.

READING 10.10 **MEASURING RADIATION: THE UNITS**

See *Student Edition,* p. 412.

READING 10.11 DOSAGE AND EFFECT

See *Student Edition,* p. 413.

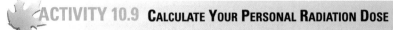

ACTIVITY 10.9 CALCULATE YOUR PERSONAL RADIATION DOSE

See *Student Edition,* p. 413.

ADVANCE PREPARATION

Before students do Activity 10.9, they should have read Readings 10.9–10.11. You may wish to review some of this material before you proceed.

SAMPLE ANSWERS TO QUESTIONS

1. In most cases, student results will be slightly below the average. Few students will be much above it.

2. Sample calculation: $360 \text{ mrem} \times 0.01 \ \dfrac{\text{mSv}}{\text{mrem}} = 3.6 \text{ mSv}$.

3. The typical student dose is well below 10 mSv, which is listed as the threshold where some evidence of increased cancer incidence **may** begin. Also, 100 mSv is listed as "no early effects" of radiation.

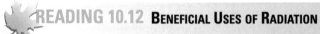

READING 10.12 BENEFICIAL USES OF RADIATION

See *Student Edition,* p. 415.

READING 10.13 THE BREEDER OPTION

See *Student Edition,* p. 415.

BLM 10.10
Transparency 10.4

READING 10.14 THE FUSION FUTURE

See *Student Edition,* p. 419.

READING 10.15 THE FUTURE OF NUCLEAR POWER

See *Student Edition,* p. 422.

CHAPTER 10 SUMMARY

See *Student Edition,* p. 422.

Name_____ Date_____

The following notes accompany the video *Radioactive Waste Disposal: The 10,000 Year Test*. This documentary does an excellent job of summarizing the nuclear waste dilemma. Students seem to get more out of videos if they have information they are accountable for. Sample answers can be found on p. 226 of the *Teacher Guide*.

RADIOACTIVE WASTE DISPOSAL: THE 10,000 YEAR TEST

VIDEO NOTES

1. A group of scientists have been given the task to predict for _____ _____, Nevada, what will happen to it from now to _____ years into the future. This is where American nuclear wastes are to be _____.

2. The entombed wastes can cause no more than _____ deaths over the next _____ years. Can science make such a prediction?

3. Used nuclear fuel rods were supposed to be temporarily stored in pools of water. Today they are _____.

4. Used spent fuel rods will be radioactive for _____ of years.

5. In the 1980s, scientists made a list of everything that could go wrong at a nuclear repository. There were _____ items on the list. It was everything anyone could think of— meteors hitting it to being hit by a nuclear bomb.

6. How could scientists know if they'd thought of everything? Answer: _____.

7. Yucca Mountain is about a two-hour drive from _____.

8. In 1956, visitors to Las Vegas got to view _____ as an added attraction to a night of gambling.

9. At Yucca Mountain, spent nuclear fuel rods will be placed in a _____ canister. These resistant canisters would then be lowered deep into the ground and delivered to and placed in a hole drilled into the repository floor—one-quarter mile below the surface.

10. Part of Yucca Mountain's shield of protection is the _____ _____ environment. Unfortunately, we can't predict for thousands of years, with ultimate certainty, how the natural system will behave.

11. Some of the rock in Yucca Mountain contains the mineral _____. This mineral "eats" radioactivity. It traps radionuclides chemically.

12. The closest volcano to Yucca Mountain probably erupted just _____ years ago. So probability is high that it will erupt again within the next _____ years.

13. Volcanic activity doesn't mean the site is _____ unless the volcano erupted right through the repository itself. The odds of that happening appear to be almost zero.

14. Computers are used to simulate a water leak from the repository over 10,000 years. The model indicated that only the _____ concentrations of waste reach the water table

in 10,000-years time. But what if there is something the computer doesn't know?

15. Water moves through simulated fractures _____. The movement is basically unpredictable. This type of behavior does not appear in the computer model of water movement.

16. If Yucca Mountain remained a desert, _____ water movement wouldn't matter. But will Yucca Mountain always be desert? For answers to that question, scientists turn to the _____.

17. A preserved pack rat nest (mitten) reveals that Yucca Mountain had a _____ climate in the past. It was much _____ and _____.

18. In the next 10,000 years, the waste depository could be _____.

19. Where will humans be 10,000 years from now? That's quite a question!

_____

_____

_____

_____

_____

_____

20. **OPINION QUESTION**

Based on what you now know, should Yucca Mountain be built? _____ If yes, why? If no, what should we do with our radioactive wastes?

_____

_____

_____

_____

_____

_____

CHAPTER 10 ASSESSMENT

Name_____ Date_____

MULTIPLE CHOICE

1. _____ The nucleus does *not* contain
   A. electrons.   C. neutrons.
   B. protons.

2. _____ The mass number represents the number of
   A. protons and neutrons.   C. electrons and neutrons.
   B. protons and electrons.   D. none of the above.

3. _____ The chemical properties of an atom are determined by its
   A. atomic number.   C. ability to fission.
   B. number of isotopes.   D. mass number.

4. _____ Atoms whose nuclei contain the same number of protons but different numbers of neutrons are
   A. isotopes.   C. radium.
   B. thorium.   D. ions.

5. _____ In the cloud chamber we used in class, the thick straight tracks were produced by
   A. gamma rays.   C. neutrons.
   B. beta particles. D. alpha particles.

6. _____ The *most penetrating* of the following radiations is
   A. alpha.   C. gamma.
   B. beta.

7. _____ Alpha particles are
   A. high-energy electromagnetic radiations.
   B. negatively charged particles.
   C. able to produce the greatest number of ions per centimeter of the three kinds of emissions from radioactive nuclei.
   D. high-speed electrons.
   E. the most penetrating of the three types of radiation emitted by radioactive elements.

8. _____ Which graph best represents how the activity of a radioactive sample changes with time? The plot is on *semi-log* paper.

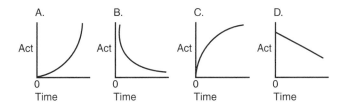

9. _____ Strontium-90 has a half-life of 30 years. If a 400 gram sample of Strontium-90 decays for 120 years, how many grams of Strontium-90 remain in the sample?
   A. 25 grams   C. 100 grams
   B. 50 grams   D. 200 grams

Ask for a periodic table to answer questions 10–16.

10. _____ How many *protons* and *electrons* does uranium have?
        A. 92   C. 235
        B. 233   D. 238

11. _____ What is the mass number of Nitrogen-14?
        A. 7   C. 21
        B. 14   D. 28

12. _____ What is the atomic number of calcium?
        A. 20   C. 60
        B. 40   D. 80

13. _____ The number of neutrons in a Plutonium-239 nucleus is
        A. 239.   C. 94.
        B. 145.   D. 333.

14. _____ In the reaction:

$$^{235}_{92}U + ^{1}_{0}n \rightarrow \underline{\hspace{1.5cm}} + ^{94}_{38}Sr + 2\,^{1}_{0}n$$

the blank is correctly filled with
        A. $^{236}_{94}Pu$ C. $^{141}_{52}Te$
        B. $^{95}_{38}Sr$ D. $^{140}_{54}Xe$

15. _____ In the reaction:

$$^{253}_{100}Fm \rightarrow \underline{\hspace{1.5cm}} + ^{4}_{2}\alpha$$

the blank is correctly filled with
        A. $^{249}_{102}No$ C. $^{257}_{98}Cf$
        B. $^{249}_{98}Cf$ D. $^{257}_{102}No$

16. _____ In the reaction:

$$^{2}_{1}D + ^{2}_{1}D \rightarrow \underline{\hspace{1.5cm}} + ^{1}_{0}n + energy$$

the blank is correctly filled with
        A. $^{3}_{0}n$ C. $^{4}_{2}He$
        B. $^{3}_{2}He$ D. $^{3}_{1}T$

17. _____ All of the following are isotopes *except*
        A. $^{2}_{1}D$ C. $^{3}_{1}T$
        B. $^{1}_{1}H$ D. $^{3}_{2}He$

18. _____ The formation of a heavier nucleus from two lighter ones with the related release of energy is
        A. fusion.   C. ionization.
        B. fission.   D. breeding.

19. _____ Scientists can get energy out of nuclei by splitting them and by combining them as follows:
        A. splitting large nuclei and fusing small nuclei.
        B. splitting small nuclei and fusing small nuclei.
        C. splitting large nuclei and fusing large nuclei.
        D. splitting small nuclei and fusing large nuclei.

20. _____ All of the following can be obtained by mining the earth's crust *except*
        A. U-235.   C. Pu-239.
        B. U-238.   D. Th-232.

21. _____ All of the following are fissionable *except*
        A. U-233.   C. U-238.
        B. U-235.   D. Pu-239.

22. _____ The primary uranium reserves in the United States are located in
A. the midwest.   C. the Pacific Northwest.
B. the Deep South.   D. the Colorado Plateau.

23. _____ The best bullet for causing nuclear fissions is the
A. proton.   C. neutron.
B. electron.   D. gamma ray.

24. _____ Which of the following occurs in the process of nuclear fission?
A. U-235 is bombarded by electrons.
B. Uranium is split into two larger atoms.
C. Heat is produced.
D. Protons are released to continue the process.

25. _____ To achieve a chain reaction, you must get more _____ out than you put in.
A. protons   C. electrons
B. neutrons   D. positrons

26. _____ All of the following are disadvantages of ordinary fission reactors *except*
A. they consume our uranium reserves as they run.
B. they produce long-lived radioactive wastes.
C. we know how to build and operate them.
D. they produce large amounts of waste heat that must be disposed of.

27. _____ The part of a nuclear reactor that is used to "soak up" neutrons and thus prevent a reactor meltdown is the
A. moderator.   C. radiation shield.
B. heat removal system. D. control rod.

28. _____ All of the following statements are true *except* one. Which statement is false?
A. A nuclear power reactor could explode like a nuclear bomb.
B. Strontium-90 and Cesium-137 are biologically active.
C. There are no operating nuclear fuel-reprocessing plants in the United States.
D. A reactor meltdown would result from a failure of the cooling system.
E. All wastes from U.S. nuclear reactors are in "temporary" storage.

29. _____ For a chain reaction to occur, you must have all of the following *except*
A. a minimum amount of fissionable material.
B. more than one neutron produced per fission.
C. fissionable nuclei.
D. a control system.

30. _____ The purpose of the moderator in a nuclear reactor is to
A. transfer heat from the reactor core to the water that will be changed to steam.
B. produce neutrons for the fission process.
C. slow down fast neutrons to increase the probability of fission.
D. absorb the dangerous gamma and neutron radiation.

31. _____ The ore-processing operation that separates the mineral(s) of interest from the rock and sand in which it is (they are) found is
A. mining.   C. storage.
B. reprocessing.   D. milling.

32. _____ As both natural thorium and uranium decay, this radioactive gas is given off.
A. carbon dioxide   C. radon
B. hydrogen   D. deuterium

33. _____ Charged particles created when radiations enter matter are
    A. isotopes.   C. gamma radiation.
    B. beta radiation.   D. ions.

34. _____ Our bodies receive radiation constantly from all of the following *except*
    A. food that has been radiated to preserve it.
    B. radioactive materials in the ground.
    C. radiation from outer space (cosmic rays).
    D. radioactive materials in our bodies.

35. _____ When dealing with the biological effects of radiation, we distinguish between *external* and *internal* hazards. Which of the following is the *least* dangerous as an *external* hazard?
    A. α C. γ
    B. β D. n

36. _____ A reactor that produces more fissionable material than it consumes is called a
    A. fission reactor.   D. burner reactor.
    B. breeder reactor.   E. conventional reactor.
    C. fusion reactor.

37. _____ Uranium-233 is made from
    A. Thorium-232.   C. Lead-212.
    B. Uranium-238.   D. Uranium-235.

38. _____ Breeder reactions do all of the following *except*
    A. make fissionable fuel as they run.
    B. produce negligible (very little) radioactive wastes.
    C. can be used to supply materials for weapons manufacturing.
    D. extend the lifetime of our uranium reserves.

39. _____ This type of reactor does *not* produce long-lived radioactive wastes.
    A. fusion   C. ordinary fission
    B. breeder   D. burner

40. _____ What can plutonium be used for besides powering nuclear reactors?
    A. Making bombs.
    B. Can be used in coal-fired power plants.
    C. Nothing.
    D. Providing energy for Pluto at Disney World.

41. _____ What kinds of pollution would probably increase with the widespread use of breeder reactors?
    A. radioactive and acid rain
    B. radioactive and thermal
    C. carbon monoxide and nitrogen oxides
    D. hydrocarbon and thermal

42. _____ This type of energy process produces more fuel than it consumes as it operates.
    A. coal gasification
    B. solar thermal energy
    C. breeder reactor
    D. ocean thermal energy conversion

43. _____ If this type of energy were developed on a large scale, it could consume a major portion of the nation's uranium supply.
    A. solar thermal energy   C. nuclear fission
    B. biomass conversion   D. oil shale

44. _____ How much would our nuclear resources increase if breeder reactors were used?
   A. double   C. 30 times
   B. triple   D. 60 times

45. _____ All of the following are of interest in the quest for obtaining energy from fusion *except*
   A. $_1^2$D   C. $_3^6$Li
   B. $_1^3$T   D. $_{36}^{95}$Kr

46. _____ A coil of current-carrying wire wrapped like a donut creates a
   A. glass bead with deuterium in the center.
   B. microwave generator.
   C. laser beam.
   D. magnetic bottle.

47. _____ Which of the following is *not* a method for producing a controlled fusion reaction?
   A. magnetic confinement
   B. laser energy
   C. use of plutonium in the reaction area

48. _____ In the United States, nuclear power is
   A. expanding rapidly.
   B. at a standstill.
   C. shrinking rapidly in terms of use.
   D. shifting to the breeder option.
   E. shifting to the fusion option.

EXTENSION

RADIOACTIVE WASTE DISPOSAL: THE 10,000 YEAR TEST

VIDEO NOTES

1. A group of scientists have been given the task to predict for <u>Yucca Mountain</u>, Nevada, what will happen to it from now to <u>10,000</u> years into the future. This is where American nuclear wastes are to be <u>buried</u>.

2. The entombed wastes can cause no more than <u>1000</u> deaths over the next <u>10,000</u> years. Can science make such a prediction?

3. Used nuclear fuel rods were supposed to be temporarily stored in pools of water. Today they are <u>still there</u>.

4. Used spent fuel rods will be radioactive for <u>thousands</u> of years.

5. In the 1980s, scientists made a list of everything that could go wrong at a nuclear repository. There were <u>57</u> items on the list. It was everything anyone could think of—meteors hitting it to being hit by a nuclear bomb.

6. How could scientists know if they'd thought of everything? Answer: <u>They couldn't</u>.

7. Yucca Mountain is about a two-hour drive from <u>Las Vegas</u>.

8. In 1956, visitors to Las Vegas got to view <u>nuclear</u> <u>bomb tests</u> as an added attraction to a night of gambling.

9. At Yucca Mountain, spent nuclear fuel rods will be placed in a <u>disposal</u> canister. These resistant canisters would then be lowered deep into the ground and delivered to and placed in a hole drilled into the repository floor—one-quarter mile below the surface.

10. Part of Yucca Mountain's shield of protection is the <u>natural geologic</u> environment. Unfortunately, we can't predict for thousands of years, with ultimate certainty, how the natural system will behave.

11. Some of the rock in Yucca Mountain contains the mineral <u>zeolite</u>. This mineral "eats" radioactivity. It traps radionuclides chemically.

12. The closest volcano to Yucca Mountain probably erupted just <u>5000</u> years ago. So probability is high that it will erupt again within the next <u>10,000</u> years.

13. Volcanic activity doesn't mean the site is <u>disqualified</u> unless the volcano erupted right through the repository itself. The odds of that happening appear to be almost zero.

14. Computers are used to simulate a water leak from the repository over 10,000 years. The model indicated that only the <u>lowest</u> concentrations of waste reach the water table in 10,000-years time. But what if there is something the computer doesn't know?

15. Water moves through simulated fractures <u>chaotically</u>. The movement is basically unpredictable. This type of behavior does not appear in the computer model of water movement.

16. If Yucca Mountain remained a desert, <u>chaotic</u> water movement wouldn't matter. But will Yucca Mountain always be desert? For answers to that question, scientists turn to the <u>pack rat</u>.

17. A preserved pack rat nest (mitten) reveals that Yucca Mountain had a <u>very different</u> climate in the past. It was much <u>lusher</u> and <u>greener</u>.

18. In the next 10,000 years, the waste depository could be <u>flooded</u>.

19. Where will humans be 10,000 years from now? That's quite a question! <u>Open ended.</u>
<u>Evaluate on depth of thought</u>.

20. **OPINION QUESTION**

Based on what you now know, should Yucca Mountain be built? _____ If yes, why? If no, what should we do with our radioactive wastes?
<u>Evaluate on quality of students' reasoning</u>.

CHAPTER 10 ASSESSMENT

1. A	25. B
2. A	26. C
3. A	27. D
4. A	28. A
5. D	29. D
6. C	30. C
7. C	31. D
8. D	32. C
9. A	33. D
10. A	34. A
11. B	35. A
12. A	36. B
13. B	37. A
14. D	38. B
15. B	39. A
16. B	40. A
17. D	41. B
18. A	42. C
19. A	43. C
20. C	44. D
21. C	45. D
22. D	46. D
23. C	47. C
24. C	48. B

CHAPTER 11

ENERGY ALTERNATIVES

LEARNING OUTCOMES

The student will:

1. explain how synthetic fuels can be used as alternatives to oil and natural gas. (C)
2. explain why our current automobile engines would not have to be modified to use gasoline from oil shale or tar sands. (C)
3. explain why it might be useful to change coal into a gas or a liquid. (C)
4. state environmental problems related to synfuel development. (C)
5. set up and analyze a working convection cell and relate the current produced to geothermal activity by completing the activity "Geothermal Convection Currents." (C,P)
6. explain why the tides and geothermal sources are useful but considered local options. (C)
7. design a solar/environmental home by drawing a future home and building a model that incorporates solar and environmental ideas. (C,P)
8. investigate various strategies for designing passive solar homes by manipulating materials and completing the activity "Passive Solar Home." (C,P)
9. graph and analyze data from the activity "Passive Solar Home." (C,P)
10. evaluate which type of passive solar home design best utilizes the sun's energy by observing, discussing, and completing the activity "Passive Solar Home." (C,A)
11. name two categories of solar heating. (C)
12. describe the advantages and disadvantages of the two types of solar heating systems. (C)
13. consider living in an underground solar-heated home and state his or her concerns and the things he or she would like in the home. (C,A)
14. design and build a solar oven and use it to cook some food by completing the activity "Build and Use a Solar Oven." (C,A,P)
15. determine the maximum output of a simple solar collector by manipulating materials and equipment and completing the activity "Analysis of a Solar Collector." (C,P)
16. calculate the approximate collector area required for heating home hot water using flat-plate collectors by completing the activity "Solar Water Heating." (C)
17. analyze the economics of solar heating and speculate on the future of solar heating for homes. (C,A)

18. calculate the power output of a solar cell by manipulating materials and equipment and by completing the activity "Solar Cells." (C,P)

19. calculate the efficiency of a solar cell as an energy converter. (C)

20. analyze factors in determining the potential of solar cells for providing electrical and heating/cooling requirements in the home by completing the activity "Solar Cells." (C)

21. state what must be done to sunlight for its energy to be used for electricity. (C)

22. list the major advantages and drawbacks of electrical generators run by solar-heated steam. (C)

23. justify the inclusion of Ocean Thermal Energy Conversion (OTEC) in the category of solar energy. (C,A)

24. design and build a model wind generator by manipulating materials and equipment from the activity "Build a Model Wind Generator." (C,P)

25. test some of the variables involved in wind generation by hypothesizing and completing the activity "Build a Model Wind Generator." (C,P)

26. list the conditions needed to take the best advantage of wind energy. (C)

27. explain why the reliability of a wind system coupled with a solar system might be much higher than the reliability of either alone. (C)

28. describe three ways that hydroelectric energy can be used. (C)

29. give examples of materials that are classified as "biomass" energy sources. (C)

30. explain how the same food grain could be used to operate farm machinery and to provide protein for cattle. (C)

31. calculate how many gallons of gasohol can be made if the number of gallons of ethanol is known and if the percent mixture of gasoline and ethanol is given. (C)

KEY TERMS

synthetic fuel
coal gasification
coal liquefaction
oil shale
kerogen
retort
tar sands
bitumen
geothermal energy
conduction
convection

tidal energy
solar energy
passive solar
thermal mass
earth-sheltered home
active solar
flat-plate collector
solar thermal energy conversion
photovoltaic
load
solar cell

photon
ammeter
voltmeter
resistor
wind generator
ocean thermal energy conversion
hydropower
bioconversion
biomass
biofuels

RECOMMENDED BLACKLINE MASTERS

11.1   Coal Gasification
11.2   Retorting Oil Shale—General Principles
11.3   Passive Solar Home
11.4   Flat-Plate Collector

11.5   Active Solar Home
11.6   Solar Cells
11.7   Fuels from Biomass

The Recommended Blackline Masters listed above are supplemental to the activity/reading, and can be found on the *Teacher Resource CD*.

CHAPTER 11: ENERGY ALTERNATIVES

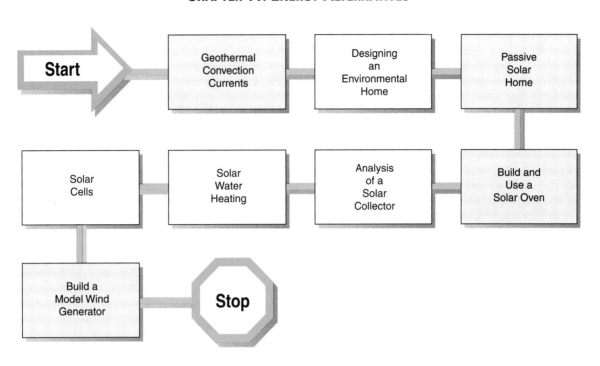

Start → Geothermal Convection Currents → Designing an Environmental Home → Passive Solar Home

Solar Cells → Solar Water Heating → Analysis of a Solar Collector → Build and Use a Solar Oven

Build a Model Wind Generator → **Stop**

NOTE: Shaded items are lower priority.

TEACHING STRATEGIES AND ANSWERS FOR ACTIVITIES

READING **SYNTHETIC FUELS**

See *Student Edition*, p. 426.

READING 11.1 **NEW FUELS FROM COAL**

See *Student Edition*, p. 426.

 11.1

READING 11.2 **OIL SHALE**

See *Student Edition*, p. 427.

 11.2

READING 11.3 **TAR SANDS**

See *Student Edition*, p. 430.

READING LOCAL OPTIONS

See *Student Edition,* p. 431.

READING 11.4 GEOTHERMAL ENERGY

See *Student Edition,* p. 431.

 4.5

ACTIVITY 11.1 GEOTHERMAL CONVECTION CURRENTS

See *Student Edition,* p. 433.

Caution students about working around open flames and with hot objects.

SAMPLE ANSWERS TO EXPLANATIONS _____

1. In Figure 11.10, heat energy is continually fed into the system. In the activity, the energy stored in the vial of hot water was fixed. Once it ran out, the convection cell stopped circulating.
2. The set up would have to be modified to look like Figure 11.10.
3. Hot water is less dense than cold water. When the vial of hot water is placed in the cold water, the hot water rises to the top of the cold water layer. Since it cannot rise farther, it spreads out near the top. More dense cold water moves into the vial to take the place of the hot water that left. Soon the temperatures equalize and the cell stops working.
4. A "thermal hot spot" would be a continuous source of energy. When groundwater comes in contact with a hot spot, the principles examined in this activity apply, and a convection cell could occur inside the earth.

READING 11.5 TIDAL ENERGY

See *Student Edition,* p. 434.

READING 11.6 OCEAN WAVES

See *Student Edition,* p. 435.

ACTIVITY 11.2 DESIGNING AN ENVIRONMENTAL HOME

See *Student Edition,* p. 436.

Decide if this activity is to be done in class or at home. If done at home, it's best to allow a weekend for completion or plan around vacation or holidays. Give extra points to those students who present their models the first day the models are due. This "lights a fire" under those who put things off. It's amazing how many models show up the next day. However, the ones that come in first are usually the best. Most models will be made out of cardboard and colored with magic markers. Some students will really get involved and use poster board, balsa wood, trees from hobby shops, and so forth. It's great to have nice looking models, however, evaluate understanding and demonstration of scientific principles. The grading rubric provided here should help. Determine your own scoring system.

TASK NO. 1: Design Environmental Home/Build Model

Check off items as you complete them:

_____ Choose location and site for home.
_____ Research climate.
_____ Know the seasons at your location.
_____ Know about the daily and seasonal movement of the sun.
_____ Think through the functions your house is to perform.
_____ Know your likes/dislikes regarding homes.
_____ Learn about energy conservation regarding homes.
_____ What materials are available for home construction at your location?
_____ Plan out lighting.
_____ Where will windows/openings be located?
_____ Where will entrances be located, and how will they minimize energy loss?
_____ How will air circulate inside your home?
_____ How will you handle humidity? air quality?

TASK NO. 2: Presentation of Home to the Class

Give a 2–3 minute talk to your class explaining the features of your home. Use the following terms correctly (as they pertain to your home):

_____ site/climate
_____ active/passive solar
_____ daily/seasonal movement of the sun
_____ deciduous/coniferous trees
_____ direction of north/south
_____ where cold/hot winds come from
_____ hills, berms, dirt banks, fences, roof design
_____ floor plan
_____ insulation, R-value, caulking
_____ windows: location, type, overhangs, recessing, drapes
_____ doors: weatherstripping, stormdoors, wingwalls, air locks
_____ thermal mass, vents, plenums, fans
_____ skylights, skyshafts
_____ humidity, air quality

TASK NO. 3: Short Paper

Turn in a two-page paper (typed) that describes the features of your home. The paper is to be in your own words. It can include reference material if you used outside sources. One-half page can be your floor plan.

11.3

Transparency 11.1

 READING 11.7 PASSIVE SOLAR

See *Student Edition,* p. 438.

READING 11.8 EARTH–SHELTERED HOMES

See *Student Edition,* p. 440.

Transparency 11.1

ACTIVITY 11.3 PASSIVE SOLAR HOME

See *Student Edition,* p. 441.

ADVANCE PREPARATION

Gather the following materials:

passive solar home kit
sun simulator
stand on which to mount the sun simulator
clock or stopwatch
ordinary graph paper (1 sheet)

STRATEGIES AND PROCEDURES

You must decide whether to do this activity outside or inside. It is nice to do it outside in direct sunlight. However, going outside involves gambling on weather conditions. Since this adds additional variables, most teachers do the activity inside and use the sun simulators. They save the flat-plate collector activity for the sunny day.

Keep these ideas in mind:

- A thermal mass also helps keep a home cooler in the summer by absorbing heat from inside the home during daylight hours.
- The cardboard house is so poorly insulated that there is little difference between the white floor, the black floor, and the reflector and black floor. Thus, you may only want to investigate black floor *vs.* thermal mass and black floor.
- The other alternative is to obtain some *thin* sheets of styrofoam and work on the improvement of the activity design.

In step 10, students may respond as follows:

- The hottest indoor temperature was achieved using a black floor and a reflector. The home heated up more slowly when the thermal mass was used. The maximum temperature achieved (in the fixed heating time) was also less when using the thermal mass.
- The most rapid cooling was observed with the home that had the black floor and the reflector. The home with the thermal mass lost its heat more slowly. Hence, the home with the large thermal mass would be the most comfortable to be in on a sunny winter day. This is because the thermal mass regulated the indoor temperature and kept it in a comfortable range.

Heat was absorbed by the mass in the daytime, which kept the home from getting too hot. At night, the heat was radiated back into the room, which kept it warm.

- We didn't attempt to keep heat in the home at night by insulating the walls and windows. Students could investigate that effect in future runs of the activity.

- At present, passive solar strategies are not economical for most people because passive homes normally are custom designed to fit a certain lot. Custom homes are more expensive to build than tract homes. Also, thermal mass is expensive. However, if the cost of home heating continues to rise, passive strategies may become more attractive to the average consumer.

ACTIVITY 11.4 BUILD AND USE A SOLAR OVEN

See *Student Edition,* p. 443.

All the information necessary for doing this activity appears in the activity. The references allow you to choose the design you want, as well as provide a choice between building or purchasing the oven. It's up to you and/or the student. Solar ovens may be purchased by contacting your Kendall/Hunt representative. See the equipment section of this teacher's guide.

READING 11.9 ACTIVE SOLAR

See *Student Edition,* p. 444.

11.4, 11.5

Transparency 11.2

ACTIVITY 11.5 ANALYSIS OF A SOLAR COLLECTOR

See *Student Edition,* p. 446.

11.4

ADVANCE PREPARATION

All the materials for this activity should be readily available in most junior and senior high science labs except the flat-plate collectors. You can build them yourself or buy them by contacting your Kendall/Hunt representative.

STRATEGIES AND PROCEDURES

For the maximum energy output determination to be reliable, proceed as follows. Align the collector directly toward the sun so that the sun's rays are at 90° to the collector face both horizontally and vertically. This is done most accurately by minimizing shadows. Then allow an initial 1000 mL of cold water to circulate through the collector and run it out onto the ground. This removes heat that was stored in the collector while it was simply facing the sun. Now immediately circulate through the collector the 2000 mL of water to be analyzed. Determine and record the temperature of both the incoming and exiting water.

All determinations in this activity are done in the English system. This is because the American heating industry operates completely with the English system and has indicated no intention to change in the foreseeable future. We want the student to relate what is learned in the classroom to what is going on in the world outside—and in this case, the English system of units must be used.

Since our goal is to determine the maximum output of the collector, this activity *must* be run on a clear day.

SAMPLE ANSWERS TO DATA

Time of day: 10:00 A.M.

1. Cloud cover blocking the sun = 0%.
3. Area of collector window = 2 ft × 2 ft = 4 ft².
4. Volume of water = 2000 mL.
5. Mass of water = 2000 grams = 2.0 kilograms.
6. Weight of water = 2.0 kg × 2.2 lb./kg = 4.4 pounds.
7.

	Water Temperature	Time of Reading
Incoming water	60°F	0 min.
Exit water	80°F	4.5 min.
Ambient (outside) air temperature	50°F	

Note: Heat losses due to large differences between collector temperature and ambient air temperature are not dealt with in this activity. However, you may choose to talk about this problem if you wish.

SAMPLE ANSWERS TO CALCULATIONS

$$\text{No. Btus} = 4.4 \text{ lbs.} \times 20 \text{ F}° \times 1 \frac{\text{Btu}}{\text{pound F}°} = 88 \text{ Btu}$$

Max. output = 88 Btu ÷ 4.0 ft² ÷ 4.5 min.
= 4.9 Btu/ft²/min.
= 294 Btu/ft²/hr.

It is unlikely that students will obtain values much above 300 Btu/ft²/hr.

ACTIVITY 11.6 SOLAR WATER HEATING

See *Student Edition*, p. 448.

Transparency 11.2

ADVANCE PREPARATION

No special preparation is necessary. However, students should have hand-held calculators available.

SAMPLE ANSWERS TO CALCULATIONS

1. Average output/day = 120 Btu/ft²/hr × 6 hr/day
= 720 Btu/ft²
2. Weight of water = 60 gal × 8.33 lb/gal
= 499.8 pounds
Temperature change = 120°F − 45°F = 75 F°

$$\text{No. Btus} = 499.8 \text{ lbs.} \times 75 \text{ F}^\circ \times 1\frac{\text{Btu}}{\text{pound F}^\circ}$$
$$= 37,485 \text{ Btu}$$

3. Area of collecting surface =
   $37,485 \text{ Btu} \div 720 \text{ Btu/ft}^2 = 52 \text{ ft}^2$
4. $4 \text{ ft} \times 8 \text{ ft} = 32 \text{ ft}^2$, $4 \text{ ft} \times 10 \text{ ft} = 40 \text{ ft}^2$. Thus, we can easily get by with
   two $4 \text{ ft} \times 8 \text{ ft}$ collector panels.
5. Since half of the roof faces north, $^1\!/_2 \times 1000 \text{ ft}^2 = 500 \text{ ft}^2$ is available.
6. $\dfrac{2 \times 32 \text{ foot}^2}{500 \text{ foot}^2} \times 100\% = 12.8\%$
7. $\text{Cost} = 64 \text{ ft}^2 \times \$50.00/\text{ft}^2 = \$3,200.00$

READING SOLAR ELECTRICITY

See *Student Edition*, p. 450.

READING 11.10 SOLAR THERMAL ENERGY CONVERSION (STEC)

See *Student Edition*, p. 450.

READING 11.11 SOLAR PHOTOVOLTAIC ENERGY (SOLAR CELLS)

See *Student Edition*, p. 451.

Transparency 11.3

ACTIVITY 11.7 SOLAR CELLS

See *Student Edition*, p. 453.

 11.6

Transparency 11.3

ADVANCE PREPARATION

To do this lab, you must have a solar cell; a load (resistor), which is matched to the cell (see p. 238) a voltmeter; and a milliammeter. You can obtain a solar cell and relatively inexpensive meters for this activity by contacting your Kendall/Hunt representative. The activity must be run on a sunny day.

STRATEGIES AND PROCEDURES

Many teachers have their students hook up the circuit before they go outside. It is easier to help them in the classroom. If a flashlight is aimed onto the solar cell, the needles on the meters will respond. Once all the circuits have been checked out, the materials can be carried outside. It is most convenient to place the circuit in the cardboard flats that cases of soda pop are sold in. This way everything is carried out and back in and nothing is broken or lost. *Note:* The voltmeter must have a high internal resistance to obtain good results. Various volt-ohm-milliammeters or multimeters also work well as metering devices.

The data for this activity can be obtained in a matter of minutes—provided all materials are available and there is direct sunlight. The remainder of class can be spent processing the data and working on the Additional Considerations.

How to Determine the Size Resistor to Use with Your Solar Cell

All measurements are to be made on a clear day with the solar cell aimed directly at the Sun. The symbols are:

SC = solar cell, V = voltmeter, mA = milliammeter, $-\!\!\!\bigwedge\!\!\!-$ = resistor.

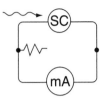

Step I:
    a. Determine the short circuit current, I_{sc}
    b. Change the current to amps.

Step II:
    a. Determine the open circuit voltage, V_{oc}
    b. Determine the maximum peak voltage
       by multiplying V_{oc} by 0.8 $V_{mpv} = 0.8 V_{oc}$.

Step III:
    Size of Resistor in ohms is given by: $R_{(ohms)} = \dfrac{V_{mpv} \text{ (volts)}}{I_{sc} \text{ (amps)}}$

SAMPLE ANSWERS TO DATA

1. Current = 30 miliamps = 0.030 amps.
2. Electrical potential = .5 volts.
3. Length of cell = 2 cm.
4. Width of cell = 1 cm.
5. Solar Input = .100 watts/cm².

SAMPLE ANSWERS TO CALCULATIONS

1. Power output of our solar cell:
   $\text{Power}_{(watts)}$ = .5 volts × 0.030 amps = 0.015 watts
2. Area of our solar cell:
   Area = length × width = 2 cm × 1 cm = 2 cm²
3. Power density of our solar cell:
   $$\text{Power} = \frac{\text{power output}}{\text{area}} = \frac{0.015 \text{ watts}}{2 \text{ cm}^2}$$
   $$= 0.0075 \frac{\text{watts}}{\text{cm}^2}$$
4. Efficiency of our solar cell as an energy converter:
   $$\text{Efficiency} = \frac{\text{power density}}{\text{Solar Input}} \times 100\%$$
   $$= \frac{0.0075}{.100} \times 100\% = \underline{7.5\%}$$

SAMPLE ANSWERS TO ADDITIONAL CONSIDERATIONS

1. No. cells = $\dfrac{100 \text{ watts}}{0.015 \dfrac{\text{watts}}{\text{cell}}}$ = 6,667 cells

2. $\text{Cost} = \dfrac{9\cancel{c}}{\text{kWh}} \times 15\ \dfrac{\text{kWh}}{\text{day}} \times 365\ \dfrac{\text{day}}{\text{yr.}} \times 30\ \text{yr.}$

$= \$14,782.50$

3. $15\ \text{kWh} = P \times 6\ \text{hr.} \qquad P = 2.5\ \text{kW}$
4. $\text{Cost} = \$7000/\text{kW} \times 2.5\ \text{kW} = \$17,500$
5. $\text{Energy} = 0.4\ \text{kWh/m}^2$
6. $\text{Amount of roof required} = \dfrac{15\text{kWh}}{.4\ \dfrac{\text{kWh}}{\text{m}^2}}\ 37.5\ \text{m}^2$

7. a. Roof area $= 1000\ \text{ft}^2 = 92.9\ \text{m}^2 \quad \left(\begin{array}{l} 1\ \text{ft} = 9,3948\ \text{m} \\ 1\ \text{ft}^2 = 0.0929\ \text{m}^2 \end{array} \right)$
   b. 40% of the roof area is required.
   c. 80% of the south-facing roof.

8. If 40% of the roof is required to provide 15 kWh/day for the electrical needs, there is not enough room available to provide for the heating. Also, the cost would be prohibitive. Passive strategies would be best.

9. If 80% of the south-facing roof is used to provide for the electrical needs, the remaining 20% can be used with flat-plate collectors for hot water needs. Activity 10.6 shows that this could easily be done—if you have the front-end money.

10. Passive solar strategies can be used to heat the home. A recycling area at the home (garage) could enable the inhabitants to save even more energy.

READING 11.12 WIND POWER

See *Student Edition,* p. 457.

ACTIVITY 11.8 BUILD A MODEL WIND GENERATOR

See *Student Edition,* p. 461.

The student section on this activity is adequate. The library research will provide background on the problems involved in designing a good wind generator. It will also familiarize the student with what is being tried in this field.

READING 11.13 OCEAN THERMAL ENERGY CONVERSION (OTEC)

See *Student Edition,* p. 463.

READING 11.14 ORBITING SOLAR SATELLITE ENERGY

See *Student Edition,* p. 464.

READING 11.15 WATER POWER

See *Student Edition,* p. 466.

 **READING** FUELS FROM THE SUN

See *Student Edition,* p. 467.

 **READING 11.16** WOOD

See *Student Edition,* p. 467.

 **READING 11.17** ENERGY FROM TRASH

See *Student Edition,* p. 467.

BLM 11.7

Transparency 11.4

READING 11.18 BIOCONVERSION

See *Student Edition,* p. 468.

CHAPTER 11 SUMMARY

See *Student Edition,* p. 471.

GENERAL OPERATIONS IN COAL GASIFICATION

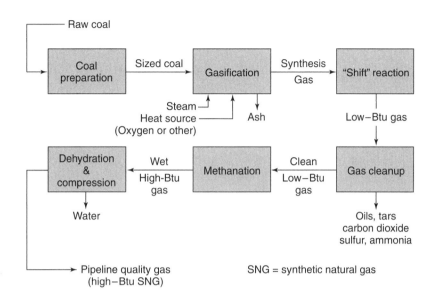

SNG = synthetic natural gas

Summary of the Chemistry of Coal Gasification

- *Gasification*

    Crushed and pulverized coal is fed into the gasification vessel. In the vessel, the coal interacts with air (or oxygen) and hot steam in an environment of high heat and pressure to produce a synthetic gas. The reactions are:

$$C + H_2O \xrightarrow{\text{Heat}} CO + H_2 \qquad \text{(gasification)}$$
$$C + O_2 \longrightarrow CO_2 + heat \qquad \text{(burning)}$$
$$C + 2H_2 \longrightarrow CH_4 \qquad \text{(direct hydrogenation)}$$

- *Synthetic gas*

    The synthetic gas produced in the gasifier is a mixture of gases:

Carbon monoxide, CO	20%
Hydrogen, H_2	40%
Methane, CH_4	11%
Carbon dioxide, CO_2	28%
Misc. impurities	1%

- *Water-gas shift*

    The shift reaction increases the energy content of the gas mixture so that it is sufficient for electric power generation.

$$CO + H_2O \longrightarrow CO_2 + H_2$$

- *Methanation*

    Methanation increases the energy content of the synthetic gas to the point where it can be directly substituted for natural gas.

$$CO + 3H_2 \longrightarrow CH_4 + H_2O$$
$$CO_2 + 4H_2 \longrightarrow CH_4 + 2H_2O$$

Name_____   Date _____

MULTIPLE CHOICE

1. _____ Why would anyone want to change coal into a gas or a liquid when it works perfectly well as a solid fuel?
   A. Homes use gas.   C. Both a and b.
   B. Cars use a liquid   D. Neither a nor b.

2. _____ The chemical symbol for methane gas is
   A. CO_2.   D. CO.
   B. H_2O.   E. CH_4.
   C. H_2.

3. _____ All of the following are arguments for gasifying coal *except*
   A. the United States has large coal reserves.
   B. processes for gasifying coal are well established and little research is necessary to make gasification a reality.
   C. gasified coal can be made into a gas that can be used in the gas furnaces we presently have in our homes.
   D. coal can be gasified into a low Btu gas for burning at electrical power generation plants.

4. _____ Which of the following is *not* an environmental problem related to coal gasification and liquefaction?
   A. The coal gasification process consumes water and water is a scarce resource in the West.
   B. The coal gasification process produces some carcinogenic by-products that must be removed from plant emissions.
   C. Coal gasification and liquefaction processes produce radioactive wastes that we don't know how to dispose of at present.
   D. Coal gasification and liquefaction processes produce some solid wastes that present a disposal problem.

5. _____ What must be added to carbon to make it a synthetic fuel?
   A. oxygen
   B. sulfur
   C. hydrogen
   D. nitrogen

6. _____ Which of the following is *not* a synfuel?
   A. oil shale from the Green River formation
   B. diesel fuel from Saudi Arabia
   C. tar sands in Alberta
   D. liquefaction of coal

7. _____ The solid organic material that turns into shale oil and gas when heated is called
   A. pyrolysis.   C. kerogen.
   B. in situ.   D. retort.

8. _____ The world's largest oil shale reserves are found in the Green River Formation, which is located in
   A. the Texas Panhandle.   C. the Rocky Mountain West.
   B. New England.   D. Southern California.

9. _____ What would be an advantage for using oil shale?
   A. It is a fossil fuel.
   B. A large amount of water is needed to process.
   C. A high cost is involved.
   D. New towns that would be created would have an adverse effect on the environment.

10. _____ All of the following are problems related to oil shale development *except*
    A. water availability.
    B. disposal of wastes.
    C. energy payoff—do we get enough to make it worthwhile?
    D. reduction of unemployment.
    E. planning for the impact on the environment and people.

11. _____ The "net energy" question asks
    A. can the energy obtained be substituted directly for oil and gas?
    B. can the energy obtained reduce the import requirements of the United States?
    C. can U.S. energy supplies exceed current U.S. demands?
    D. do you receive enough energy from a project to justify the energy expenditure that went into doing it?

12. _____ The tar sands are
    A. new oils that lacked sufficient heat and pressure to be changed to a liquid and/or a gas.
    B. old oil deposits from which the light hydrocarbons escaped leaving the heavy residue behind.
    C. pumped from the ground and refined into petroleum products.
    D. converted into gas by bacterial action at processing plants.

13. _____ Energy from tides and geothermal power are very small sources in the United States. Why should we still use them as energy sources?
    A. Because any energy source can help.
    B. Because locally they may be a large source of energy.
    C. We shouldn't because they're too small to waste money on.
    D. We shouldn't because we should rely on one or two major forms of energy.
    E. Both a and b are good reasons.

14. _____ The use of Earth's heat as an energy source is
    A. geothermal.   C. potential.
    B. solar.   D. nonrenewable.

15. _____ How is geothermal energy used in homes?
    A. Gas is transferred from geysers to home heating systems.
    B. Hot water is provided for radiators.
    C. Geothermal energy is transmitted by microwave to homes.
    D. None of the above.

16. _____ The sun produces energy by
    A. fission.   C. ionization.
    B. fusion.   D. breeding.

17. _____ Which of the following is *not* a main part of a solar collector?
- A. a transparent cover or glass
- B. solar radiation
- C. an absorbent surface
- D. a heat transfer medium

18. _____ If you have a solar collector that captures 720 Btu/sq. ft./day and you need 600,000 Btu/day, how many square feet of solar collector would you need?
- A. 230
- B. 833
- C. 972
- D. 1076

19. _____ If a solar collector is 2-ft. square and has the ability to raise the temperature of a volume of water 17F degrees, how many Btus are gained?
- A. 15
- B. 19
- C. 34
- D. 44
- E. not enough information

20. _____ The British Thermal Unit is
- A. a unit of solar energy.
- B. a hot English rock group.
- C. a unit for measuring energy.
- D. a unit for measuring light energy.

21. _____ If your home needs 910 sq. ft. for a solar heating system, and it costs $50 per square foot, how much would the system cost?
- A. $960
- B. $40,500
- C. $45,500
- D. $54,500

22. _____ If you have a solar heating system that costs $50,000 and your winter heating bills average $500, what is the payoff time for the system?
- A. 10 years
- B. 100 years
- C. 50 years
- D. 500 years

23. _____ Most current solar energy units for homes are
- A. cheap to buy and cheap to operate.
- B. cheap to buy and expensive to operate.
- C. expensive to buy and cheap to operate.
- D. expensive to buy and expensive to operate.

24. _____ What are the two categories of solar heating?
- A. heating and cooling
- B. ocean thermal and solar satellites
- C. active and passive
- D. positive and negative

25. _____ A passive solar home has
- A. maximum south-facing window area.
- B. roof overhangs or recessed windows.
- C. thermal mass.
- D. deciduous trees on the south, coniferous trees on the north.
- E. all of the above.

26. _____ Which of the following is a *disadvantage* of passive solar systems?
- A. Not simple to maintain.
- B. Does not produce heat "on demand."
- C. Does not reduce energy needs.
- D. None of these.

27. _____ Which of the following is a *disadvantage* for using solar-heated steam electrical generators?
- A. Energy is free.
- B. Energy is embargo proof.
- C. Can be installed on poor land.
- D. Operates in the day.

28. _____ A solar cell converts
   A. light into electrical energy.   C. mechanical into electrical energy.
   B. electrical energy into light.   D. chemical into electrical energy.

29. _____ This alternative collects solar energy to make large quantities of steam for electricity.
   A. breeder reactor   C. geothermal energy
   B. photovoltaic conversion   D. solar thermal energy conversion

30. _____ The power output of a solar cell is measured in watts, which is a product of
   A. ohms × volts.   C. ohms × amps.
   B. volts × amps.   D. watts × volts.

31. _____ A large solar collector absorbs 50 kilowatts of power for a period of 7 hours. How much
   energy is available from the collector?
   A. 150 kWh   C. 350 kWh
   B. 250 kWh   D. 450 kWh

32. _____ Electricity for residential use costs about 8 cents/kWh in most areas of the United States. At
   that rate, how much will it cost to provide for the household electrical needs of an average
   home for a 30-year period? (Assume the average home needs 17 kWh a day.)
   A. $1862   C. $496
   B. $449   D. $14,892

33. _____ Electrical energy is sold by the kWh. The formula is kWh = P × time. If an average house
   needs 16 kWh/day and we assume we have an average of 7 hours collecting time per day
   for producing energy from solar cells, what must be the output for our solar cell system?
   A. 2.3 kW   C. 23 kW
   B. 9 kW   D. 112 kW

34. _____ If the power output of a solar cell is 0.02 watts and you need to light a 100 watt bulb, then
   how many solar cells would you need?
   A. 500   C. 2
   B. 5000   D. 20,000

35. _____ How many watts of power can be obtained from a solar cell that generates 0.8 volts and
   0.018 amps?
   A. 0.01 watts   C. 0.782 watts
   B. 0.0144 watts   D. 0.818 watts

36. _____ What is the major drawback of wind machines?
   A. residues given off   C. decapitation
   B. air pollution   D. land use

37. _____ What does the power output of a wind machine depend on?
   A. cloudiness and temperature
   B. wind velocity and diameter of blades
   C. height of wind machine and temperature
   D. geothermal technology and mechanical losses

38. _____ Where would it be *advantageous* to use wind energy today?
   A. In places where energy is very expensive.
   B. Where air pollution is a real problem.
   C. At remote locations where long transmission lines are too expensive.
   D. All of the above.

39. _____ Why is Ocean Thermal Gradient Energy included with solar energy?
   A. The sun is the energy source that makes it work.
   B. The sun heats the top ocean layer.
   C. The temperature difference results from properties of solar radiation.
   D. All of the above.

40. _____ This method extracts energy from crops and organic waste.
   A. coal gasification
   B. biomass conversion
   C. solar thermal energy conversion
   D. ocean thermal energy conversion

41. _____ Biofuels can be made from
   A. sawdust.
   B. manures.
   C. rice hulls.
   D. municipal sewage.
   E. all of these.

42. _____ Biofuels are of interest because
   A. liquid fuels can be produced.
   B. gaseous fuels can be produced.
   C. waste volumes can be reduced.
   D. all of the above.
   E. none of these.

43. _____ In terms of biomass processes, how can grain be used to operate farm machinery and provide protein for cattle?
   A. Sell some grain to buy gasoline and feed the remaining grain to cattle.
   B. Sell the grain to buy gasoline and hay.
   C. Ferment the grain to make alcohol and then feed high protein mash to cattle.
   D. It cannot.

44. _____ A biomass energy source uses materials that were once
   A. dead.
   B. living.
   C. massive.
   D. happy.

45. _____ Why don't we supply all of our energy from our forests?
   A. Wood is needed for lumber and paper.
   B. Forests are renewable, but not every year.
   C. It took years to grow what is now standing.
   D. All of the above.

CHAPTER 11 ASSESSMENT

1. C	24. C
2. E	25. E
3. B	26. B
4. C	27. D
5. C	28. A
6. B	29. D
7. C	30. B
8. C	31. C
9. A	32. D
10. D	33. A
11. D	34. B
12. B	35. B
13. E	36. D
14. A	37. B
15. B	38. D
16. B	39. D
17. B	40. B
18. B	41. E
19. E	42. D
20. C	43. C
21. C	44. B
22. B	45. D
23. C	

CHAPTER
12

STRATEGIES FOR USING ENERGY

LEARNING OUTCOMES

The student will:

1. develop a home energy plan by determining the present energy situation in his or her home in each of six categories and then suggest how to improve energy use when necessary using information from the textbook and outside sources by completing the activity "Home Energy Plan." (C,P)

2. distinguish between a commercial vehicle and limited production, prototype, concept, and hybrid vehicles. (C)

3. graph the fuel economy *vs.* curb weight of various commercial vehicles and formulate a conclusion by completing the activity "Fuel Efficiency *vs.* Weight." (C,P)

4. graph the fuel economy *vs.* 1/weight of various commercial vehicles and formulate a conclusion by completing the activity "Fuel Efficiency *vs.* Weight." (C,P)

5. plot a point for a hybrid vehicle on a previously plotted graph and speculate on the significance of the point. (C,P,A)

6. operate and analyze a mini fuel cell by completing the fuel cell activity. (C,P)

7. analyze one or more choices consumers and society are faced with in everyday life. The choice(s) must be based on data and information gathered. The analysis will involve both the use of data and speculation on the reliability of the source of data. This analysis is the purpose of the activity "Appropriate Technology." (C,A)

8. analyze data and related maps regarding world oil sources, demand, and per capita use.

9. distinguish between nonrenewable and continuous energy sources. (C)

10. define, clarify, and analyze various energy sources and strategies that could lessen our dependence on crude oil. (C)

11. formulate a personal and/or national energy plan by completing the activity "Sorting Out Your Options." (C,A)

KEY TERMS

conservation
insulation
R-value
heat exchanger
production vehicle
prototype vehicle
concept vehicle

hybrid vehicle
composite
appliance
cogeneration
fluidized-bed combustion
heat pump
fuel cell

electrolyte
catalyst
hydrogen storage
pumped storage
continuous sources
appropriate technology
energy policy

RECOMMENDED BLACKLINE MASTERS

The Recommended Blackline Masters listed above are supplemental to the activity/reading, and can be found on the *Teacher Resource CD*.

ACTIVITIES FLOW CHART

CHAPTER 12: STRATEGIES FOR USING ENERGY

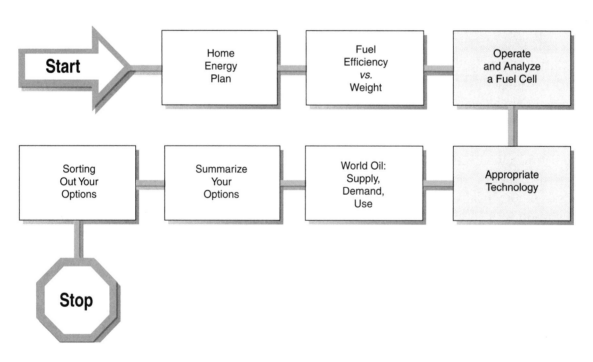

NOTE: Shaded items are lower priority.

TEACHING STRATEGIES AND ANSWERS FOR ACTIVITIES

READING THE FIRST PRIORITY: CONSERVATION

See *Student Edition,* p. 476.

ACTIVITY 12.1 HOME ENERGY PLAN

See *Student Edition,* p. 476.

12.1, 12.2

Transparency 12.1

Having students design a home energy plan helps them both localize and personalize many of the key concepts in this chapter.

Start by having them examine Figure 12.2 and the six items/regions emphasized. Allow students to redraw the figure if it is nothing like the house they live in. Also, point out where insulation and windows are most likely located. Then examine Figure 12.3 and discuss what students are to do to complete the activity. Point out that Figure 12.1 suggests where the greatest savings might be made. Sections 12.1–12.3 of the textbook are loaded with ideas and data. Students can also gather information from listed references, in libraries, on the Internet, from the local utility, and from state energy conservation offices and manufacturers of insulation, windows, lighting devices, and so forth.

Students' final plan can consist of completed Figure 12.3, a written report, an illustration, and/or an oral report.

READING 12.1 WELL-INSULATED BUILDINGS

See *Student Edition,* p. 478.

12.3

READING 12.2 MORE EFFICIENT VEHICLES

See *Student Edition,* p. 482.

SPECIAL FOCUS THE CAR OF THE FUTURE: THE ULTRALIGHT HYBRID

See *Student Edition,* p. 484.

ACTIVITY 12.2 FUEL EFFICIENCY VS. WEIGHT

See *Student Edition,* p. 484.

This is essentially a graphing activity. The graphs obtained give only an approximation. It is difficult to compare vehicles because they come with so many choices regarding accessories. If you want to expand this activity, get the EPA mileage ratings and weights off the stickers of new vehicles at auto dealerships. The employees can help you with collecting the data.

1. The Fuel Economy (mph) *vs.* Curb Weight (lb) graph is a simple reciprocal curve. The amount of bend in the curve depends on the scales chosen for the graph. In general, as the weight increases, the fuel economy drops.

2. Because metric units are directly proportional to U.S. Customary units, the metric graph is the same as the U.S. Customary graph and so the conclusion is the same.

3. This graph is a straight line (essentially) that extrapolates through the origin. Thus, fuel economy is inversely proportional to weight (or mass). This means that if the weight of a vehicle is cut in half, the fuel economy will double (approximately).

4. The point helps verify that as the weight (or mass) is lowered, the fuel economy increases. In these cases, however, the gain is even greater than the graphs suggest because these two vehicles are more efficient than the 2004 commercial vehicles plotted. This is due to their design and engineering. The power strategy is different.

 READING 12.3 MORE EFFICIENT APPLIANCES

See *Student Edition,* p. 485.

 READING ENERGY CONVERSION AND STORAGE

See *Student Edition,* p. 486.

 READING 12.4 ENERGY CONVERSION TECHNOLOGIES

See *Student Edition,* p. 486.

D. FUEL CELLS

The designation of the cathode and anode for fuel cell technology is the opposite of what it is in many science textbooks. The designation in *Global Science* is the one used in the fuel cell industry. It may be confusing, but it is important to adjust your thinking because this is the way it is done.

 ACTIVITY 12.3 OPERATE AND ANALYZE A FUEL CELL

See *Student Edition,* p. 490.

ADVANCE PREPARATION

This activity is designed around the use of a solar hydrogen fuel cell, which can be obtained by contacting your Kendall/Hunt representative. Everything needed for assembling and operating the miniature solar-hydrogen plant is included with the kit except for the illuminating lamp, the clear 100-watt filament light bulb, distilled water, and a squeeze-type wash bottle.

Set-up instructions are summarized in the text of Activity 12.3.

_____

Students should carefully analyze the operation of the solar-hydrogen plant. The four observation items should help them focus on the important ideas.

ANALYSIS _____

1. Two volumes of hydrogen are generated for every one volume of oxygen produced.
2. To establish a hydrogen economy based on fuel cells, hydrogen must be generated and an infrastructure established that can deliver it to where fuel cells are operating.
3. a. Electricity from the power grid can be used to electrolyze water.
   b. Reformers can extract hydrogen from natural gas, ethanol, methanol, or gasoline.
   c. Research scientists are working on a variety of chemical and biological processes that can produce hydrogen.

TAKING APART AND STORING YOUR FUEL CELL PLANT

1. Turn off the 100 W light source.
2. Remove the tubing stoppers (plugs) from the lower outlets of both the hydrogen and oxygen side of the fuel cell. This purges the lines and drains the water from the overflow pipes.
3. Remove the rubbery stoppers from the storage cylinders on the electrolyzer.
4. Store the rubbery stoppers in their overflow tubes so the small transfer tubes are *inside* the overflow tubes. This protects them during storage.
5. Dump the water out of the electrolyser.
6. Store both the electrolyser and the fuel cell in plastic zip-lock bags. Place a moist paper towel in each bag to prevent surfaces from drying out.

READING 12.5 ENERGY STORAGE TECHNIQUES

See *Student Edition*, p. 493.

READING COMPARING SOURCES—HOW MUCH IS AVAILABLE?

See *Student Edition*, p. 494.

Transparency 12.2

READING 12.6 ENERGY AVAILABLE FROM NONRENEWABLE RESERVES

See *Student Edition,* p. 494.

BLM 12.4

Transparency 12.3

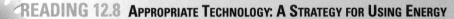

READING 12.7 THE CONTINUOUS RESOURCES—A COMPARISON

See *Student Edition,* p. 495.

READING 12.8 APPROPRIATE TECHNOLOGY: A STRATEGY FOR USING ENERGY

See *Student Edition,* p. 496.

BLM 12.5

ACTIVITY 12.4 APPROPRIATE TECHNOLOGY

See *Student Edition,* p. 498.

1. Less energy is involved in sending and receiving an e-mail message than in sending a letter. The letter is written on paper, placed in an envelope, and travels by car/truck/train/bus/plane/etc. However, e-mail doesn't always have the same personal touch as a nice handwritten letter.

2. It is obviously more efficient to drive the fuel efficient car to and from work. However, there may be safety or other considerations. Also, most people use their cars for more than going to and from work. These factors are all part of the decision.

3. It is better for the environment to swat insects than to use chemical sprays. However, if the insect population is out of control or the person swatting can suffer severe health effects from an insect bite or sting, then sprays may be appropriate. Also, many insect sprays are biodegradable.

4. Trimming trees with a hand saw uses less energy than a chain saw. However, the decision has a lot to do with how much wood must be cut, how much time is available, and how thick the logs are. Hand saws are best for small jobs. Chain saws should be saved for the big ones.

5. Passive strategies are more energy efficient. However, the costs of passive strategies are usually front-end loaded. The important thing is that individuals analyze their home energy use situation and form a home energy plan.

6. The important numbers are the cost of the photovoltaic system and the amount the local utility charges to bring power to a site 1/2 mile from the nearest utility pole.

7. This is a difficult one for students to obtain sufficient data. The big question is: Can the conservation efforts save 500 mW of power or more? A group such as the Rocky Mountain Institute (www.rmi.org and e-mail: outreach@rmi.org) may provide suggestions on how to proceed.

8. An attic fan is more efficient than an air conditioner. Other considerations are: Does the fan get the home cool enough for sleeping? Are pollens in the air a problem? How many hot days and nights are of concern?

9. The hybrid vehicle is more efficient, *but* is it available at a price one can afford? How does it perform?

10. Biomass fuels are friendlier to the environment, *but* are they available? At what price?

11. Compact fluorescents are more efficient, *but* can they be easily fitted into existing sockets? How much will a major conversion to compact fluorescents cost initially?

12. What is the cost of the insulation, improved windows, and caulking? Will there be adequate air exchange once the house is "sealed" up?

13. This may soon become a hot political issue. Do an Internet search or contact the Rocky Mountain Institute (www.rmi.org) to get started.

14. Students will need data for specific metals. Data will include what percent is recycled now, if alloy constituents pose a problem, and future projections.

15. The amount of energy to produce the container and the recycling rate are key. Container manufacturers and Franklin Associates, Ltd., have this type of data.

READING 12.9 CAN APPROPRIATE TECHNOLOGIES POWER A NATION?

See *Student Edition,* p. 500.

ACTIVITY 12.5 WORLD OIL: SUPPLY, DEMAND, USE

See *Student Edition,* p. 502.

ADVANCE PREPARATION

None required. You could get out a world atlas.

ANSWERS TO ITEMS

1. Middle East
2. Asia Pacific, North America
3. Russia (214.6), Middle East (161.1), North Africa (87.3)
4. South America (119.2), Middle East (114.7), Canada (95.5)
5. Middle East (195.4), Indonesia (28.3)

6.

Country	GDP (2000) (billion dollars)	Rel. Size Econ.
U.S.	10,082	6.86
China*	5,560	3.78
Japan	3,450	2.35
India	2,500	1.70
Germany	2,174	1.48
France	1,510	1.03
U.K.	1,470	1.00

*China's GDP will vary depending on who reported the data and how Hong Kong is included.

7. U.S., Iceland, Netherlands, Saudi Arabia
8. China, India, Indonesia, Brazil

9. a. Develop hybrid cars and SUVs.

   b. Develop fuel cell powered vehicles.

   c. Reduce weight/vehicle using lightweight structural components.

   d. Develop mass transit in urban areas.

   e. Raise gasoline taxes. (Politically unpopular.) World politics/supplies could lead to higher prices even if taxes are not raised.

   f. Develop the ceramic engine, which doesn't dump as much heat into space. More of the fuel produces motion.

READING 12.10 ENERGY POLICY

See *Student Edition,* p. 504.

12.6

Transparency 12.4

ACTIVITY 12.6 SUMMARIZE YOUR OPTIONS

See *Student Edition,* p. 506.

In Figure 12.40, the dashed arrow after fusion is meant to indicate that fusion is difficult to classify. If the deuterium—deuterium reaction can be used on a large scale in future reactors, and if several other engineering problems are solved, the amount of energy available from this option is fantastic! This may imply that fusion is a sustainable source. Student answers may be summarized as follows:

Source or Strategy	Brief Description	Advantage	Related Problem
Coal	A solid carbon-based fuel that can be mined.	The remaining reserves and resources are very large.	Coal is a solid. Preventing and cleaning up pollution is a major challenge.
Oil shale	A rock that can be mined, crushed, and retorted to release oil and gas.	The world economy runs on oil. Oil shale development could reduce U.S. imports.	The energy payoff seems low. Related waste and pollution problems are large.
Tar sands	Sandy natural deposits that contain a tarlike fuel that can be mined and changed to oil and gas.	The world economy runs primarily on oil and gas.	Mined sites must be reclaimed and pollutants removed at the processing plants.
Coal gasification	The process of changing coal into a fuel-like natural gas.	The gas produced can substitute for natural gas.	The gasification process uses energy, water, and produces pollutants.
Coal liquefaction	The process of changing coal into a liquid fuel.	The world economy runs mainly on liquid hydrocarbon fuels.	The liquefaction process uses energy and produces pollutants.
Ordinary fission reactors	The splitting of heavy nuclei to release energy and neutrons.	We already know how build and operate reactors. We want electricity.	We can't agree on what to do with the radioactive wastes. Terrorism.

Source or Strategy	Brief Description	Advantage	Related Problem
Breeder reactors	Fission reactors that produce new fuel as they run.	Greatly increase the amount of energy available from uranium and thorium reserves.	They would greatly increase the quantity of radioactive waste.
Fusion	The combining of light nuclei to produce heavier nuclei and large amounts of energy.	If we can figure out how to do fusion continually, huge amounts of energy are available.	Scientists haven't been able to contain the plasma long enough to achieve a controlled energy payoff.
Passive solar	The use of the sun and building design to heat and cool buildings.	Little pollution. Sun's reliability. Simple in concept.	It is difficult to store energy for cloudy days. Initial costs can be high.
Active solar (solar panels)	The use of panels to collect solar energy but require outside energy to run fans or pumps.	Little pollution. Simple in concept. Economical in long term.	High front-end cost. The system requires some maintenance.
STEC	Strategies for collecting and concentrating enough solar energy to make large quantities of steam.	The steam is used to generate electricity—a desirable form of energy.	The collection systems require a large area, and it is difficult to store energy for cloudy days.
Photovoltaic cells	Devices that convert sunlight directly into electricity.	Can produce electricity at remote locations. Electricity is a very desirable product.	The initial costs are relatively high. The collection area can be large.
Solar satellites	The use of orbiting satellites to beam microwaves back to Earth.	The microwaves can be converted to electricity—a desirable product.	Expensive to build, launch, maintain, and defend.
Wind	The use of wind to turn turbines to power generators to produce electricity.	Reduces our demand for oil, gas, coal, and nuclear fuels.	Wind is unreliable. Visual pollution. Economic payoff is a barrier.
Hydroelectric	Converts the gravitational energy of water stored behind a dam to produce electricity.	Relatively clean. Economical.	Only works at some locations. Less power available in dry years. Dams silt up.
Bioconversion	Plants convert sunlight to chemical energy in photosynthesis.	There is a lot of plant material that can be burned or decomposed to provide energy.	Burning and decomposition produce pollutants. The energy density is low.
Energy from trash	Burning trash to recover the energy stored in paper and yard wastes.	Reduces the quantity of trash that becomes landfill.	Trash contains metals, glass, and other materials that clog boilers.
OTEC	Uses temperature differences in ocean water to generate electricity.	Less pollution. Electricity is a desired product.	Not cost effective. Primarily of local interest—mainly in the tropics.

(continued)

Source or Strategy	Brief Description	Advantage	Related Problem
Ocean waves and Ocean currents	Uses the mechanical energy of waves and currents to produce electricity.	Less pollution. Electricity is a desired product.	Not much energy available. Primarily of local interest.
Geothermal	Energy originating in Earth's crust used to produce steam to generate electric power.	Electricity is a desired product. Reduces demand for oil, gas, and nuclear power.	Pollution at the sites. Primarily of local interest.
Tidal	Uses the kinetic energy of moving tides to generate electricity.	Less pollution. Electricity is a desired product.	Only economical at a very *few* locations.
Cogeneration	The production of two useful forms of energy from the same fuel source.	Cogeneration increases the efficiency of a variety of industrial processes such as electric power generation.	Higher initial cost to build. The use of gas turbines increase the demand for natural gas and drives up the price.
Fluidized-bed combustion	The mixing of powdered coal, air, and limestone to produce heat to generate electricity.	Cleaner and more efficient than ordinary power plants.	Not perfected.
Heat pumps	Devices that move heat from a cooler region to a warmer one using mechanical or electrical energy.	Heat pumps are more efficient than electric heaters and gas furnaces.	High initial cost.
Fuel cells	A device that converts chemical energy into electrical energy as it is supplied with fuel.	Hydrogen should be readily available. Water is the only by-product.	Providing hydrogen in large quantities. Providing instant power under severe conditions.
Hydrogen storage	The storage of chemical energy in hydrogen gas as a fuel.	Hydrogen gas burns clean, producing only water.	Finding a safe way to store hydrogen and easily and quickly transfer it to vehicles.
Pumped storage	Pumping water uphill during low demand so it can be used to generate electricity during high demand.	The process helps smooth out a power company's demand curve.	The process might be an economic gain but it is an energy loss.
Heat storage	The storage of heat in thermal mass, water, or eutectic salts.	Solar heat is gathered in the day for release at night when it is needed.	The initial costs are relatively high.
Reduce	Cutting waste by cutting down on consumption.	Less waste, less pollution, cleaner environment.	Could lower one's lifestyle—less comfort.

Source or Strategy	Brief Description	Advantage	Related Problem
Reuse	Using items longer. The buying of used clothing and products.	Reduces demand for energy and resources.	Could lower one's lifestyle—not as up-to-date. Hurts consumption-driven economy.
Recycle	The process of converting waste materials into new products.	Energy and resources are usually saved in the process.	Not all wastes are recyclable. It takes energy to recycle.
Improved efficiency	Design devices to do a task but use less energy.	More efficient devices do the same task for less energy.	The more efficient device may cost more.
Government: Directions and goals	Governing bodies set goals for groups of people and often enforce them.	The achievement of the goal helps solve a problem.	Usually the goal is not desired by *all* those it affects.
Government: Funded R & D	Tax funds are used to solve a problem.	Desired products may be developed faster than under free market conditions.	Tax funds may not be used as efficiently as in research supported solely by private funds.
Tax to influence behavior	Raise taxes to cause people to change behavior.	The new behavior helps solve a problem.	Behavior change is forced economically, not done by choice.
Regulate use	Pass laws to cause people to change behavior.	The new behavior helps solve a problem.	Individual freedom is reduced.

ACTIVITY 12.7 SORTING OUT YOUR OPTIONS

See *Student Edition,* p. 507.

STRATEGIES AND PROCEDURES

This activity can be used as a homework assignment, a group assignment, or a chapter (unit) assessment. If done as a chapter (unit) assessment, you might want students to use only the chart they built in Activity 12.6 and no other resources. This is an incentive to do a good job on Activity 12.6. It is your choice.

1. a. Coal gasification, coal liquefaction, oil shale, tar sands, methane generation.
   b. Fuels like oil and gas can be transported using *existing* systems. They can be used by today's utilities and vehicles.
2. We already know how to use nuclear power; we've been using it for years. Disposing of radioactive waste. Conventional reactors use up a finite fuel. The nuclear proliferation problem.
3. a. Coal, nuclear, oil shale, tar sands.
   b. Evaluate on depth of thought.
4. No energy alternatives have absolutely no negative environmental impact. However, the solar options (in general) have the least environmental impact.

5. Active solar (solar panels), passive solar, solar cells, STEC, OTEC, wind power, bioconversion, hydroelectric power, energy from trash, solar satellites.

6. Tidal power, tar sands (in the United States), OTEC, geothermal, ocean waves and currents.

7. Solar power—especially STEC, photovoltaic cells, wind power, and bioconversion. The sun normally cannot produce very high temperatures. For everyday life, that is good. That's why the sun doesn't cause forest fires! However, when it comes to producing electricity or cutting steel, very high temperatures are often required. That is why we talk about matching the source to the end use. Under special conditions, engineers can use sunlight to produce very high temperatures. However, these methods require the gathering of sunlight from a large area using lenses and mirrors.

8. Fusion. Other possible answers are breeder reactors and solar cells (cost still must drop).

9. Evaluate on depth of thought.

CHAPTER 12 SUMMARY

See *Student Edition*, p. 508.

Name_____   Date_____

MULTIPLE CHOICE

1. _____ A well-insulated home should have all of these features *except*
   A. a well-insulated building shell.
   B. a vapor barrier.
   C. a large, high-capacity furnace.
   D. double, or triple-paned windows that are properly placed.
   E. a controlled ventilation system.

2. _____ Which statement about high-mileage cars is *untrue?*
   A. High-mileage cars are unsafe to drive.
   B. At present, a person can buy several different cars that are rated at near or above 40 miles per gallon.
   C. High-mileage cars weigh less than ordinary cars.
   D. Lighter-gauge steel, aluminum, and composites all reduce the weight of cars.
   E. Hybrid cars are available to consumers throughout the United States.

3. _____ Benefits of strong conservation efforts include all of the following *except*
   A. cleaner environment.
   B. reduced world tensions.
   C. increased energy options worldwide.
   D. more primitive lifestyles.
   E. greater opportunity for more people to enjoy the "good life."

4. _____ Which of the following is a good conservation practice for home lighting?
   A. Turning off lights when not in use.
   B. Removing lights where not needed.
   C. Switching to fluorescent lighting.
   D. Use of dimmer switches.
   E. All of the above.

5. _____ How can we conserve energy in buildings? Adjust the inside temperatures to be
   A. higher summer temperatures and lower winter temperatures.
   B. lower summer temperatures and lower winter temperatures.
   C. higher summer temperatures and higher winter temperatures.
   D. lower summer temperatures and higher winter temperatures.

6. _____ Which of the following is a way in which the structure of a building can influence energy use?
   A. Building materials used.
   B. Type and placement of insulation.
   C. Building site and orientation.
   D. Window area and design.
   E. All of the above.

7. _____ This energy conversion technique results in the production of two useful forms of energy from the same fuel source.
   A. Cogeneration
   B. fuel cell
   C. fluidized-bed
   D. pumped storage

COMPARISON OF CONTINUOUS ENERGY SOURCES—U.S.

	kW/acre	kW/hectare
Solar energy at ground level	720	1800
All the winds (at surface)	43	110
U.S. tides	0.02	0.05
U.S. geothermal	0.02	0.05
All photosynthesis	0.4	1.0
U.S. hydroelectric power	0.2	0.4
U.S. consumption rate	1.7	4.1

8. _____ According to the table, which compares U.S. continuous energy sources, all of the following are true statements *except*
   A. solar energy at ground level could provide more than enough energy to supply all of our needs.
   B. geothermal energy can only make a small contribution toward satisfying our total energy requirements.
   C. if we had the technology and funds to fully use wind energy, there is enough energy in all surface winds to power our nation completely.
   D. a combination of tidal power and hydroelectric power could provide more than enough energy to satisfy U.S. energy demand.

9. _____ Which one of these energy strategies/options reverses the trend of our becoming more dependent on large energy systems?
   A. fission
   B. solar satellites
   C. fusion
   D. appropriate technology

10. _____ Which source to end-use match is best in most cases?
   A. electricity → home heating
   B. nuclear reactor → electric power generation
   C. passive and active solar → home heating
   D. solar (photovoltaic) cells → home heating
   E. electric power generation → electric automobiles

11. _____ All of the following are *true* statements about the way appropriate technology advocates view the energy situation *except*
   A. a country that runs on oil can't afford to run short.
   B. in general, smaller is better.
   C. we should become less dependent on technology instead of more dependent.
   D. whenever possible, the largest number of people should be able to understand and control the devices and systems on which they depend.

12. _____ From biology, we learn that genetic variation increases the chance of survival. How is this idea used in the appropriate technology strategy?
   A. Different regions have different power needs.
   B. Adapt to what is available.
   C. Don't be dependent primarily on one or two energy sources.
   D. All of the above.

13. _____ Which statement about the appropriate technology strategy is *not* true?
   A. Complex, centralized systems are less accessible to the poor.
   B. Complex, centralized grid systems increase the size of equipment failures, mistakes, and deliberate disruptions.
   C. Appropriate technologies are simpler and easier for the masses to understand.
   D. A switch to appropriate technologies could be made in as little as five years.
   E. Appropriate technologies could help us solve the problem of energy availability to poorer nations.

14. _____ Arguments *against* the wide-scale use of appropriate technologies include all of the following *except*
   A. it is easier to control pollution at one large power plant than at individual chimneys.
   B. only technically trained people understand how appropriate technologies work.
   C. interconnected power grids provide a backup system when local systems fail.
   D. it is unrealistic to assume that advanced nations could (or would) switch to an appropriate technology base in only 20 to 25 years.

15. _____ Which of the following is an alternative to oil and natural gas that results in the production of a fuel that is like oil and/or natural gas?
   A. coal liquefaction
   B. coal gasification
   C. oil shale
   D. tar sands
   E. all of these

16. _____ Which of the following is an energy option that could provide huge amounts of energy, but its development requires a major research breakthrough?
   A. ordinary nuclear fission
   B. nuclear fusion
   C. passive solar
   D. tar sands
   E. tidal energy

17. _____ Which *one* of the following energy options has the *least* environmental impact?
   A. coal
   B. nuclear fission
   C. oil shale
   D. coal gasification
   E. solar cells

18. _____ Which *one* of the following does *not* involve a renewable energy source?
   A. passive solar
   B. wood
   C. oil shale
   D. wind power
   E. flat-plate collectors

19. _____ A continuous energy source
   A. can be used again and again.
   B. is a nonrenewable resource.
   C. depends entirely on stored energy.
   D. will eventually run out.

20. _____ All of the following are finite sources of energy (called nonrenewable) in that their reserves can be exhausted *except*
   A. oil shale.
   B. natural gas.
   C. biomass.
   D. tar sands.

21. _____ Although nonrenewable, this energy source is of interest because its reserves are huge and it can be used right now.
   A. oil shale
   B. tar sands
   C. coal gasification
   D. nuclear fission
   E. coal

22. _____ Which statement about fuel cells is *not* true?
   A. A fuel cell is a device that converts chemical energy to electrical energy as it is supplied with fuel.
   B. The electrolyte in a fuel cell conducts electric current.
   C. The only by-product of a hydrogen fuel cell is water.
   D. Fuel cells weigh more than our present internal combustion engines.
   E. Fuel cells can be stacked together to produce a wide range of power.

23. _____ All of the following are ways to store energy for future use *except*
   A. hydrogen gas.
   B. fuel cell.
   C. eutectic salts.
   D. water pumping.

24. _____ On a yearly basis, which *one* of the following uses the most home energy?
   A. heating and cooling rooms
   B. water heating
   C. lighting
   D. refrigeration
   E. cooking food

25. _____ A concept car is
   A. available for consumers to purchase.
   B. built and tested, but not sold.
   C. put together on a computer, but not as yet built.
   D. available to consumers, but only at some locations.

CHAPTER 12 ASSESSMENT

1. C
2. A
3. D
4. E
5. A
6. E
7. A
8. D
9. D
10. C
11. A
12. C
13. D
14. B
15. E
16. B
17. E
18. C
19. A
20. C
21. E
22. D
23. B
24. A
25. C

WATER: QUANTITY AND QUALITY

LEARNING OUTCOMES

The student will:

1. describe where the world's water is located and determine how much is accessible for human use by completing the activity "Water, Water Everywhere." (C)

2. develop a way to determine how much water he or she uses each day by completing the activity "How Much Water Do You Use?" (C)

3. analyze water use per person in the United States and his or her own water use as a basis for developing strategies for wiser water use. (C,A)

4. examine water management strategies. (C)

5. evaluate information about the Florida Everglades. (C)

6. analyze the quality of water samples by manipulating materials and equipment and completing the activity "How Clean Is Your Water?" (C,P)

7. make recommendations about the best use of the waters that were tested in no. 6. (C,A)

8. design an inquiry investigation to test the effects of nitrates and phosphates on pond water by completing the activity "The Effects of Pollutants on Pond Water." (C,P)

9. list the major categories of water pollutants. (C)

10. identify the main steps in the municipal water treatment process. (C)

11. identify the main steps in wastewater treatment. (C)

KEY TERMS

surface water	water diversion	pollution	pH
groundwater	watershed	effluent	dissolved oxygen (DO)
recharge	subsidence	point source	biological oxygen demand (BOD)
fresh water	desalination	non-point source	coliform bacteria
water budget	cloud seeding	pollutant	oligotrophic
aquifer	drip irrigation	thermal pollution	eutrophic

RECOMMENDED BLACKLINE MASTERS

13.1   The Global Water Supply
13.2   Average U.S. Indoor Home Water Use
13.3   Municipal Water System
13.4   Water Testing Data Table
13.5   Wastewater Treatment
13.6   Solids Processing (from Metro Wastewater Reclamation District)

The Recommended Blackline Masters listed above are supplemental to the activity/reading, and can be found on the *Teacher Resource CD*. Blackline Masters 13.7–13.10 are essential to teaching the activity/reading, and so are included in the *Teacher Guide* (pp. 277–280) as well as on the *Teacher Resource CD*.

ACTIVITIES FLOW CHART

CHAPTER 13: WATER: QUANTITY AND QUALITY

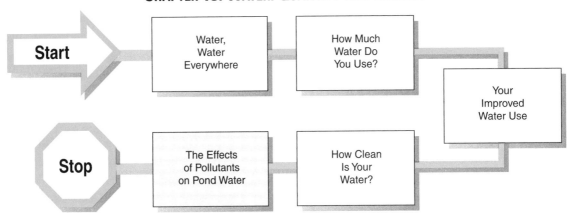

TEACHING STRATEGIES AND ANSWERS FOR ACTIVITIES

CHAPTER OPENER, See *Student Edition*, p. 511.

As students look at the photograph, ask them to describe the range of experiences they have had with water. It will not take long to realize the important and complex relationship between human activities and water.

13.1 READING EARTH'S WATER

See *Student Edition*, p. 512.

See *Student Edition,* p. 512.

ADVANCE PREPARATION

Put 1000 mL of water in a large beaker. You can color it blue to help the students see it.

Have a 1000-mL graduated cylinder, three 25 mL beakers, two droppers, and some salt ready for the demonstration.

STRATEGIES AND PROCEDURES

For the first part of this activity, tell your students that the water in the large beaker represents all the water on Earth. Then, explain that you are going to divide that 1000 mL into the categories Earth's water falls into. Ask them to predict the categories and how much water belongs in each one. After the students have made their predictions, conduct the demonstration according to the information in the following chart.

Category	Percent of Earth's Water	Action for Demonstration (All water is removed from 1000 original mL.)
Ocean water	97.2%	Pour 972 mL into a large graduated cylinder; add salt.
Icecaps and glaciers	2.15%	Pour 21.5 mL in a small beaker and put in the freezer.
Deep groundwater	0.31%	Pour 3.1 mL in a small beaker and set out of reach.
Saline lakes and inland seas	.008%	Take 2 drops out of the large beaker and put out of reach.
Fresh surface water	.009%	Take 2 drops out of the large beaker and keep nearby.
Accessible groundwater	0.31%	Pour the remaining water (3.1 mL) into a small beaker and keep nearby.

Ask students what they think of the demonstration. What does it mean to them?

In the second part of this activity, the students analyze additional data about the availability of the world's water supply. This section could be assigned for homework with a follow-up discussion in class.

In step 1 (questions to discuss after the demonstration), students may respond as follows:

1. a. In the oceans.
   b. Saline lakes and inland seas or fresh surface water.
   c. Accept reasonable responses.

In step 2 (questions to follow data analysis of Figure 13.3), students may respond as follows. Project Blackline Master 13.1.

2. a. There are many ways to respond to this question. Some ideas include:

   ❧ The majority of water is in the "other" category.
   ❧ All but a very small percentage of water is unavailable for human use.
   ❧ Even a small percentage of water is many cubic miles of water.
   ❧ There is a lot of water tied up in icecaps and glaciers.

b. The oceans.

c. Students may have difficulty with this question depending on their life experiences or ability to deduce information. The easiest water to access is the surface water. Remind students that there is a difference between being easy to access and being useful.

d. Anything deep, frozen, or in the atmosphere is difficult to access.

READING 13.1 WATER DISTRIBUTION IN THE WORLD

See *Student Edition*, p. 514.

READING 13.2 WATER IN THE UNITED STATES

See *Student Edition*, p. 517.

READING WATER MANAGEMENT

See *Student Edition*, p. 520.

READING 13.3 DAMS AND RESERVOIRS

See *Student Edition*, p. 521.

READING 13.4 WATER DIVERSION PROJECTS

See *Student Edition*, p. 522.

SPECIAL FOCUS THE COLORADO RIVER BASIN AND WATER LAW

See *Student Edition*, p. 523.

READING 13.5 MANAGING GROUNDWATER

See *Student Edition*, p. 528.

READING 13.6 DESALINATION

See *Student Edition*, p. 529.

READING 13.7 WATER FROM ICEBERGS

See *Student Edition*, p. 529.

READING 13.8 CLOUD SEEDING

See *Student Edition*, p. 530.

ACTIVITY 13.2 HOW MUCH WATER DO YOU USE?

See *Student Edition,* p. 531.

ADVANCE PREPARATION

Prepare your students in advance to keep their water use diary. The success of this activity is dependent on the students participating fully and honestly. You may be able to get some typical home water-use data from your local water district and/or plumbing supply store.

STRATEGIES AND PROCEDURES

After you have data from all your students, prepare a class data table. Use the data table to guide a discussion of the wrap-up questions. If students come up with ways to conserve water at school, look for opportunities to help them implement their ideas. Save the students' data for use in Activity 13.3.

SAMPLE ANSWERS TO ANALYSIS QUESTIONS

1. & 2. The variance will probably be great. You may want to discuss differences in lifestyles. For instance, athletes may take multiple showers in a day, or people with large lawns and gardens may use more water for their yards than others do.

3. The numbers are not accurate because they do not include the industrial uses of water that are part of producing the products we buy or use. The water used to produce the food we eat is also not included. The table is only for home use.

4. Most Americans can lower the amount of water they use by doing simple things like turning off the water when soaping hands or brushing teeth, running the dishwasher only when it is full, watering yards early in the morning or in the evening, and so on. The benefit to lowering the amount of water one uses is that it helps conserve the limited supply of fresh water.

READING 13.9 WATER CONSERVATION

See *Student Edition,* p. 532.

ACTIVITY 13.3 YOUR IMPROVED WATER USE

See *Student Edition,* p. 533.

Students will need to access the data they collected in Activity 13.2. Discuss with students just one change they are willing to make in their water usage. One of the points of this lesson is that if we all do a little, then we all gain a lot. This lesson relies heavily on the students collecting accurate data and being able to analyze the differences in class water use.

1. Hopefully students will make at least one consistent change and be able to discuss that change.
2. One small change is usually not difficult.
3. Once the change becomes habit, most people can keep it up.
4. If everyone made a small change and kept it up consistently, you should see a significant change.
5. Students may realize that all of us working together can make a difference. Or, conversely, if the whole class does not participate, the students may see that it does take most people making a small change to see an effect.

 SPECIAL FOCUS THE FLORIDA EVERGLADES

See *Student Edition,* p. 534.

 READING POLLUTION OF WATER

See *Student Edition,* p. 538.

 READING 13.10 POINT AND NON-POINT SOURCES

See *Student Edition,* p. 538.

 13.3

READING 13.11 MAJOR WATER POLLUTANTS (CATEGORIES)

See *Student Edition,* p. 538.

 13.4, 13.7, 13.8, 13.9, 13.10

ACTIVITY 13.4 HOW CLEAN IS YOUR WATER?

See *Student Edition,* p. 544.

ADVANCE PREPARATION

Laboratory directions depend on the equipment you purchase to do the testing. For accuracy, ease of use, and economy, we recommend the following kits available by contacting your Kendall/Hunt representative.

GREEN Water Monitoring Kit (Classroom Set)
Tests 8 variables: pH, DO, BOD, nitrate, phosphate, coliform bacteria, turbidity, and benthic macroinvertebrates. Contains Test Tabs to perform 100 tests (44 tests for coliform bacteria) and unlimited for benthic macroinvertibrates and turbidity.

GREEN Low Cost Monitoring Kit
Tests 8 variables. Test Tabs to do 10 samples (3 for coliform).

GREEN Low Cost Estuary Monitoring Kit
Tests 8 variables. Test Tabs to do 10 samples (3 for coliform).

If you wish to divide up the equipment in the GREEN Water Monitoring Kit (Classroom Set) so that several groups can take equipment into the field, we recommend using a smaller plastic carrying case, which can be obtained by contacting your Kendall/Hunt representative.

Due to liability/safety considerations, you may need to collect the samples before school. If you get 5 gallons of each, they shouldn't change too much as the day progresses. Also test the school's tap water. As an alternative, you can organize your students to collect water samples from two different sources. Remind them to be careful where they collect and *inform a responsible adult.* They are not to work alone!

The best samples are collected by submerging the collection jar under the water, filling it, and putting the cap on under the water. This helps maintain a relatively accurate dissolved oxygen and pH reading.

STRATEGIES AND PROCEDURES

You may wish to set up lab stations around the room for students to conduct each test. The fecal coliform test and dissolved oxygen are the most complicated tests, so you may want to plan the flow of students accordingly. The table in Figure 13.37 should be expanded to include the temperature and possibly a *brief* description of each sample.

After students have recorded their data, they should be able to respond to the wrap-up questions and be ready to participate in a class discussion. They will have to read the background material to give informed responses during the discussion. Blackline Masters 13.7–13.10 should help students organize their information.

SAMPLE ANSWERS TO ANALYSIS QUESTIONS

1. Answers will vary based on student water samples. All students should be able to relate their results accurately to the information in the background section.
2. Assessing the overall quality of the sample requires the students to make some judgments. For example, if the pH is fairly low and the fecal coliform count is very low, is that a "good" water sample? If so, what or who is it good for? What if the pH is 7, but the fecal coliform or the nitrates are borderline high? Encourage the students to think critically about their responses.
3. In general, students should be extremely cautious about what they would agree to drink. Even if students label something as safe to drink, remind them it is *never* safe to drink liquids used in lab activities.

4. Based on just these particular tests, it is probably safe to swim, except in waters with unsafe levels of fecal coliform.

5. This question connects the test results back to the real world setting. If a body of water is not designated for drinking or swimming or other human/animal use, then could we accept varying levels of quality?

6. This question helps students think about the match between use and quality. If a high-quality water source is being used for activities that do not require high quality, is that the best use of that water? What if the water is low quality, but is being used for activities that students think need a higher quality of water?

7. Students should reflect on how carefully they collected their samples and conducted their tests. This is part of being a good scientist—to reflect on the quality of your work.

8. There are errors related to collecting the samples, reading the test strips, waiting the designated amount of time, and so forth.

 READING 13.12 **POLLUTION OF AQUATIC ECOSYSTEMS**

See *Student Edition,* p. 547.

 ACTIVITY 13.5 **THE EFFECTS OF POLLUTANTS ON POND WATER**

See *Student Edition,* p. 550.

ADVANCE PREPARATION

This activity also requires the use of a resource kit. Please see the kits listed on pp. 272-273 of this *Teacher Guide.* The materials from these kits can be used for this activity, or you can obtain a water pollution study kit—(at a greater expense) by contacting your Kendall/Hunt representative.

If you choose to make the nitrate and phosphate solutions on your own, the directions are as follows:

* To make a "rough" 0.5% nitrate solution, dissolve 5 grams of sodium nitrate ($NaNo_3$) in enough deionized water to build the volume to 1000 mL.

* To make a "rough" 0.5% phosphate solution, dissolve 5 grams of sodium phosphate tribasic ($Na_3PO_4 \cdot 12H_2O$) in enough deionized water to build the volume to 1000 mL.

STRATEGIES AND PROCEDURES

Begin this activity with a discussion to review phosphates and nitrates as pollutants so students understand where the chemicals they are testing for come from. This activity requires a day at the beginning for discussion and prelab work; a day of setup; nine days, where just 15 minutes is used to observe and record changes; and then a day at the end to conclude the activity.

After the prelab discussion about pollutants, ask students to make a prediction about what will happen to the pond water after they add nitrates and phosphates to the water. Then, let the students design simple experiments to test their ideas. In general, the students will be comparing the changes in the water based on how much of each solution is added. You may wish to guide your students in such a way that you have a step-wise approach to testing the various amounts of phosphates and nitrates. You will probably also want some setups with only phosphate or only nitrate to isolate the variables.

SAMPLE ANSWERS TO ANALYSIS QUESTIONS _____

1. In general, students will find that the more phosphates and/or nitrates a sample has, the greater the algal bloom.
2. Students should recognize that the chemicals made the difference, and if the algae grew more, then they function as a nutrient for the plant.
3. If the students used varying amounts of phosphates and nitrates, they will notice that greater amounts of chemicals produced algal blooms more quickly.
4. The samples varied based on what was added to them.
5. Students will probably suggest that effluents be controlled so we do not get excessive algae growth.

READING 13.13 EUTROPHICATION OF LAKES
See *Student Edition,* p. 551.

READING 13.14 POLLUTION OF GROUNDWATER
See *Student Edition,* p. 553.

SPECIAL FOCUS INVASIVE SPECIES (BIOLOGICAL POLLUTION)
See *Student Edition,* p. 554.

SAMPLE ANSWERS TO QUESTIONS _____

1. Invasive species generally spread rapidly because they have few to no natural enemies in their new habitat.
2. No. Almost all the food we eat comes from plants and animals that were introduced from somewhere else. Invasives are unwelcome when they are in superabundance and/or in the wrong place.
3. The SciLinks feature and library/internet research should provide students with ample information to do this item.
4. Personal actions such as learning to identify the problem invasive species in one's area, consulting local natural resource agencies, and inspecting boats, trailers, and draining water before leaving a boating area are helpful.

Farmers, ranchers, forest owners, and homeowners must have access to the best scientific information and the necessary defensive weapons.

Biotechnology may/can provide powerful, diverse, and defensive measures. What might some of these be? Make a class list.

READING **WASTEWATER TREATMENT**

See *Student Edition,* p. 555.

BLM 13.5

READING 13.15 **PRIMARY TREATMENT**

See *Student Edition,* p. 556.

BLM 13.5

READING 13.16 **SECONDARY TREATMENT**

See *Student Edition,* p. 557.

BLM 13.5

READING 13.17 **TERTIARY TREATMENT**

See *Student Edition,* p. 559.

BLM 13.6

READING 13.18 **SOLIDS PROCESSING**

See *Student Edition,* p. 559.

SPECIAL FOCUS **EVALUATING "SCIENTIFIC" INFORMATION**

See *Student Edition,* p. 561.

READING 13.19 **ON-SITE SEWAGE TREATMENT SYSTEMS**

See *Student Edition,* p. 561.

READING **SOLVING WATER PROBLEMS**

See *Student Edition,* p. 563.

CHAPTER 13 **SUMMARY**

See *Student Edition,* p. 564.

TESTING FOR WATER QUALITY

< = Less than / Source			
Date			
Brief description			
pH and meaning			
Water temp. (°C & °F)		___°C ___°F	___°C ___°F
DO		___mg/L (or ppm)	___mg/L (or ppm)
Do interpretation			
Coliform bacteria		24 hr. / 48 hr.	24 hr. / 48 hr.
Coliform bacteria interpretation			
Nitrate level		___mg/L (or ppm)	___mg/L (or ppm)
Nitrate interpretation			
Phosphate level		___ppm (or mg/L)	___ppm (or mg/L)
Phosphate interpretation			

Some Freshwater Fish

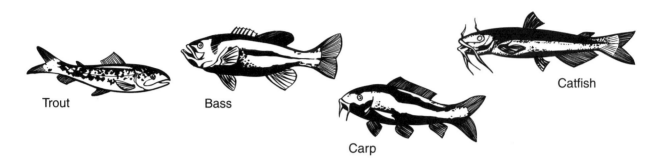

Trout

Bass

Carp

Catfish

Some Aquatic Insects

Mayfly
2.8 cm

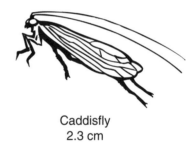

Caddisfly
2.3 cm

Water Strider
1.0 cm

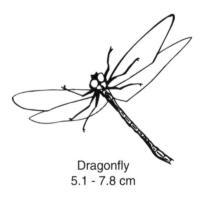

Dragonfly
5.1 - 7.8 cm

NOTE: Not to scale; average sizes indicated.

BLACKLINE MASTER 13.9
DESCRIPTION OF TESTS

TESTING FOR WATER QUALITY

Name _____   Date _____

Condition	Why Test?	Comments
pH		
DO		
Coliform bacteria		
Nitrates		
Phosphates		

Water: Quantity and Quality

TESTING FOR WATER QUALITY

Condition	Why Test?	Comments
pH	*Changes* in pH indicate that contaminants have been introduced.	Healthy aquatic organisms prefer a pH range of 6.0–9.0.
DO	*Low* DO levels indicate organic wastes in water; unhealthy conditions.	*High* DO indicates healthy, well-aerated water.
Coliform bacteria	*If* Coliform bacteria are present, *then* disease-causing organisms are probably there as well.	This is a *key* first test for water safety.
Nitrates	High nitrates are harmful to humans. High nitrates cause *eutrophication*.	Nitrates come from fertilizer, wastewater, and agricultural runoff (including feedlots).
Phosphates	High phosphate levels cause *eutrophication*.	Phosphates come from agricultural and lawn runoff and *detergents*.

Name _____   Date _____

MULTIPLE CHOICE

1. _____ Which sequence shows the correct order for total water supply progressing from *largest* to *smallest?*
   A. icecaps/glaciers, oceans, groundwater, freshwater lakes
   B. freshwater lakes, oceans, groundwater, icecaps/glaciers
   C. oceans, icecaps/glaciers, groundwater, freshwater lakes
   D. groundwater, icecaps/glaciers, oceans, freshwater lakes
   E. oceans, freshwater lakes, groundwater, icecaps/glaciers

2. _____ The amount of water used by the average American, both directly and indirectly, can be totaled up and analyzed. Which of the following is the correct sequence for daily water use moving from *largest* to *smallest* use? (Note: Industrial does not include electric power generation.)
   A. home use, agricultural, industrial/commercial
   B. agricultural, home use, industrial/commercial
   C. industrial/commercial, home use, agricultural
   D. industrial/commercial, agricultural, home use
   E. agricultural, industrial/commercial, home use

3. _____ The pumping of groundwater can result in
   A. groundwater depletion.
   B. land subsidence.
   C. saltwater intrusion.
   D. all of the above.
   E. none of the above.

4. _____ Problems related to building large dams and creating related reservoirs include all of the following *except*
   A. evaporation losses from reservoirs.
   B. water seepage into the ground.
   C. salt buildup in water related to the evaporative losses.
   D. siltation due to reduced stream flow.
   E. recreational fishing and sailing.

5. _____ The Colorado River Compact
   A. allocates less water than normally exists in the river each year.
   B. allocates more water than normally exists in the river each year.
   C. is an agreement between Colorado and Utah.
   D. protects agriculture from the mining industry.
   E. classifies the Colorado River as a wild and scenic river.

6. _____ Measures to reduce salinity (salt) in the Colorado River include all of the following *except*
   A. lining irrigation ditches to prevent loss.
   B. techniques to increase irrigation efficiency once water reaches the crop.
   C. diversion of water away from natural sources of salt.
   D. all of the above.
   E. none of the above.

7. _____ Icebergs towed from the Antarctic into the Los Angeles area
   A. would melt long before they arrived.
   B. are filled with so much silt that they would severely damage the ecology of the area.
   C. could provide for significant water needs if delivered on a continuous basis.
   D. would attract so many penguins that Santa Catalina Island would have to be closed to tourists.
   E. could enable Los Angeles to host the Winter Olympics in 2024.

8. _____ Which statement about the Florida Everglades is *not* true?
   A. Water does not flow through the Everglades in rivers but rather as a wide shallow sheet across the land.
   B. Rains drench the Everglades from May through October, followed by a six-month dry season.
   C. Lightning-caused fires are part of a natural cycle that is important to the Everglades ecosystem.
   D. A large canal designed to get large quantities of water to the Everglades quickly helped restore the region.
   E. Efforts to restore the sheet flow of water to portions of the park are beginning to pay off in measurable recovery.

9. _____ Biological oxygen demand (BOD) is a measure of the
   A. amount of oxygen gas dissolved in water.
   B. depletion of oxygen in water by decomposers.
   C. number of coliform bacteria colonies per 100 mL of water.
   D. pH level of a sample of water.
   E. concentration of inorganic pollutants in water.

10. _____ Just below the point where organic sewage enters a river, the
    A. DO is low.
    B. DO is high.
    C. BOD is low.
    D. ammonia (NH_4) level is low.
    E. algae concentration is high.

11. _____ A term meaning nutrient poor is
    A. eutrophic
    B. slough.
    C. oligotrophic.
    D. sludge.
    E. succession.

12. ____ All of the following are characteristics of a eutropic lake *except*
    A. the blue-green algae population is large.
    B. the DO level at the surface is high.
    C. carp and bullheads are representative fish.
    D. the DO level at the bottom is low.
    E. the water is crystal clear.

13. ____ Which of the following statements about disease-causing agents in water is *not* true?
    A. Disease-causing agents in water include bacteria, viruses, protozoans, and roundworms.
    B. Chlorine kills bacteria but not all of the viruses that can be waterborne.
    C. Disease-causing agents are removed the same way inorganic chemicals are.
    D. Disease-causing agents are associated with water contaminated by human and/or animal feces.
    E. In 75% of the world, water purification standards are low or absent.

Match the water pollutant category on the left with the set of examples on the right.

14. _____ synthetic organic compounds   A. salt, acids

15. _____ agricultural runoff   B. sewage, animal manure

16. _____ sediments   C. detergents, oil, solvents

17. _____ oxygent-demanding wastes   D. nitrates and phosphates

18. _____ inorganic chemicals   E. silt, soil, and clay

ADDITIONAL MULTIPLE CHOICE

19. _____ Which sequence is the correct order for the flow of wastewater through a treatment plant?
    A. disinfection—barscreen—secondary treatment—primary clarification
    B. barscreen—primary clarification—secondary treatment—disinfection
    C. secondary treatment—barscreen—disinfection—primary clarification
    D. disinfection—secondary treatment—primary clarification—barscreen
    E. barscreen—disinfection—primary clarification—secondary treatment

20. _____ The purpose of *clarifiers* is to
    A. inject air into wastewater to satisfy the needs of the microorganisms.
    B. add chlorine gas to wastewater to kill infectious germs.
    C. allow suspended solids to settle out and draw off water.
    D. produce compost for use as a soil conditioner.
    E. remove rags, disposable diapers, and other debris from incoming wastewater.

21. _____ The step in most wastewater (sewage) treatment systems in which microorganisms consume dissolved organic matter.
    A. primary treatment   D. chlorination
    B. secondary treatment   E. composting
    C. tertiary treatment

22. _____ Biochemical decomposition (breakup) of organic matter is called
    A. aerobic.   D. digestion.
    B. pollution.   E. microorganisms.
    C. effluent.

23. _____ Anaerobic bacteria can live without access to
    A. oxygen.   D. moisture.
    B. nutrients.   E. food.
    C. warmth.

24. _____ This flammable gas is a common by-product of anaerobic digestion.
    A. oxygen   D. carbon monoxide
    B. nitrogen   E. methane
    C. hydrogen

25. _____ Failure to remove this pollutant results in suds floating on a river near the discharge of a sewer plant.
    A. chlorine   D. carbon dioxide
    B. sludge   E. suspended solids
    C. phosphorus

26. _____ The liquid that comes out of a treatment plant after completion of the treatment process is called the
    A. wastewater.   D. sludge.
    B. effluent.   E. aeration.
    C. sewage.

SHORT ANSWER

27. Why must we use our supplies of fresh water carefully?

28. List two serious threats to groundwater supplies.

29. Describe the two major approaches for managing water.

30. What is desalination, and why is it of interest?

31. Trace the route of your drinking water through the hydrologic cycle.

32. What are the greatest problems your community has with regard to

    a. water quantity?

    b. water quality?

c. pollution of streams or groundwater?

_____

_____

d. treatment of special problems in your water supply?

_____

_____

33. Give examples of point and non-point pollution sources. How can each of these be controlled?

_____

_____

34. Distinguish between natural eutrophication and cultural eutrophication and explain how eutrophication depletes the DO in a lake.

_____

_____

35. If groundwater is a renewable resource, how can it be "mined" and thus depleted like a nonrenewable resource?

_____

_____

36. Explain why land subsides when groundwater is depleted.

_____

_____

37. What practices led to problems in the Everglades? How is this area being restored?

_____

_____

38. What can you do personally and as a citizen to solve some problems of water pollution?

_____

_____

CHAPTER 13 ASSESSMENT

1. C	14. C
2. E	15. D
3. D	16. E
4. E	17. B
5. B	18. A
6. D	19. B
7. C	20. C
8. D	21. B
9. B	22. D
10. A	23. A
11. C	24. E
12. E	25. C
13. C	26. B

27. Less than 1% of the world's water is usable fresh water. If current trends of population growth and increased water use continue, the lack of fresh water will threaten the vitality of agriculture and industry.

28. Increased pollution, overuse.

29. Increasing the water supply in a region by building dams and diverting water into the region. Using water more efficiently by conserving the existing supply and getting more uses from it.

30. Desalination is the removal of salt from water to make it drinkable or suitable for agriculture.

31. Students should respond based on local water treatments and weather patterns.

32. Responses will vary based on the community and class discussions.

33. A point source is an easily discernible source of pollution, such as a factory. A non-point source is spread out and more difficult to identify and control.

34. Eutrophication is the accumulation of nutrients in a lake. Cultural eutrophication refers to the buildup of nutrients based on human activities. Eutrophication helps aquatic plants grow, but when those plants die their decaying process uses up the dissolved oxygen that fish and other organisms need to live.

35. When the water in an aquifer is pumped out faster than the water is replaced by the natural water cycle, eventually the groundwater level drops and people in the area have limited access to water.

36. As water is removed from water-holding rock layers, empty spaces are created. Pressure from the layers above compresses the empty aquifer and subsidence occurs.

37. The ecological importance of swamps was not appreciated. Consequently, much of the Everglades was dredged, ditched, and drained. Agricultural runoff resulted in eutrophication. Restoring the sheet flow of water to the eastern part of the Everglades and making the water delivery schedule more in tune with the seasonal needs of the swamp have helped reclaim the Everglades.

38. Students should respond based on class discussions, activities based on personal water use, and field trips.

RESOURCE MANAGEMENT: AIR

The student will:

1. list three ways in which ecosystems can be damaged. (C)
2. explain how energy consumption and mineral use are related to environmental problems. (C)
3. list the major layers of the atmosphere and briefly describe each one by completing the activity "What's Up There?" (C)
4. quantitatively analyze and evaluate the link between the automobile and air pollution by completing the activity "Driving Our Atmosphere Crazy." (C,P)
5. develop a chart of the five major air pollutants by including type of pollutant, main source of the pollutant, harmful effects, and method of reducing each pollutant. (C)
6. explain how air pollutants are trapped in a thermal inversion.
7. measure and record the pH of various solutions by manipulating materials and equipment and completing the activity "Home Sweet Lab—Testing pH." (C,P)
8. manipulate materials and equipment and produce acid rain by completing the activity "Acid Rain—Just the Facts." (C,P)
9. analyze information gained on acid rain production to recommend possible solutions to the acid rain problem. (C,A)
10. investigate the effects of acid precipitation on plants by manipulating materials and equipment and completing the activity "Effects of Acid Precipitation on Plants." (C,P)
11. manipulate materials and equipment to determine some basic properties of electrical charges. (C,P)
12. explain how an electrostatic precipitator works using concepts discovered in the activity "Charge It! For Cleaner Air." (C)
13. list some of the strategies for reducing the pollution caused by the automobile. (C)
14. develop a chart to summarize two ways that electric power plants can reduce their harmful emissions. (C)
15. simulate the greenhouse effect by manipulating materials and equipment and completing the activity "The Greenhouse Effect Model." (C,P)
16. suggest individual and societal actions that can reduce human contributions to the greenhouse effect. (A)

17. explain why the greenhouse effect tends to make Earth warmer and the particle effect tends to make Earth colder. (C)

18. describe how the melting of the land-based Antarctic ice cap could affect world climate. (C)

19. investigate possible relationships between global carbon dioxide measurements and global temperature readings by completing the activity "CO$_2$ and Climate Trends: You Decide." (C,P)

20. use diagrams, pictures, and ideas to explain ozone hole depletion. (C,A)

KEY TERMS

troposphere
stratosphere
thermosphere
combustion
air pollutant
Environmental Protection Agency
carbon monoxide (CO)
unburned hydrocarbons
photochemical smog

ozone
nitrogen oxides (NO$_x$)
smog
catalytic converter
sulfur oxides (SO$_x$)
scrubbing
wet scrubber
particulates
thermal inversion

acid deposition
bag house
electrostatic precipitator
climate
greenhouse effect
greenhouse gases
chlorofluorocarbons (CFCs)
methane
aerosols

RECOMMENDED BLACKLINE MASTERS

14.1 Damaging Ecosystems
14.2 Energy Use and Air Pollution
14.3 Thermal Inversions
14.4 Acid Rain
14.5 The Greenhouse Effect
14.6 The Particle Effect

The Recommended Blackline Masters listed above are supplemental to the activity/reading, and can be found on the *Teacher Resource CD*. Blackline Masters 14.7-14.8 are essential to teaching the activity/reading, and so are included in the *Teacher Guide* (pp. 305–306) as well as on the *Teacher Resource CD*.

CHAPTER 14: RESOURCE MANAGEMENT: AIR

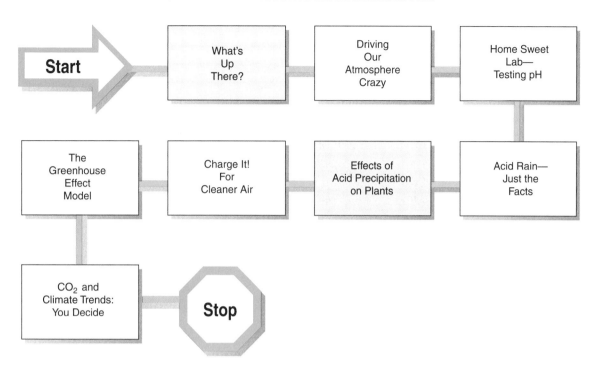

NOTE: Shaded items are lower priority.

TEACHING STRATEGIES AND ANSWERS FOR ACTIVITIES

READING 14.1 HUMAN ACTIONS AND OUR ENVIRONMENT

See *Student Edition*, p. 568.

 14.1

Transparency 14.1

ACTIVITY 14.1 WHAT'S UP THERE?

See *Student Edition*, p. 569.

STRATEGIES AND PROCEDURES

Emphasize that our atmosphere is a protective resource. From the surface, our atmosphere is an "ocean of air," but from space it resembles a thin, blue haze. As students study Figure 14.2, obvious features include clouds, contrails, and color. Hidden features include its chemical composition and phenomena too small to perceive at this scale (local weather, rain, dust, pollution, etc.)

Reinforce the idea that nitrogen, not oxygen, is the most abundant gas in our atmosphere by a ratio of more than 3:1. Another key concept is that atmospheric gases are colorless and difficult to detect by sight or smell alone.

Finally, note that the gas **ozone** is introduced here for the first time. Ozone is triatomic molecular oxygen, consisting of 3 oxygen atoms (O_3) and is highly reactive (unlike 2 atom oxygen O_2). Small amounts of ozone exist as a pollutant in the lower atmosphere, but most ozone resides high in Earth's atmosphere (more about this in Reading 14.12).

In step 1, students may respond as follows:

- Oxygen is necessary for respiration.
- Carbon dioxide is necessary for photosynthesis.
- Regulates temperature extremes.
- Nitrogen gas gets incorporated into living things (e.g., as part of DNA and other organic molecules).
- Protects Earth from small meteors.
- Provides medium for sound.
- Allows both living things (birds, insects) and nonliving things (aircraft) to fly.

In step 3, students may respond as follows:

Gas	Chemical Formula	% in Atmosphere	Property or Fact about This Gas
Nitrogen	N_2	78.00%	most abundant gas
Oxygen	O_2	21.00%	by-product of photosynthesis
Argon	Ar	0.90%	inert gas
Carbon dioxide	CO_2	0.030%	one of the principal, naturally occurring "greenhouse gases"
Water vapor	H_2O	<.001%	varies widely; is invisible
Nitrous oxide	N_2O	<.001%	a trace gas; considered a natural greenhouse gas
Ozone	O_3	<.001%	shields against UV rays in stratosphere
Methane	CH_4	<.001%	by-product of biologic activity
Neon	Ne	<.001%	inert gas
Helium	He	<.001%	inert gas

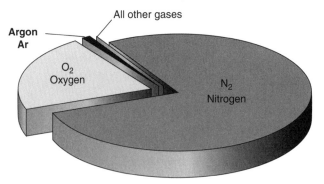

Gases in the Atmosphere

In step 5, students may respond as follows:

Layer	Location	Temperature	Facts
Troposphere	Over North/South Pole: 0–6 miles (0–10 km) thick: Over equator 0–10 miles (16 km) thick.	Varies from 130°F to −75°F at ground level.	Layer in which we live. Usually cools with height (except during "Inversions"). 90% of atmosphere's mass is concentrated here. Most weather occurs here. Upper part contains "jet stream."
Stratosphere	Above the troposphere: 6–10 miles (~48 km) thick.	Varies from −67°F at lowest point to −28°F at upper layers.	Very dry; mostly cloud-free. Airflow mostly horizontal. Layer most suitable for air travel due to lack of most weather disturbances. Zone of ozone concentration. Warm because of ozone's reaction with UV radiation.
Thermosphere	50 miles (80 km) to outer space	At lowest part, −80°C (−112°F), temperature of some molecules can exceed 1100°F (600°C) at 120 miles above Earth.	Highest and thickest of all layers. Extremely thin air is easily warmed by the absorption of UV solar radiation.

Extension

At scale of 1 foot = 1000 miles, Earth's radius would be 4 feet. Using a chalk line as Earth's surface, the upper layers of the atmosphere would lie about 2 inches above the chalk mark.

 **READING 14.2** AIR QUALITY

See *Student Edition*, p. 571.

 14.2

Transparency 14.2

 **ACTIVITY 14.2** DRIVING OUR ATMOSPHERE CRAZY

See *Student Edition*, p. 573.

ADVANCE PREPARATION

Students can prepare their charts in their lab notebook or on a separate sheet of graph paper.

Assign students to work with their parents to estimate the number of miles driven by their family each year. Convert this total to kilometers by multiplying by 1.62.

Make an overhead transparency of Blackline Master 14.7 for use in the prelab and postlab discussions.

Prelab Discussion

1. Use the sugar and other props listed in the activity to reinforce how many tons of NO_x are produced by automobiles. A teaspoon of sugar is a good way to visualize small units such as grams. Use the toy dump truck to visualize large units like tons. A real dump truck holds about 15 tons of solid material.
2. The overhead transparency will help to explain the procedure.
3. The air pollution data are real, although the units combine particulates (dust, salt, and soot) with gases (carbon dioxide, carbon monoxide, SO_2, NO_x, etc.).
4. The rush hour peaks on the graph illustrate the contribution of cars, buses, and trucks to the problem.
5. The questions should provide a driving force for postlab discussion.
6. The possibilities for discussion are endless; for example:

   - How much of the pollution in a brown cloud is visible? Can invisible gases be harmful?
   - What effects do all of these pollutants have on the atmosphere as a whole?
   - Do the pollutants stay in one place or do they move around?
   - Does smog interact with rain or clouds?
   - Can anything be done to help solve the problems?
   - Does positive action require laws?
   - Are students willing to do their share to help?
   - What are some strategies that could make a difference?

Other Tips

- Globally, humans produce about 5.5 billion metric tons of CO_2 each year.
- In the United States alone, 20 million metric tons of NO_x and 22 metric tons of SO_2 are released into the atmosphere each year.

Extensions

- Although invisible, CO (carbon monoxide) and O_3 (ozone) are also monitored in cities with air quality problems. Have students research the sources and affects of these gases.
- There are several good large-number-realization activities, such as Activity 5.2. A printed page holds about 4000 x's. Make an overhead of a page full of printed x's and have students count them. Then, have them decide how many sheets of paper it would take to print 1,000,000 x's. It would take 250 sheets, which is half a ream of paper. It would, therefore, take 500 reams of paper to print a billion x's. If students assign one x, for every kilogram of pollutants, they can calculate how much paper would be needed to print the x's. (The amount is staggering!)
- A similar study of the amount of trash produced by a family for one year can be very eye-opening for students. Have students weigh their

trash for a week and multiply the result by 52 to see how much material is going to the landfill from their family, the community, the country, and so on.

 READING 14.3 **AIR POLLUTION: THE BIG FIVE**

See *Student Edition*, p. 575.

 14.2

Transparency 14.2

 SPECIAL FOCUS **THERMAL INVERSIONS**

See *Student Edition*, p. 579.

 14.3

SAMPLE ANSWERS TO QUESTIONS

1. Air gets cooler and thinner as elevation increases.
2. A thermal inversion is a situation where a layer of dense cool air is trapped under a layer of warm air. Thermal inversions occur when warm air moves toward cooler air in a valley. The warm air moves over the more dense cooler air in the valley.
3. Health hazards occur because the pollutants can't escape by rising upward, so they build up to harmful levels in a fixed volume of air.

 READING 14.4 **INDOOR AIR POLLUTION**

See *Student Edition*, p. 580.

SAMPLE ANSWERS TO QUESTIONS

1. Most people spend more time inside than outside. Indoor air circulates slowly so pollutants remain "trapped" for a time inside.
2. a. **Bacteria/Mold**—Prevent moisture buildup. Dust floors and change air filters regularly.
   b. **Tobacco Smoke**—Do not smoke in the house or in buildings.
   c. **CO**—Keep furnaces serviced. Never let a car idle in the garage!
   d. **CO_2**—Maintain good air circulation in the building. Open windows on nice days to air out the house.
   e. **Radon**—Have home checked. Improve air exchange if there is a problem.
   f. **VOCs**—Close paint/cleaner containers after use. Don't store excess materials. Get rid of them.
   g. **Noise**—Turn down the stereo!

 READING 14.5 **ACID PRECIPITATION**

See *Student Edition*, p. 582.

 14.4

Transparency 14.3

 ACTIVITY 14.3 **HOME SWEET LAB—TESTING pH**

See *Student Edition*, p. 583.

Over the past two decades, acid precipitation has sparked lively debate among concerned citizens, environmentalists, scientists, and industry owners whose factories are widely blamed for causing acid precipitation. The goal here is not to settle the debate but rather to take an objective and factual view of the problem. This activity provides students with scientific proficiency to discuss more clearly what acid rain is and how it affects the environment.

Before students are allowed to study the effects of acid precipitation on plants (Activity 14.5 "Effects of Acid Precipitation on Plants"), they should be given an opportunity to learn about the concept of pH and how they can measure it. This activity was developed to afford students that opportunity as well as to give them a "feel" for the acidities of common household liquids as compared to samples of acidic precipitation.

ADVANCE PREPARATION

Hydrion paper (pH paper) is paper that has been soaked in a number of different indicators, each changing color at its own characteristic pH. It is, then, a "universal" indicator. Hydrion paper kits always contain color comparison charts inside the plastic dispensers. It facilitates the distribution of pH paper if you precut the paper in quantities of 2 cm segments. Also, we recommend that you post several color comparison charts around the classroom to prevent the bottleneck that will certainly develop if only one or two dispensers are used for the entire class.

Students will soon discover that their pH-measuring skills can be honed by "interpolating" between any two adjacent colors shown on the comparison charts. Encourage them to estimate intermediate pHs corresponding to intermediate colors. Interpolating is not critical to the success of this activity, however, because the goal is to develop a chart (and a seat-of-the-pants intuition) of solutions arranged in descending order of acidity.

During the postlab discussion, pool the class data on the board. Soliciting student assistance, you should refine the pH chart until it represents the students' best efforts. Where does your sample of acidic precipitation fit in the chart? Remember that acid precipitation is, by definition, any precipitation having a pH less than 5.6.

Lab teams should complete the Data Interpretation section on their own time. Discuss the three questions in light of the class data chart before you conclude the postlab discussion.

If you intend to use real acidic precipitation, don't forget to collect it ahead of time. It should be stored in a glass or plastic container in your science refrigerator until ready for use.

If you need to manufacture some acid rain, use the following two recipes. Wear safety goggles. Work under a fume hood. Report any problems:

1. Solutions using nitric acid. (*Note:* Be sure that these solutions are mixed thoroughly and that the pH of each is stable before it is used.)
   a. pH 1 = 6.5 mL concentrated HNO_3 per liter of solution. This solution of nitric acid and spring water may be used as a stock solution. It is a 0.1 M solution.

b. pH 2 = 2 mL of 0.1 M solution (pH 1) + 198 mL spring water, creating a 0.01 M solution.

c. pH 3 = 2 mL of 0.01 M solution (pH 2) + 198 mL spring water, creating a 0.001 M solution.

d. pH 4 = 2 mL of 0.001 M solution (pH 3) + 198 mL spring water, creating a 0.0001 M solution.

e. pH 5 = 2 mL of 0.0001 M solution (pH 4) + 198 mL spring water, creating a 0.00001 M solution.

f. pH 6 = 2 mL of 0.00001 M solution (pH 5) + 198 mL spring water, creating a 0.000001 M solution. (Plain spring water, which is close to pH 6, may be substituted.)

2. Solutions using sulfuric acid. The following pH solutions of H_2SO_4 may be used in place of the HNO_3 solutions. (*Note*: The pH of the stock solutions must be stable before they are used. As you add drops of H_2SO_4, be sure the solution is stirred thoroughly and that you measure the pH carefully. The number of drops recommended for each solution is approximate, so it is important that you take several pH measurements for each solution.)

a. 500 mL of spring water $\simeq$ pH 6

b. 500 mL of spring water + approximately 5 drops $\simeq$ pH 5
of 10% H_2SO_4

c. 500 mL of spring water + approximately 15 drops $\simeq$ pH 4
of 10% H_2SO_4

d. 500 mL of spring water + approximately 25 drops $\simeq$ pH 3
of 10% H_2SO_4

e. 500 mL of spring water + approximately 30 drops $\simeq$ pH 2
of 10% H_2SO_4

f. 500 mL of spring water + approximately 35 drops $\simeq$ pH 1
of 10% H_2SO_4

STRATEGIES AND PROCEDURES

You should expect that this activity will probably require two or three class periods for implementation, including the postlab discussion.

Depending on the average level of sophistication of your students, you may or may not wish to present a more mathematically elaborate discussion of pH. For example, chemistry students learn that pH is defined as the logarithm of the reciprocal of the hydrogen ion concentration (i.e., $pH = \log 1/(H^+)$). Thus, if one is given the concentration of hydrogen ion in a solution, he or she can compute the pH. Conversely, given the pH, one can calculate the hydrogen ion concentration.

Whatever their levels of sophistication, students should understand that the pH scale is a logarithmic scale and that, for example, the acidity of a rain sample with, say, pH = 5, is two orders of magnitude or 100 times more acidic than a solution of distilled water (pH = 7).

You may wish to have students omit reading the Background section, which deals with the concerns related to acid precipitation, and opt instead for them to become involved first with the definition of pH and laboratory procedure. If you decide to introduce the subject with the activity itself, then the relevance of the Background section can be brought out during the postlab discussion. Or, you may wish to proceed according to the sequence described.

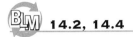

14.2, 14.4

Transparency 14.2, 14.3

ACTIVITY 14.4 ACID RAIN—JUST THE FACTS

See *Student Edition,* p. 585.

ADVANCE PREPARATION

The materials for this activity should not be difficult to gather. Baby jars and lids can be obtained from friends or from local day-care centers. Straws, masking tape, and kitchen matches can be purchased at the supermarket. The chemicals are prepared as follows.

WARNING

If you have never prepared these chemicals before, have a chemistry teacher assist you. Concentrated acetic acid and ammonium hydroxide are dangerous chemicals. Prepare chemical solutions under a fume hood. If you don't have your own, most biology teachers have bromthymol blue powder. Chemicals and premade solutions can be purchased by contacting your Kendall/Hunt representative.

PREPARATION OF SOLUTIONS

- *Bromthymol blue* (BTB). See Activity 2.3 "Investigating Ecosystems" in the *Global Science* Teacher's Guide for directions on preparing BTB solution.
- *Acetic acid,* I.O M. Add 14.3 mL of 17.4 M acid (99–100%) to 200 mL distilled H_2O and continue diluting to 250 mL.
- *Ammonium hydroxide,* I.O M. Add 16.7 mL of concentrated solution (14.8 M, 28% NH_3) to 200 mL distilled water and continue diluting to 250mL.
- *Limewater* is 0.02 M calcium hydroxide. This saturated solution is prepared by dissolving 0.375 g of calcium hydroxide in distilled water and diluting to 250 mL. We recommend that you add a little excess calcium hydroxide and filter off any $CaCO_3$ that forms as a (cloudy) solid. You need to store in a sealed bottle to protect from CO_2 in the air.

Notes: White vinegar can substitute for acetic acid. Household ammonia can substitute for the ammonium hydroxide.

SAMPLE ANSWERS TO QUESTIONS

1. BTB is *yellow* in the presence of an acid and *blue* in the presence of a base.
2. *Acids* are formed when the oxides of various elements are dissolved in water.
3. Exhaled air contains carbon dioxide. $CO_2 + H_2O \rightarrow$ an acid.
4. Ordinary air contains some CO_2 • CO_2 + natural rain water $\rightarrow$ an acid.
5. The match head contains some sulfur and phosphorus. During combustion, oxides of sulfur and phosphorus are formed.

6. Lime reacts with water to form slaked lime, which is a base. Bases neutralize acids.

7. ❧ Burn less coal. (Conserve and/or use nuclear, solar, natural gas.)
   ❧ Remove the sulfur before the coal is burned.
   ❧ Remove the SO_x before it goes up the chimney (scrubber).
   ❧ Blend coal (mix low-sulfur coal with higher-sulfur coal).

8. ❧ Develop engines that run cooler.
   ❧ Remove or alter the NO_x before it leaves the tailpipe.
   ❧ Build more oxygen into the fuel so that less air is needed. Air contains nitrogen.
   ❧ Higher efficiency cars → less fuel must be burned.

 READING 14.6 THE EFFECTS OF ACID PRECIPITATION

See *Student Edition,* p. 589.

ACTIVITY 14.5 EFFECTS OF ACID PRECIPITATION ON PLANTS

See *Student Edition,* p. 590.

This activity was developed to follow Activity 14.3 "Home Sweet Lab—Testing pH." Its purpose is to demonstrate the effects of acidic precipitation on the rates of growth of certain leafy plants.

ADVANCE PREPARATION

If you have stored samples of real acidic precipitation, you may elect to use them, or you may wish to make up your own "acid rain" according to one or both recipes listed under Advanced Preparation in Activity 14.3.

This activity does not have to be limited to the leaf samples suggested under the Materials section (coleus, begonia, and African violet). You may want to ask students to bring in their own plant cuttings from home.

STRATEGIES AND PROCEDURES

Approximately one class period will be required for lab teams to "pot" the three leaves of the plant they have been assigned and to make an appropriate data table. More time will be required on the subsequent days for students to "water" their plants, to make observations, and to record data and/or drawings of their leaf roots as the roots begin to show growth.

Be sure that each lab team places its containers so that the leaves will be exposed to the same conditions of illumination and temperature. Although the textbook does not explain it explicitly, students will need to "water" their plants on a regular basis, measuring out with a graduated cylinder equal amounts of the three liquids.

Students should be able to determine the pH of each liquid you provide with no difficulty if they have participated in Activity 14.3.

If you manufactured your own "acid rain" by following the recipe using nitric acid, your students may find that some plants' growth rates may be affected positively. This is due, of course, to the addition of the nitrate radical (which is a fertilizer) to the potting soil or vermiculite.

A few interested students might appreciate the opportunity to work together conducting the first experiment listed in the Extension section. Following the conclusion of their work, they could present the results to the class.

In your postlab discussion, be sure to conclude your study of acid precipitation by emphasizing its controversial nature. Environmentalists (as well as the Canadians) believe that enough evidence has been gathered to prove that coal-fired power plants are the sources of acid precipitation and, thus, are responsible for the elimination of acid emission. Others do not believe the data are conclusive at all.

READING 14.7 STRATEGIES FOR REDUCING AIR POLLUTION

See *Student Edition*, p. 592.

ACTIVITY 14.6 CHARGE IT! FOR CLEANER AIR

See *Student Edition*, p. 595.

ADVANCE PREPARATION

The materials used in this activity are common in high school physics labs. They also can be purchased by contacting your Kendall/Hunt representative. See the equipment section of this *Teacher Guide*.

Experimentation will provide information on the best way to charge the plastic strips and other objects. Most people obtain the best charge by rubbing in only one direction. The cloth is pulled the length of the plastic strip using a slight pinching action. This is repeated several times.

SAMPLE ANSWERS TO DATA/CONCLUSIONS

Part A
1. Cellulose acetate rubbed with cotton becomes *positively* charged.
2. Vinylite rubbed with wool becomes *negatively* charged.
3. Like charges *repel*.
4. Unlike charges *attract*.
5. Dissimilar materials rubbed together become *oppositely* charged.
6. There appear to be only *two* kinds of charge.
7. Electrical charges *do not* have to touch to influence each other. An *electric field* exists around an electric charge.
8. The charge obtained on an object that is rubbed with another object depends on what it is being rubbed with. Sometimes the results seem temperature/humidity related. Thus, no answers are given here. It appears many objects show charges or electrical properties when rubbed against dissimilar materials.

Part B
Correct numbering of the drawing should not be difficult.

READING 14.8 THE GREENHOUSE EFFECT

See *Student Edition*, p. 598.

ACTIVITY 14.7 THE GREENHOUSE EFFECT MODEL

See *Student Edition*, p. 601.

STRATEGIES AND PROCEDURES

In steps 9 and 10, students may respond as follows:

9. a. Trial 2, with lid.

    b. The lid returned heat radiated from the soil back into the box. With the lid off, heat escaped into space.

    c. The lid of the box simulates the carbon dioxide and other gases in Earth's atmosphere that temporarily absorb, and thus trap, escaping long wavelength (infrared) radiation.

10.

Light	Sun
Soil	*Ground cover*
Air in the box	*Atmosphere*
Lid	*Greenhouse gases*

11. a. The lab model is a static model. The global greenhouse effect is active.

    b. The lab model has no carbon sinks—the Global model has ways to store carbon.

12. It is unacceptable to change Earth's atmosphere for experimental purposes and the time span is too long.

13. All models are incomplete and the implications have serious climactic and economic consequences.

14. This appears to be a valid argument. Analysis of fossils and sediments from previous geological periods seem to bear this out.

Extensions

1. ❧ Drive less.
    ❧ Drive more efficient cars.
    ❧ Use alternative fuels (plant-based alcohols, hydrogen).
    ❧ Use less electricity.
    ❧ Insulate homes better.
    ❧ Stop deforestation (especially rainforests).
    ❧ Plant trees.

2. ❧ Drive less.
    ❧ Choose a more efficient automobile.
    ❧ Use alternative fuels.
    ❧ Buy more energy-efficient electrical appliances.
    ❧ Insulate my home/turn down the thermostat.
    ❧ Write letters against deforestation.
    ❧ Plant a tree.

3. Purposeful large-scale experiments on the atmosphere are not permissible because they alter climate; however, analysis of volcanic eruptions,

geologic evidence, and current carbon dioxide levels probably provide sufficient opportunities to study these types of questions.

READING 14.9 THE CLIMATE QUESTION

See *Student Edition*, p. 603.

ACTIVITY 14.8 CO₂ AND CLIMATE TRENDS: YOU DECIDE

See *Student Edition*, p. 605.

Global warming is among the most controversial topics in science. The purpose of this activity is to allow students to look at data scientists themselves have access to and, with your guidance, form their own conclusions. By doing so, you encourage healthy debate. Allow them to see trends and make them aware of the uncertainties of long-term climate models. (Students can update temperature and CO₂ data sets by referring to the web pages given at the end of this section). Finally, global warming is inherently difficult to study because it deals with a small set of known facts about a fully unknown future.

One of the most difficult aspects of studying complex topics, such as atmospheric systems, is the tendency to oversimplify to make lessons easy to digest.

Here are some distinctions to keep in mind:

* Ozone is naturally created and destroyed within the stratosphere. This balance is now upset as CFCs tend to *destroy more ozone than is naturally replaced*.
* Thinning ozone may cause more UV rays to filter through to the troposphere, but UV rays *do not* lead to increased heating.
* CFCs *do* absorb infrared radiation and serve as another (but minor) type of greenhouse gas.
* Ozone layer depletion is *not* caused by global warming.

STRATEGIES AND PROCEDURES

This activity is straightforward. Students must use the data to construct a line graph and then use the information in their textbook (and from other resources you provide) to draw conclusions.

SAMPLE ANSWERS TO ITEMS

1. See graph.
2. Fossil fuels emissions, cement manufacture, and gas flaring
3. Increased population coupled with the widespread use of automobiles during the mid-twentieth century.
4. $24.2 - 4.8 = 19.4$ billion metric tons of CO₂. $24.2/4.8 = 5.04$ times or 504% rise.
5. $1900 \sim -0.4, 2000 \sim 0.4 \rightarrow 0.8C°$ in 100 years, or $0.008C°$ per year.
6. $1°/0.008°/\text{year} = 125$ years $3.5°/0.008 = 437$ years. Hence, 125 to 437 years.

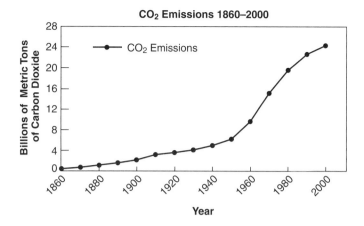

CO_2 Emissions 1860–2000

Year

7. Factors that would accelerate warming or cause cooling; factors that would influence rise in sea level other than temperature rise.
8. CH_4, NO_x water vapor, CFC's.
9. More data (years of measurement); other instruments (e.g., satellites) that could validate ground-based temperature readings. Ice core data.

READING 14.10 THE DEBATE ABOUT OUR FUTURE CLIMATE

See *Student Edition,* p. 606.

READING 14.11 THE EFFECTS OF PARTICLES ON GLOBAL COOLING

See *Student Edition,* p. 607.

 14.6

READING 14.12 DEPLETION OF THE OZONE LAYER ("GOOD OZONE")

See *Student Edition,* p. 609.

CHAPTER 14 SUMMARY

See *Student Edition,* p. 611.

ACTIVITY WHY IS THE SKY BLUE (OR ORANGE OR RED OR BROWN)?

See *Teacher Guide,* p. 304.

This activity introduces students to two concepts at once: light scattering and how particles influence sky color. Remind students that although scattering can cause other colors to be visible in our atmosphere, it is the blue/violet wavelengths that are preferentially scattered.

Some students may inquire about "red" sunsets and sunrises. Emphasize that the more the light is scattered (to blue and violet), the more the complementary spectral colors (reds and oranges) become visible.

Finally, clouds appear white because there are many particles of varying sizes. Taken together they scatter all wavelengths of light allowing us to see a combination of all color-white.

Smog is a combination of smoke and fog. Smog occurs most commonly in and around large metropolitan and/or industrialized areas.

If your school is located within or near an urban area, you may want to assign students a time to observe or photograph the sky. Be on the lookout for smoggy conditions, "brown clouds," or temperature inversions.

Name_____ Date_____

ACID RAIN: THE INVISIBLE THREAT (20 MIN.)

See *Teacher Guide* p. 309 for answers.

VIDEO NOTES

1. In lakes attacked by acid rain, fish populations _____, loons don't _____, and on nearby hills _____ die.
2. Water solutions are acid, base, or _____.
3. pH stands for potential _____.
4. If a liquid is neutral, its pH = _____.
5. Unpolluted rain has a pH of _____.
6. Sulfur dioxide comes primarily from the burning of _____.
7. Nitric oxide comes primarily from _____ (cars and trucks).
8. Wet and dry forms of acidic fallout are called acid _____.
9. In the past, we built taller _____ to move pollutants farther away. This resulted in acid deposition in someone else's neighborhood.
10. Acid deposition problems are influenced by the _____ of industrial plants, _____ patterns, and topography (the lay of the land).
11. Many scientists believe acidic waters cause the release of toxic metals that are killing the _____ in Adirondack lakes (upstate New York).
12. Calcium _____ in the soil can buffer acids and reduce the effect of acid deposition in ecosystems.
13. _____ is often dumped in lakes to counter the effects of acid rain.
14. Statues, buildings, and monuments made of _____ and _____ are corroding in acidic rainfall.
15. _____ at coal-burning power plants reduce sulfur oxide emissions.
16. Cleaner, more _____ energy sources (such as photovoltaics and wind power) reduce the acid deposition problem.

Name _____ Date _____

ACTIVITY: WHY IS THE SKY BLUE (OR ORANGE OR RED OR BROWN)?

PURPOSE

To determine why the sky is usually blue—but not always.

BACKGROUND

Blue (or any other color) skies exist because of a scientific phenomena called light scattering. This is a process by which particles in the atmosphere remove light from a beam and send it off in another direction. White light is made up of all the colors of the rainbow, each with a different wavelength. When white light gets scattered, though, you may notice a single wavelength or color predominating-like the blue in the sky overhead.

MATERIALS

- dark room or closet
- bag of chalk dust and/or flour
- 8 ounces of milk

- flashlight
- empty 2-liter soda bottle with cap

PROCEDURE

PART A

1. Turn on a flashlight in a darkened room. Prop the light, and position it so that you are looking at the beam from the side.
2. Sift flour or chalk dust over the beam of light so that the particles will fall through it. What do you see? Record your answer in your science notebook.
3. Describe how chalk or flour dust "scatters" white light.

   High in the atmosphere, the particles that do the scattering are much smaller than dust. These particles, in fact, are molecules. They are just the size the right size to scatter wavelengths of light in the blue and violet range. These molecules are also spread evenly across the sky.

4. If you used colored flour or chalk, what colors would you see?

   Clouds contain particles of many different sizes; hence they scatter light from all wavelengths. What is the result of scattering light in this manner?

304   **Chapter 14**

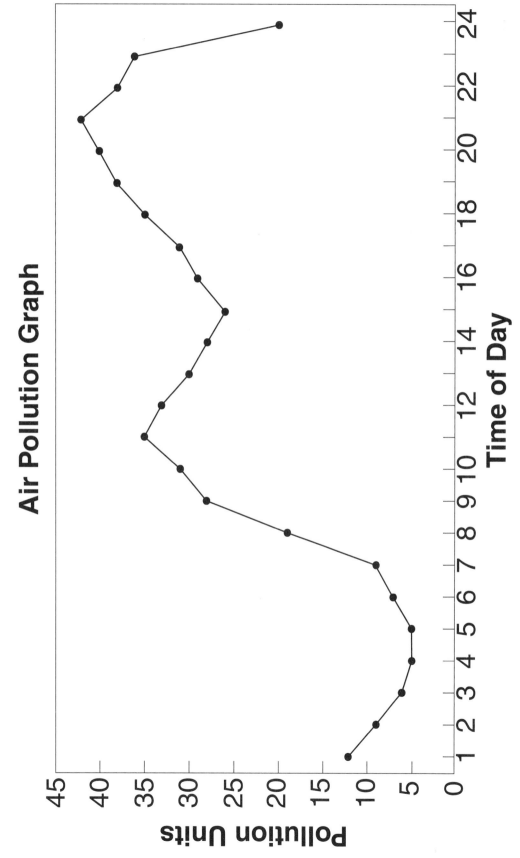

Air Pollution Graph

Pollution Units

Time of Day

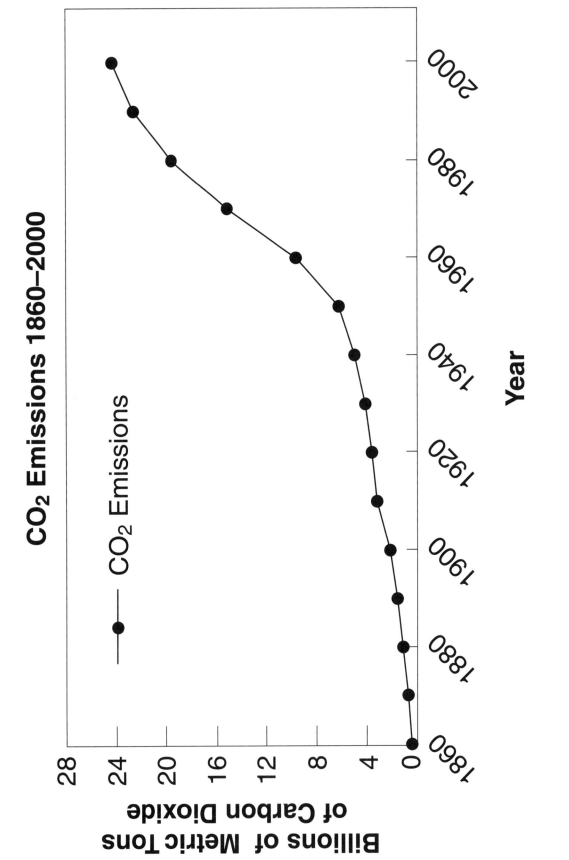

CO₂ Emissions 1860–2000

— CO₂ Emissions

Year

Billions of Metric Tons of Carbon Dioxide

Name_____ Date_____

MULTIPLE CHOICE

1. _____ Which one of the following is *not* an example of ecosystem disruption?
   A. the widespread use of artificial fertilizers, herbicides, and pesticides
   B. water vapor condensing and falling as rain
   C. increased particulate matter in the air reflecting sunlight
   D. one-crop farming on great expanses of land

2. _____ The flow of energy through the ecosphere is most influenced by
   A. the widespread use of artificial fertilizers.
   B. the dumping of pollutants and CO_2 into the atmosphere.
   C. one-crop farming on great expanses of land.

3. _____ The impact of humans on the environment
   A. comes almost entirely from our use of energy and mineral resources.
   B. has little to do with our use of energy and mineral resources.
   C. is in no way influenced by our use of energy and mineral resources.
   D. is mostly positive.

4. _____ Energy and mineral use affect the environment for all of the following reasons *except*
   A. the extraction of resources disturbs ecosystems.
   B. the use of resources puts foreign substances into existing ecosystems.
   C. resources can be isolated from their surroundings.
   D. resources are spilled as they are transported from one place to another.

5. _____ Unburned hydrocarbons are most closely related to this pollutant.
   A. sulfur dioxide   D. ozone
   B. carbon monoxide   E. water
   C. carbon dioxide

6. _____ Nitrogen normally will not combine with oxygen. Nitrogen will combine if
   A. a car has a catalytic converter.
   B. the temperature is low enough.
   C. high-test gasoline is used.
   D. water gets into the gas tank.
   E. the temperature is hot enough.

7. _____ The most abundant gas in our atmosphere is
   A. oxygen.   C. nitrogen.
   B. carbon dioxide.   D. water vapor.

8. _____ Which of the following is considered a "trace" gas?
   A. water vapor   D. none of these
   B. carbon dioxide   E. all of these
   C. ozone

9. _____ This atmospheric layer contains most of Earth's weather.
   A. ozone layer   C. troposphere
   B. stratosphere   D. hydrosphere

Match the air pollutant to the related piece of information.

10. _____ particulates

A. Produced mainly from the burning of impure coal.

11. _____ hydrocarbons

B. Comes from the incomplete combustion of gasoline and from evaporation of petroleum fuels.

12. _____ sulfur oxide (SO_x)

C. Causes oxygen deprivation in the blood.

13. _____ nitrogen oxide (NO_x)

D. The pollutant we have been most successful in reducing.

14. _____ carbon monoxide (CO)

E. Produced when fuel is burned at high temperatures.

ADDITIONAL MULTIPLE CHOICE

15. _____ Catalytic converters change carbon monoxide into carbon dioxide and unburned hydrocarbons into carbon dioxide and
   A. ethanol.
   B. sulfur dioxide.
   C. particulator.
   D. ozone.
   E. water.

16. _____ Air quality in many of our large cities is often reduced because of thermal inversions. These hold the polluted air on the ground because
   A. the warm air sinks.
   B. polluted air near the surface is trapped by warmer air at a higher level.
   C. the particulates warm up the air.
   D. winds cool the upper level air and hold the warmer air down.

17. _____ SO_x is related to
   A. unburned hydrocarbons.
   B. pollutants from industrial sources and volcanoes.
   C. devices used to catch airborne particulates.
   D. the shape of inversion layers over smog-choked cities.

18. _____ Common indoor air pollutants include all of the following *except*
   A. carbon monoxide (CO).
   B. radon gas.
   C. sulfur dioxide.
   D. tobacco smoke.
   E. bacteria/mold.

19. _____ All of the following statements about acid rain are true *except*
   A. acid rain kills fish and trees and damages soil.
   B. automobiles and electric power plants are probably the main causes of acid rain.
   C. tall smokestacks built to ease local pollution most likely contribute to acidic rainfall in distant places.
   D. acid rain did not exist before the Industrial Revolution.

Methods for reducing pollution related to automobiles are listed on the left. Match the method with the correct short description given on the right.

20. _____ improved efficiency

A. Require small, quiet, electric cars be used in certain metropolitan areas.

21. _____ improved fuels

B. Burn oxygenated fuels, plant-based alcohols, or hydrogen instead of gasoline.

22. _____ economic restraints

C. Require afterburners and /or catalytic converters.

23. _____ lowered emissions

D. The use of plastics, fibers, and ceramics to reduce total mass.

24. _____ smaller vehicles

E. Tax gasoline, raise downtown parking fees, and charge fees to enter certain areas during rush hour.

ADDITIONAL MULTIPLE CHOICE

25. _____ Which of the following is *true* about the effects of acid precipitation?
   A. skin burns
   B. red sunsets
   C. increased global warming
   D. locally induced environmental stress
   E. melting ice caps

26. _____ Electric generating plants *always* produce a certain amount of
   A. nuclear wastes.
   B. smoke particles.
   C. thermal pollution.
   D. sulfur gases.

27. _____ All of the following are devices for reducing stack emissions (air pollution) at electric power plants *except*
   A. bag house.
   B. electrostatic precipitator.
   C. pulverizer.
   D. scrubber.

28. _____ Cooling towers help condense steam to make this device more efficient.
   A. pulverizer
   B. bag house
   C. power lines
   D. turbine
   E. furnace

29. _____ The greenhouse effect causes Earth to become warmer because
   A. CO_2 molecules reflect incoming sunlight.
   B. CO_2 molecules change sunlight into heat.
   C. CO_2 molecules are transparent to incoming sunlight, but they absorb infrared (heat) radiation.
   D. CO_2 molecules capture X-rays and change them into electrical signals.

30. _____ The depletion of the ozone layer is most closely associated with
   A. acid rain.
   B. carbon dioxide.
   C. chlorofluorocarbons (CFCs).
   D. particles in the upper atmosphere.
   E. high-occupancy vehicles (HOVs).

31. _____ In studying ecosystems influenced by acid precipitation, which of the following is *not* important?
   A. location of coal-fired power plants
   B. weather patterns
   C. soil type
   D. forest fires
   E. All are important.

32. _____ Which of the following is considered a greenhouse gas?
   A. particulates
   B. water vapor
   C. nitrogen
   D. carbon monoxide

33. _____ All of the following are true about ozone *except*
   A. ozone is a pollutant when found in the lower atmosphere.
   B. ozone (O_3) is a highly reactive gas.
   C. the ozone layer screens out ultraviolet radiation.
   D. satellites give off emissions that are damaging the ozone layer.
   E. troposphere ozone causes eye, throat, and lung irritations.

34. _____ Which of the following is the most common naturally occurring acid in our atmosphere?
   A. acetic acid
   B. citric acid
   C. hydrochloric acid
   D. carbonic acid

35. _____ Which of the following best illustrates how the greenhouse effect works?
   A. Measuring the temperature inside a closed automobile on a sunny day.
   B. Testing water in a rainbarrel with pH paper.
   C. Studying the effects of airplane contrails.
   D. Watching smoke rise from an extinguished match in a closed container.
   E. None of the above.

ACID RAIN: THE INVISIBLE THREAT (20 MIN.)

VIDEO NOTES

1. In lakes attacked by acid rain, fish populations <u>die</u>, loons don't <u>nest</u>, and on nearby hills <u>trees</u> die.
2. Water solutions are acid, base, or <u>neutral</u>.
3. pH stands for potential <u>hydrogen</u>.
4. If a liquid is neutral, its pH = <u>7</u>.
5. Unpolluted rain has a pH of <u>5.6</u>.
6. Sulfur dioxide comes primarily from the burning of <u>coal</u>.
7. Nitric oxide comes primarily from <u>gasoline engines</u> (cars and trucks).
8. Wet and dry forms of acidic fallout are called acid <u>deposition</u>.
9. In the past, we built taller <u>smokestacks</u> to move pollutants farther away. This resulted in acid deposition in someone else's neighborhood.
10. Acid deposition problems are influenced by the <u>location</u> of industrial plants, <u>weather</u> patterns, and topography (the lay of the land).
11. Many scientists believe acidic waters cause the release of toxic metals that are killing the <u>fish</u> in Adirondack lakes (upstate New York).
12. Calcium <u>carbonate</u> in the soil can buffer acids and reduce the effect of acid deposition in ecosystems.
13. <u>Limestone</u> is often dumped in lakes to counter the effects of acid rain.
14. Statues, buildings, and monuments made of <u>limestone</u> and <u>marble</u> are corroding in acidic rainfall.
15. <u>Scrubbers</u> at coal-burning power plants reduce sulfur oxide emissions.
16. Cleaner, more <u>renewable</u> energy sources (such as photovoltaics and wind power) reduce the acid deposition problem.

CHAPTER 14 ASSESSMENT

1. B		19. D	
2. B		20. D	
3. A		21. B	
4. C		22. E	
5. D		23. C	
6. E		24. A	
7. C		25. D	
8. D		26. C	
9. C		27. C	
10. D		28. D	
11. B		29. C	
12. A		30. C	
13. E		31. E	
14. C		32. B	
15. E		33. D	
16. B		34. D	
17. B		35. A	
18. C			

RESOURCE MANAGEMENT: LAND

LEARNING OUTCOMES

The student will:

1. **examine** present land use cover in the United States and how land use decisions are made. (C)

2. **examine** a hypothetical land use situation by **completing** the activity "Land Use Decision. You Make the Call." (C,A)

3. **design** an environmental landscape for the yard of a home by **completing** the activity "Environmental Landscaping." (C,A,P)

4. **define** public lands and **be familiar** with the federal agencies that manage them. (C)

5. **state** what happens to the overburden when strip mining is carried out in a responsible manner. (C)

6. **analyze** a mined land reclamation project by **completing** the activity "Mined Land Reclamation." (C,P)

7. **Analyze** land use planning in general and at the local level by **completing** the activity "Land Use Analysis." (C,A)

8. **examine** land use challenges, as they relate to various ecosystems by **reading** 15.8–15.13 and **answering** the related questions. (C)

9. **Prioritize** various strategies for managing western (U.S.) forests by **completing** the activity "Western Forest Management." (C)

10. **describe** the average composition of municipal solid waste. (C)

11. **develop** a plan for handling municipal solid waste by **completing** the activity "Not in My Backyard!" (C,A)

12. **describe** how waste is classified according to its characteristics. (C)

13. **investigate** the properties of conducting solutions by **completing** the activities "Conducting Solutions" and "Copper Plating." (C,P)

14. **summarize** and **analyze** the various strategies humans use to dispose of toxic waste by **completing** the activity "Disposing of Toxic Waste: The Decision." (C,A)

15. **use** knowledge of the composition of municipal solid waste to **recommend** solutions to America's waste dilemma. (C,A)

16. **consider** the dilemma caused by the fact that science (technology) comes with no instructions on how to use it. (A)

KEY TERMS

land use
environmental impact statement
reclamation
fragmentation
desertification
wetlands
biodegradable
recycling

nonbiodegradable
hazardous waste
toxic waste
integrated circuit
printed circuit
electrolyte
electroplating
dilution

chemical alteration
containment
environmental impact
municipal solid waste (MSW)
incinerator
sanitary landfill
technology

RECOMMENDED BLACKLINE MASTERS

15.1 Land Use Decision

15.2 Municipal Solid Waste (MSW)

15.3 Hazardous Wastes

15.4 Conducting Solutions

15.5 Disposing of Toxic Waste

The Recommended Blackline Masters listed above are supplemental to the activity/reading, and can be found on the *Teacher Resource CD*. Blackline Masters 15.6–15.12 are essential to teaching the activity/reading, and so are included in the *Teacher Guide* (pp. 328-341) as well as on the *Teacher Resource CD*.

ACTIVITIES FLOW CHART

CHAPTER 15: RESOURCE MANAGEMENT: LAND

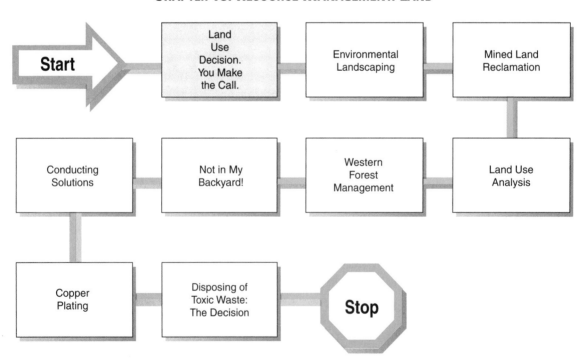

NOTE: Shaded items are lower priority.

TEACHING STRATEGIES AND ANSWERS FOR ACTIVITIES

READING 15.1 LAND USE/COVER CATEGORIES

See *Student Edition,* p. 616.

See *Student Edition,* p. 616.

ANSWERS TO QUESTIONS

1. forest, range, grassland, cropland, wetland, desert
2. farming, forest use, residential, parks, refuges

READING 15.2 LAND OWNERSHIP AND PAST LAND USE

See *Student Edition,* p. 617.

READING 15.3 PRESENT LAND USE

See *Student Edition,* p. 618.

READING 15.4 PRESENT LAND USE DECISION-MAKING STRUCTURES

See *Student Edition,* p. 619.

ACTIVITY 15.1 LAND USE DECISION. YOU MAKE THE CALL.

See *Student Edition,* p. 621.

 15.1

STRATEGIES AND PROCEDURES

The situation in this activity is typical of land use decisions going on all over the modern world today. The map of Figure 14.5 is also Blackline Master 15.1.

In steps 2–5, students may respond as follows:

2. Proposal	Advantage	Disadvantage
a. Keep agricultural	Farm land is preserved.	Wheatland has other needs.
b. Park/recreation	Area needs more parks.	Doesn't feed the economy.
c. Trucking center	Jobs/tax income.	Loss of farmland.
d. Technical college	Wheatland area needs.	Less economic gain than some of the other alternatives.
e. Shopping mall	Maximum economic gain.	Loss of farmland/future park.
f. Mixed use	Meets several needs.	Loss of farmland/future park.

3. We don't know the full economic and cultural needs of the town, the quality of the agricultural land, or if other alternative sites are available.

4. a. This type of activity can give students a better picture of how land use decisions are actually made.

   b. If not handled well, this can degenerate into creating the stereotypes that all developers are evil, county commissioners are corrupt, and environmentalists are always right.

5. The best decision can only be made when all the facts are available, out in the open, and clearly understood. This is not only hard to simulate, it doesn't always happen in the real world.

ACTIVITY 15.2 ENVIRONMENTAL LANDSCAPING

See *Student Edition*, p. 622.

MATERIALS

Recommended video: CD: Water Wise Gardening: See video section of the *Teacher Guide*.

Graph paper: 10 squares to the inch (example: National 12–280); light green grid graph paper is sold by office supply stores, stationary stores, college bookstores, and by contacting your Kendall/Hunt representative.

Pamphlets on xeriscaping and low-water landscaping can be obtained from most water districts and at many commercial nurseries.

STRATEGIES AND PROCEDURES

The following lesson plan works well with this activity.

Purpose. To develop a landscape plan for a home that is both attractive and resource efficient (water/energy/mineral).

Background. Probably the most important land use decision most people make in a lifetime is the landscaping of their yard.

Day 1

1. View CD (the main portions).
2. Review the xeriscaping strategy (postCD).
3. Obtain Activity 15.2 and graph paper.
4. Decide where **streets, roads,** and **sidewalks** are in relation to the **lot** (70 × 100).
5. Show, with an arrow, where **north** is.
6. Think about **site features** and **uses.**
7. Block out your house **floor plan** (25 × 40). Do you want a garage? Use symbols to show walls, windows, doors, and sliding doors.

Day 2

1. Analyze your **site** (items 1–11).

2. Sketch landscape plan (use symbols).
3. Color your plan.
4. List **native plants**
5. Follow up on **other** ideas (items 2–5).
6. Prepare your report.

 READING 15.5 PUBLIC LANDS

See *Student Edition*, p. 624.

 15.3

 READING 15.6 PUBLIC LAND MANAGEMENT ISSUES

See *Student Edition*, p. 625.

ANSWERS TO QUESTIONS

1. a. Bureau of Land Management (BLM)—manages ~1/8 of land area of United States.
   b. Forest Service (USFS)—manages and protects federal forests and grasslands.
   c. National Park Service (NPS)—manages our national parks, monuments, and important historic sites.
   d. Fish and Wildlife Service (FWS)—manages national wildlife refuges, fish hatcheries, and many small wetlands and special management areas.
2. Multiple use implies that land areas can be used in a variety of ways all at the same time (e.g., a single forest can have recreational, grazing, and timbering uses all going on at once).
3. 1. an analysis of the need for project.
   2. a rigorous comparison of reasonable alternative projects.
   3. a description of the environment affected by the project.
   4. a discussion of the environmental impacts of the proposed project and those of the possible alternatives.

 READING 15.7 MINED LAND RECLAMATION

See *Student Edition*, p. 629.

ANSWERS TO QUESTIONS

1. Yes. Many examples of reclamation exist in the United States and abroad. See Activity 15.3 for documentation.
2. 1. Top soil removed and stored nearby.
   2. Mine developed and resources extracted.
   3. Broken overburden placed back into the mine pit.
   4. Bulldozers shape overburden surface to resemble original surface contour.
   5. Topsoil placed onto the new surface.
   6. Topsoil seeded with a mixture of good starter seeds and seeds of native plants. Fertilizer added. (This is Stage 1 of ecological succession.)
   7. In dry regions, the seeds are watered until they take hold.

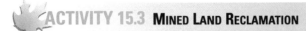

ACTIVITY 15.3 MINED LAND RECLAMATION

See *Student Edition*, p. 631.

Part A is set up assuming you don't have several computers and color copiers in your classroom. After Part A is done, students bring their information to class where they can complete their poster. Grade posters on quality and thoroughness.

SAMPLE ANSWERS TO QUESTIONS

1. What type mixture of good starter grass and native plant seeds was used? Were erosion barriers used after the seeds were planted? In dry regions, did they irrigate for a time?
2. It probably is approaching the climax community for the type of biome in which it is located. This is what would happen naturally.

SPECIAL FOCUS ISLAND BIOGEOGRAPHY

See *Student Edition*, p. 633.

ANSWER TO ASSIGNMENT

To create the most stable biotic community, the open space must be adequate in size and habitat diversity to maintain a minimum population that will not undergo the serious genetic difficulties that occur in small populations.

ANSWER TO EXTENSION

The greater the variety of topography (hills, cliffs, depressions), the more niches that can be filled. This means for the same size islands, the ones with the most varied topography will support more diverse habitats.

SPECIAL FOCUS LAND FRAGMENTATION

See *Student Edition*, p. 634.

ANSWERS TO PROBLEM

1. Area $= (1000 \text{ m})^2 = 1,000,000 \text{ m}^2$.
   Perimeter $= 1000 \text{ m} \times 4 = 4,000 \text{ m}$.
   Safe Area $= (800 \text{ m})^2 = 640,000 \text{ m}^2$.
2. For each quadrant:
   Area $= (495 \text{ m})^2 = 245,025 \text{ m}^2$.
   Perimeter $= 495 \text{ m} \times 4 = 1980 \text{ m}$.
   Safe Area $= (295 \text{ m})^2 = 87,025 \text{ m}^2$.
3. TOTAL safe area after the road and railroad were built $= 87,025 \text{ m}^2 \times 4 = 348,100 \text{ m}^2$.

   % of original safe area $= 87,025 \text{ m}^2/640,000 \text{ m}^2 \times 100\% = 54.4\%$.

4. a. Try to preserve larger habitats.

    b. If larger habitats are not possible, provide corridors (such as tunnels under the road and railroad) where organisms can move from one habitat to another.

 ACTIVITY 15.4 LAND USE ANALYSIS

See *Student Edition,* p. 635.

COMMENTS ON THE TASKS

1. Good land use planning should provide for as many diversified uses as possible while maintaining the quality of the environment.
2. If you live in a city, the city probably has a planning department. Most counties have county commissioners plus a planning office. In addition, public lands are administered by various state and federal agencies. Because of regulations, proposed projects on private land often must file an environmental impact statement.
3. This item is location dependent.
4. Golf courses, city parks, trails along creeks and rivers, and closed industries and government facilities often become restoration projects.
5. Most of the larger cities and counties use GISs. How extensive that use is depends on size of staff and funds available. Cities and counties with smaller populations and budgets probably don't use GISs.
6. Emphasize the positive. In almost all cases, local industries strive to be a positive influence on the communities they serve—both economically and environmentally.

 READING LAND MANAGEMENT CHALLENGES

See *Student Edition,* p. 636.

 READING 15.8 AGRICULTURAL LAND

See *Student Edition,* p. 636.

ANSWERS TO QUESTIONS

1. Cropland: 388 million acres/2,263 million acres = 17%.
   If the data from Figure 15.1 is used, the answer becomes 455/2,263 = 20%.
2. Livestock: 788 million acres for range and grazing/2,263 million acres =34.8%. If the data from Figure 15.1 is used, the answer becomes 588/2,263 = 26%. This figure doesn't include forest land used for grazing.
3. Agricultural land is needed to produce food, fiber, and renewable fuels. Keeping it in production in the United States ensures a safe, domestic food supply; helps improve the balance of trade; provides habitat for wildlife; and enhances the environment.

READING 15.9 FOREST LANDS

See *Student Edition*, p. 637.

1. a. Draft animals were replaced by internal combustion engines. This meant farms could be smaller and produce the same crop.
   b. Farm productivity rose due to improved crops and farming techniques. Less farmland was needed.
2. Most of America's forested land is on private property.
3. Most of America's forested land is located in the eastern half of the country.

15.6, 15.7, 15.8, 15.9, 15.10, 15.11

ACTIVITY 15.5 WESTERN FOREST MANAGEMENT

See *Student Edition*, p. 638.

The following Blackline Masters are for this activity:

15.6   A Clear-Cut Drought Solution?
15.7   Thicker Forests, Hotter Fires
15.8   Adopt-a-Forest
15.9   Fire Plan Carries Opportunity, Risk
15.10   Fire Risk-Ratings: An Idea Whose Time Has Come
15.11   Activity 15.5 Western Forest Management

BLMs 15.6–15.10 are the five articles. BLM 15.11 is a chart on which the five articles are to be summarized.

After summarizing the five articles, the class will vote on the eight proposed bills.

Bills that pass will be prioritized. This list represents the class's western forest management plan.

READING 15.10 WILDERNESS AND PRESERVES

See *Student Edition*, p. 639.

1. Being a wilderness stakeholder means being actively familiar with the area and knowledgeable about policies that may affect wilderness. Stakeholders often attend meetings which address wilderness policy issues and sometimes help resolve resource conflicts.
2. Wilderness areas are used for camping, hiking, fishing, hunting, and canoeing. Others visit wilderness areas for wildlife viewing. Still others enjoy skiing and snowshoeing. Only low-impact recreation is allowed.
3. When traveling through wilderness areas, one can follow the policy of the U.S. Park Service by leaving only foot-prints and taking only pictures. Carrying out trash, not disturbing wildlife, and using resources of the wilderness wisely are important when visiting these areas. Community members who promote these values and understand wilderness are good

contributors to advisory boards. This includes scientists, resource users, and people from surrounding communities.

READING 15.11 DESERTS AND DESERTIFICATION

See *Student Edition,* p. 642.

ANSWERS TO QUESTIONS

1. On a desert hike, one should wear a hat and carry plenty of water. Sun block and sunglasses are a must. Reflective clothing also helps one adapt to extreme conditions. A map and compass are also important.
2. Deserts are best explored on foot rather than using vehicles that damage plants, soils, and wildlife. While dunes are fun to explore, they also provide habitat for sensitive plants. It is important not to trample their root structures. Water sources should only be disturbed if completely necessary.
3. Strategies which minimize desertification include planting native, desert tolerant, trees and plants. Water sources can be maintained through conservation practices such as xeriscape and drip irrigation. Improving habitat for pollinators also is helpful.

READING 15.12 WETLANDS

See *Student Edition,* p. 644.

1. If you live near an ocean, wetlands provide important benefits to both humans and ocean ecosystems. Runoff is filtered so the water is clear for marine life and swimming. Waterfront land and property is protected from erosion while flooding from storms and high waves are minimized. Coastal wetlands also provide nutrients, hatchery, and nursery areas for fish.
2. Rather than filling in wetlands, housing could be elevated above wetlands. Water could be channeled around housing. Additional wetlands and habitats could be created in adjacent areas to minimize impact. Environmentally-friendly construction materials can be used to minimize wetland impact. Students should debate the effects of many single houses versus one large housing project. This is a challenge many developers face.

READING 15.13 URBAN ENVIRONMENTS

See *Student Edition,* p. 674.

ANSWERS TO QUESTIONS

1. a. a flow of energy (sunlight, food, fuel)
   b. a supply of material resources (vitamins, minerals, water, air)
   c. a waste removal system
2. Most people on Earth live in urban areas.

3. Increased population may be planned for by creating more housing and jobs which minimize the impact on urban environments. Housing may be built on developed areas close to mass-transit. Land use plans which limit sprawl, vehicles, and pollution all help.

 READING **THE PROBLEM OF WASTE**

See *Student Edition,* p. 648.

 15.2

ACTIVITY 15.6 **NOT IN MY BACK YARD!**

See *Student Edition,* p. 649.

This activity is best used as an introduction to the problem of waste management. Students can work in small groups. The background information can be read quietly at the beginning of class (or one of the students in each group can slowly read it to the others—helping those that can't read). Students then fill out the decision-making chart. You may want to check and make sure each group has correctly stated/identified the problem. Provide help as you deem necessary. After ample time for discussion, you may choose to fill out a class decision-making chart. This can serve as the basis for your unit discussion of waste management.

 READING 15.14 **DISPOSING OF OUR SOLID WASTES**

See *Student Edition,* p. 652.

 15.3

READING 15.15 **CLASSIFYING WASTES**

See *Student Edition,* p. 653.

READING 15.16 **INDUSTRIAL PROCESSES**

See *Student Edition,* p. 655.

 15.4

ACTIVITY 15.7 **CONDUCTING SOLUTIONS**

See *Student Edition,* p. 656.

ADVANCE PREPARATION

Activities 15.7 and 15.8 are the first 2 activities from the kit (module) "Toxic Waste: A Teaching Simulation," which is sold by Lab-aids. This kit comes with complete directions and contains 7 experiments that focus on the problem of properly disposing of a toxic substance. It is designed to be used with 5 classes of 32 students working in teams of 2. If you choose to do all 7 activities in the Toxic Waste kit, it will require an additional 8 class periods and you will need to purchase a tray package containing 16 trays, 16 plastic droppers and 24 measuring/mixing spatulas.

MATERIALS

If you purchase the SEPUP Kits, you do a total of seven experiments that focus on the problem of properly disposing a toxic substance. Activities 15.7 and 15.8 are the first two of the seven. The remaining five activities will require about eight more class periods.

If you choose to do Activities 15.7 and 15.8, all of the necessary materials for the Copper Plating activity can be found on the materials list and may be purchased by contacting your Kendall/Hunt representative.

Prepare a 50,000 ppm Copper Chloride Solution as follows:

Dissolve 134 g. of $CuCl_2 \cdot 2H_2O$ crystals in 866 mL water to make 1 liter of solution (0.79 M)

STRATEGIES AND PROCEDURES

Many teachers place the equipment for these two activities in the cardboard flats that cases of soda pop come in. These are available free at the grocery store. The flats are then numbered, and this way equipment can be quickly organized, handed out to groups, and returned and checked for readiness for the next class.

Some teachers assign students in a group a role as follows:

1. *EPA*. Keeps the group on task; turns in the group's report.
2. *Site Engineer*. Gets/returns the equipment.
3. *Chemist*. Does the experiment.
4. *Safety Officer*. Makes sure safety goggles are worn. Cleans up the lab station.

Roles are indicated by each name on the group's lab report.

Lab Rules

1. Work as a group. No wandering.
2. Safety goggles *must* be worn.
3. No food or drink in the lab.
4. No "side" experiments with the equipment.
5. Lab technique (conduct) is part of the grade.
6. Turn in equipment as a group.
7. You will be dismissed from class as a group. (The first group that turns in its completed report and clean equipment goes first, etc.)

In steps 4-11, students may respond as follows:

4. Water is not a good conductor. The bulb did not glow.
5. As salt is added, the bulb begins to glow.
6. The bulb gets brighter as more salt is added.

7. When salt is added to water, it breaks up into ions. The ions conduct electric current through the solution.
9. The bulb does *not* glow when sugar dissolves in the water.
10. Sugar does not form ions when it dissolves in water.
11. The bulb didn't glow.

1. a. **Toxic:** poisonous; harmful to living things.
1. b. **Waste:** Useless material.
2. Garden sprays, insect repellents, rat/mouse poison.
3. Some students will say, "We throw them out with the trash." Ideally, they should be disposed of *safely, economically,* and in an *environmentally* sound manner.

Conductor: a material that is capable of transferring electric charge (or energy).

Conducting solution: a solution that can carry electric current.

Ion: a small particle that carries an electric charge.

Electrolyte: a substance that breaks up into ions when it dissolves in water.

Nonelectrolyte: a substance that does not break up into ions when it dissolves in water.

  15.4

READING 15.17 WHY SOME SUBSTANCES DISSOLVE AND SOME SOLUTIONS CONDUCT

See *Student Edition,* p. 657.

ACTIVITY 15.8 COPPER PLATING

See *Student Edition,* p. 659.

In step 4, (Figure 15.39) students may respond as follows:

Appearance	Paper Clip	Plating Solution	Copper Strip
Before	silver colored	blue	copper colored, shiny
After	reddish-brown coating	blue-green	copper colored, but dull

1. The paper clip became coated with a reddish-brown solid. Copper; since the question says "seems," rust can also be counted.
2. Negative clip (black clip). By reading the instructions carefully.
3. • Recycle the copper if you can. This way it isn't wasted. (Make pennies out of it.)
   • If the copper chloride must be disposed of, **dilute** it (dump it down the drain with lots of water); **change** it to a nontoxic substance and dispose; **tie it up** in something like concrete so it can't get into the environment; or **contain** it in a special toxic waste dump.

- Dumping it into landfills, lakes/rivers, or the ocean is totally unacceptable.
- Drop it into a volcano.
- Don't use toxic products in the first place.
- Shoot it into space.

ACTIVITY 15.9 DISPOSING OF TOXIC WASTE: THE DECISION

See *Student Edition*, p. 661.

BLM 15.5 OR 15.12

The following chart contains sample answers to each item in Figure 15.20. An alternative approach is to use Blackline Master 15.12.

Method	Dilution	Out of Sight	Waste Reclamation	Chemical Alteration	Containment	Waste Minimization
Description and/or examples	Add H$_2$O until down to legal level and dispose.	• Shoot into space • Bury it • Dump in ocean	Change waste to valuable product Recover and sell	Change waste to nontoxic substance and dispose	Tie up in concrete, a barrel, or special dump	• Only buy what you need • Substitute nontoxic for toxic
Environmental Impact	• Requires lots of water • Toxins still in environment • Toxins can be biologically concentrated	No longer an accepted method of toxic waste disposal	Lowers the impact significantly	Works in many cases, but acid leaching can free some toxins	The only acceptable method for most toxic substances	By far the best strategy
Economic Analysis	• Water is expensive • Convenient and less expensive than some solutions	Cleanup costs are extremely high	Can be an economic gain	Can be expensive	Expensive in short run, but economic in long run.	• Buying less saves money • Substitutes may cost more

READING 15.18 WASTE MANAGEMENT

See *Student Edition,* p. 661.

READING 15.19 DISPOSAL OF MUNICIPAL SOLID WASTE

See *Student Edition,* p. 664.

Transparency 15.1

READING TECHNOLOGY: FRIEND OR FOE?

See *Student Edition,* p. 667.

The questions at the end of this reading should enable you to cover the major ideas—especially question 2. You may also want to discuss the following definitions:

- **Information:** a fact (including data) or group of facts.
- **Knowledge:** information organized in a meaningful or useful way.
- **Wisdom:** knowledge tempered with judgment.

CHAPTER 15 SUMMARY

See *Student Edition,* p. 669.

Name _____ Date _____

DISPOSING OF TOXIC WASTE

The following is a list of six strategies for disposing of toxic waste. Rank these six strategies from 1 = best to 6 = worst and then justify your ranking.

Method	Description and/or examples	Ranking (1 = Best)	Justification of Ranking
Dilution	Add H_2O until down to legal level and dispose	5	• Toxins still in environment • Uses lots of water • Can be biologically concentrated
Out of Sight	• Shoot into space • Bury it • Dump in ocean	6	• Puts toxins in the environment • Very expensive to clean up
Waste Reclamation	Change waste to valuable product. Recover and sell	2	Gets rid of waste and profit can be made
Chemical Alteration	Change waste to nontoxic substance and dispose	3	Less expensive than containment
Containment	Tie up in concrete, a barrel, or special dump	4	Toxins fixed in a known location can be monitored
Waste Minimization	• Only buy what you need • Substitute nontoxic for toxic	1	Greatly reduces the quantity of waste

See page 341 for student handout.

A Clear-Cut Drought Solution?

Logging urged to boost runoff, but eco-groups object

By Theo Stein, Denver Post Environment Writer. © 2002 The Denver Post

State officials intend to push a program of aggressive logging that would change the face of Colorado's high-country forests for decades in hopes of increasing the water supply.

Up to half a million acre-feet of new water—enough to supply a million families—could be created by sawing out clear-cuts in clumps and thinning trees on broad swaths of federal and state land, according to Kent Holsinger, the top water official in the Colorado Department of Natural Resources.

Cutting mountain forests to produce water has been studied on small plots since the Depression, but has never been applied as broadly as officials of Gov. Bill Owens' administration now advocate. With Republicans in control of the statehouse and in Washington, big projects are now expected to get serious consideration from state and federal officials.

"The idea of more actively managing forests to mitigate wildfire and help restore water yields holds tremendous promise," Holsinger said.

Holsinger and other officials have been stumping across the state for several months, promising drought-stricken communities that new water will follow new logging projects.

"With scientific data showing active management can result in more water for Coloradans, this is right near the top of the list of things we need to look at," said U.S. Rep. Scott McInnis, R-Grand Junction, who chairs the House Forest Health Subcommittee. "Heaven knows we can use all the water we can get."

Mark Rey, an undersecretary with the U.S. Department of Agriculture and a former timber lobbyist, said existing forest plans, which direct logging on federal land, could be changed to help achieve state goals.

"We are eager to work with the state as we go through the forest plan revision process to see under what circumstances we can agree to increase water yield for aquatic species and downstream users," he said.

ENVIRONMENTALISTS CRY FOUL

Environmentalists have universally panned the concept, which they say doesn't work everywhere but is guaranteed to increase flooding and degrade mountain streams.

"This is beyond harebrained," said Chris Wood, who was an adviser to Forest Service chief Mike Dombeck during the Clinton administration. "This will produce a tremendous backlash when people see what this looks like on the ground."

The idea is simple: Removing trees allows more snow to fall to the ground, where it runs off into streams and rivers during the spring. Some forest researchers and many water users complain that Colorado's high country has grown too many trees in the last few decades, trees that intercept snow which would otherwise add to the snowpack that melts and runs downhill to farmers and cities every spring.

Huge amounts of forest—between 25 percent and 40 percent of a watershed—have to be cut to achieve this increased water yield, according to the research being used to support the effort. And land managers would have to maintain those clear-cuts or keep making new ones to keep that extra water flowing.

But those same studies show that removing tree cover only produces extra water during the spring runoff—when it's not needed. And the largest increases are in wet years, not during drought. So logging for water would require new and enlarged reservoirs, something that Owens has already indicated is a top priority.

The Owens administration has been careful to cast this as a forest health effort, saying that increased logging can serve the dual benefit of reducing wildfire risk while providing more water as forests are returned to a more "natural" state.

But the dry, over-dense pine forests that burned last summer never get enough snow to be sources of water to begin with. And a major logging effort in the

---

*Due to permission restrictions, Blackline Master 15.6 does **not** appear on the *Teacher Resource CD*.

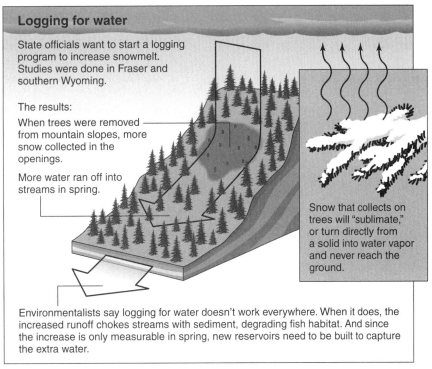

Logging for water

State officials want to start a logging program to increase snowmelt. Studies were done in Fraser and southern Wyoming.

The results:

When trees were removed from mountain slopes, more snow collected in the openings.

More water ran off into streams in spring.

Snow that collects on trees will "sublimate," or turn directly from a solid into water vapor and never reach the ground.

Environmentalists say logging for water doesn't work everywhere. When it does, the increased runoff chokes streams with sediment, degrading fish habitat. And since the increase is only measurable in spring, new reservoirs need to be built to capture the extra water.

Source: Denver Post research.

high country will necessarily mean less money, is available to thin the Front Range red zone that burned so fiercely in 2002.

Generating water requires cutting the moist high snow forests that only burn once every few centuries, when drought makes them so flammable that no amount of thinning or firebreaks will help.

"The link between logging for fire mitigation and logging for water is a false one," said environmental hydrologist Dan Luecke of Boulder.

EXPERIMENT TRIED IN FRASER

Most of the research on how logging can increase runoff in the Rockies has been done at the experimental forest in Fraser, where water yield from the 714-acre Fool Creek watershed has been continuously monitored for 60 years.

Foresters removed 40 percent of the watershed's trees with alternating strips of clear-cuts in 1956, and documented a 40 percent increase in water flowing through a gauge at the bottom of the valley when compared with a nearby watershed that was not cut.

And the yield has been long-lived—four decades later, half of the increase can still be measured at a stream gauge at the foot of the valley, said retired Forest Service researcher Chuck Troendle, whose work underpins much of the support for logging for water.

Flows increased the most during wet years, and almost not at all during droughts, he said. That means the

surplus water has to be captured in reservoirs and stored—perhaps for many years—until it's needed.

But Troendle also found that the number of high-flow days each spring doubled, resulting in increased scouring of the stream channel.

The only large-scale demonstration of the concept was implemented on the 4,100-acre Coon Creek watershed of the Encampment River in southern Wyoming. Twenty-four percent of the watershed was removed in patch cuts during the early 1990s, producing a 17 percent increase in flow, said Troendle.

Two years ago, Troendle calculated that 185,000 acre-feet of water a year could be created by a logging program that cut half of the 1.1 million acres of national forest land in the North Platte watershed over a 120-year period.

But he also said any increase in streamflow downstream of the forest would be so small that it would be undetectable.

Holsinger said the state intends to—increase logging on the 70,000-acre Colorado State Forest in Jackson County immediately. And he said the Owens administration wants all national forest plans to identify increasing water yield as a primary goal.

Clear-cutting would be required on lodgepole pine stands, a practice that would eat away at habitat favored by the federally threatened lynx and other interior forest species. The result would be the clusters of openings found at Coon Creek, which Troendle acknowledges have a significant environmental impact.

"It's pure destruction," said Luecke, as he examined a photo of the watershed. "It looks like it was carpet-bombed. This is an outrageous idea. There's no way it can be economically viable."

Troendle said thinning could be used in the spruce-fir forests where most of Colorado's water-bearing snowpack collects. But the proportion of trees removed—25 percent to 40 percent—would have to be the same.

SUCCESS ELSEWHERE DOUBTED

Many scientists, however, doubt that logging for water would be as successful in other parts of Colorado. In the 1970s. Richard Gandagno studied what happened to runoff after ski runs were cut at Eldora Mountain.

He discovered that deep snow collected in the spruce-fir stands, while the open runs were scoured almost bare by the winds — the exact opposite of what Troendle found in the Fraser study just a few miles away.

Troendle's studies also showed that cutting on the slopes with the wrong exposure or too much wind would result in no new water.

And the environmental cost could be immense. Removing trees causes erosion, which clogs streams with sediment that stifles habitat for fish and aquatic insects, environmentalists said.

"You're completely altering the hydrology of these systems for a short-term gain in water quantity," said Wood, now the vice president for conservation programs at Trout Unlimited. "But the long-term impacts on water quality and wildlife are immense."

Greg Aplet, a forest ecologist with the Wilderness Society, said that the amount of water flowing off Colorado's middle-aged forests is about to naturally increase as they mature into old-growth stands. The uniform tops of today's forests may intercept snowfall, but gaps caused by insects and storm damage in old-growth forests help capture snowfall.

"These forests are just at the point where water yield should come back on its own," Aplet said. "Why reset the clock now?"

Despite the official support, many environmentalists think economics will be the idea's undoing.

"You have to ask two questions: How much will it cost and what else could we be doing with the money?" said Luecke.

"The Forest Service has been losing money on logging projects in Colorado for a long time," he said. "It's expensive to build roads and log on steep slopes, and Colorado trees just don't get that big. That's why the timber industry has largely abandoned the state."

"The fact you do need to virtually clear-cut an entire area to get some measurable runoff—and then only in certain years—makes this such a long shot it doesn't seem to be worth all that effort," said former Colorado Natural Resources director David Getches, now a law professor at the University of Colorado.

"We haven't done any planning for the state's water future, and we're growing like crazy," Getches said. "Frankly, decision-makers have been caught flat-footed, and they want to do something. I hope they don't do something destructive."

"We're not going to solve water problems in the West by focusing on the supply side," said Wood. "We need to find ways to be more efficient with the water we have."

TASKS

Sample answers are provided on p. 346 of the *Teacher Guide.*

1. Give three arguments supporting massive clear-cutting of forests in the mountains of southwestern portions of the United States.

_____

_____

_____

2. Give three arguments against the massive clear-cutting of forests in the mountains of southwestern portions of the United States.

_____

_____

_____

Thicker Forests, Hotter Fires

We should strive for conditions that are ecologically sustainable and reduce wildfire risk

By Merrill R. Kaufmann

As a forest ecologist who has studied the area now being transformed by the Hayman Fire, I have been called by journalists and others asking if the fire is burning naturally and should be accepted as an essential ecosystem process. Are recent fires really worse than they were historically?

Some suggest that the fires are natural and should be left to burn, even if they destroy manmade structures. Others argue that land managers should reduce wildfire hazards only through careful use of prescribed fire—without any mechanical treatment to reduce forest fuels before igniting the forest.

Some answers are in fact available and research sheds some light on the challenge before us. Scientific investigation in the Upper South Platte Watershed Restoration Project, and at other research sites from Arizona's Grand Canyon rim to South Dakota's Black Hills to Montana's Bitterroot Mountains, have revealed much about fire history in low-elevation ponderosa pine forests.

Although many ponderosa pine forests across the West are in much the same condition, I'll focus my comments on lower-elevation forests along the Colorado Front Range where my own scientific investigations and the work of associates reveal much about the Hayman and other recent fires near Denver.

These forests have been severely impacted by logging, grazing and fire suppression. Historically, they were dominated by fire-resistant ponderosa pine, with lesser amounts of Douglas fir and other more fire-sensitive species that aren't as well adapted to surviving fire as are mature ponderosa pine. Current forests are younger, far denser and have many more fire-sensitive trees. Our research near Cheesman Reservoir, for instance, shows that fires in the ponderosa pine forests there occurred every 20 to 60 years, more frequently at lower elevations and less frequently at higher or drier sites.

The ponderosa pine zone covers about 4 million acres along the Colorado Front Range. If we assume an average interval between fires of 40 years, we could expect about 2.5 percent of the area, or 100,000 acres, to burn each year. Of course, more could have burned in severe fire years and less in wetter years.

Yet, we view the Buffalo Creek, Hi Meadow, Bobcat Gulch, Schoonover and Hayman fires as extreme—even though the total area burned is well below the historical annual average, Why?

Studies by my colleagues, and especially our research at Cheesman Reservoir, provide much-needed insight into our local historical fire behavior. Before the Hayman Fire burned this forest on June 10, we studied the frequency, size and severity of fires from the year 1197 to the present. Between 1534 and 1880, eight fires had a major influence on the density and species of trees covering the landscape.

These fires were relatively large, some of them 10,000 acres or more, and were "mixed" in severity. They spread primarily on the surface, with patches of locally more intense fire that killed some of the trees. The fires produced variable burn patterns and patchy forests, with rapid recovery of grasses, forbs and shrubs that protect the soil and minimize erosion. They created openings of 1 to perhaps 100 acres, generally by torching or scorching of individual trees. The openings were interspersed with woodlands having five to 50 trees per acre and with a few more densely forested areas. The openings created averaged less than 20 percent of the total area burned. The fires limited Douglas fir primarily to north slopes.

So, how do recent fires compare with the size of historical fires? Except for the Hayman Fire, the size of most

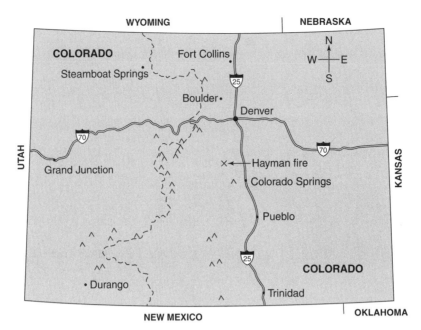

In Colorado, roughly 40%, of the land west of I-25 is forested. X marks the location of the Hayman-fire. The dashed line marks the continental divide. The ^ symbols show the locations of half of Colorado's 14-thousand foot peaks.

recent fires has been no more than 12,000 acres, well within the historical norm, though all were suppressed.

Fire severity is another matter. In the Buffalo Creek, Hi Meadow and Bobcat Gulch fires, crown fires created openings of 2,000 to 7,500 acres. Undoubtedly, the Hayman Fire is creating equally large intensely burned areas. Based on our research, it appears that recent fires are considerably more severe than occurred historically because they create much larger openings.

Crown fires now occur in place of the historically more typical mixed severity fires—because current forests have 10 to 20 times or more as many trees as historical forests. Our more severe modern wildfires kill more understory vegetation, destabilizing soils for several years until new vegetation develops. Extreme erosion occurred after the 1996 Buffalo Creek Fire and other large fires since then. We can expect the same from the Schoonover and Hayman fires this year.

So what can be done? One option is doing nothing except fire suppression, but the damage to Denver's municipal watershed and the many homes burned show the frightening consequences of that choice. A second option is reintroducing fire to restore forests to a sustainable condition. A third option is to use mechanical thinning to reduce biomass in the forest as a way to limit fire spread and severity. And a fourth option is using both prescribed fire and mechanical thinning.

Most agree that we should strive for a forest condition that is ecologically sustainable and that provides an acceptably low level of wildfire risk to vital watersheds, fish and wildlife, human lives and property. Restoring the open and patchy structure that forest landscapes had historically would help achieve what most people tell us they want.

Reintroducing fire by itself cannot solve the problems created by the current forest structure. Wildfires in recent years leave little doubt that fire is too unpredictable and too severe in these dense forests. Fire behavior specialists do not believe it is safe or even possible to create the spatial heterogeneity and openness desired without physically removing some of the biomass from current forests.

Demonstration treatments in the South Platte watershed illustrate the effectiveness of combining overstory thinning with burning of slash to create suitable stand densities and openings, and the restored conditions were acceptable to land owners.

As a scientist and resident of a Front Range community, I am troubled that we still have room for 400 more 10,000 acre fires or 40 more Hayman-size fires—any of which could occur in much more populated areas.

The National Fire Plan has injected important new funding into our research, which is helping us to better understand how to restore fire-dependent forests and protect critical water-sheds. Answers to scientific questions about forest ecosystems and water-sheds are now closer. Perhaps more difficult, Front Range communities must pull together to find ways to address the social and economic issues not as easily addressed by science.

Merrill R. Kaufmann is a research forest ecologist working for the U.S. Forest Service's Rocky Mountain Research Station in Fort Collins.

QUESTION

Sample answers are provided on p. 346 of the *Teacher Guide*.

How does Merrill R. Kaufmann, research forest ecologist, propose we better manage lower-elevation ponderosa pine forests? List three proposals.

_____

_____

_____

Adopt-a-Forest

Private, commercial help needed to speed up the tree-thinning process.

© 2002, Rocky Mountain News, by Dick Foster

President Bush will ask Coloradans to adopt a forest and clean out it's brush and light timber, much as they now adopt stretches of highway to clean up litter.

Interior Secretary Gale Norton said Bush's National Fire Plan revisions, announced in Oregon Thursday, will enlist private and commercial efforts to speed the cleanup of Western forests to prevent a repeat of the massive fires seen this summer.

Bush cited the 2002 fire season as one of the worst in modern history, with more than 5.9 million acres burned, 20 firefighters killed and 2,000 homes destroyed.

He called for sharply increased efforts to thin out forests clogged with decades of undergrowth that fuels blazes like the Hayman Fire, which burned out the heart of Colorado's Pike National Forest, charring more than 137,000 acres in 24 days this summer.

For decades, national policy had leaned toward fire suppression, which created the current predicament, the growth of fuels that feed the huge fires like this summer's. Grass, small trees and brush provide a "ladder" for the fire to climb into treetops of the forest's big trees and race uncontrollably for miles.

The National Fire Plan signed by President Clinton in 2000 increased funds to thin the forests either mechanically or through controlled burns. But even with federal funding increases, the job of thinning the 197 million acres of forest is monumental.

"At the current rate, as the president pointed out today, our thinning process would take 100 years to complete," Norton said.

Colorado alone has 14 million acres of national forest. Last year the U.S. Forest Service was able to thin about 50,000 acres through the National Fire Plan.

"That's a drop in the bucket," said Forest Service spokesman Dave Steinke. Private cooperation, and lots of it, is needed to speed the process of thinning the vast expanses of forest across the West, Norton said.

"For us, the best benefit is through innovative ideas that would come through stewardship contracts that the Forest Service or a Department of Interior agency would enter into with an organization to take care of a particular area of forest," Norton said after meeting Thursday with Bush.

"Those organizations might be local governments or nonprofit organizations or commercial enterprises," she said. In some states, commercial logging will probably be increased to speed forest thinning, and Bush has urged reducing regulatory obstacles that slow down the clearing projects.

But Colorado may not be among the states that see an increase in commercial timbering, Norton said.

"Colorado forests are not the highest-value commercial timber areas," she said. When Colorado forests are thinned of small trees, "We have to find creative ways of using those small trees."

But if there is no commerical appeal to thinning Colorado forests, there are public safety and economic necessities in protecting the state's burgeoning mountain communities and tourist attractions, Norton said. "If there are communities that want to volunteer to do some of the thinning, or if the tourism industry wants to volunteer to protect some of its investment, we are trying to build partnerships," she said. "There are all kinds of things that we might want to examine. When you get people involved in trying to solve a problem, they come up with solutions you never thought of."

QUESTIONS

Sample answers are provided on p. 346 of the *Teacher Guide*.

1. Why was the adopt-a-forest plan proposed?

_____

_____

_____

2. How does adopt-a-forest work?

_____

_____

_____

3. Is liability insurance a concern here? Explain.

_____

_____

_____

Fire Plan Carries Opportunity, Risk

By Greg Aplet

For decades, scientists have recognized that the exclusion of fire from forests results in negative consequences to forest health. Because of fire's many benefits, including cycling of nutrients, regeneration of seedlings and the maintenance of healthy forest conditions, scientists have called for the restoration of fire as a key ecological process. The work involved is expensive, though, and historically, Congress has not made the funds available to federal land managers.

In 2000, wildfires burned more acreage than had burned in any single year since the 1940s, costing almost $2 billion in taxpayer money to fight. In response, politicians wishing to "do something" joined fiscal conservatives concerned about the mounting expense of fire fighting to fund a $2 billion program to improve fire-fighting effectiveness and reduce the threat of fire before it starts. In 2001, Congress again allocated more than $1.6 billion dollars to this "National Fire Plan" (an amalgamation of agency policies and congressional direction), and some expect this level of spending to continue for 10 or more years. If focused on the right priorities, such a massive federal expenditure could result in real benefits to wildland ecosystems. If misdirected, though, the National Fire Plan may make matters worse.

The National Fire Plan represents Congress' first significant effort to address the fuel issue and could lead to the restoration of fire to fire-dependent ecosystems. Alternatively, the plan may result simply in more money being poured into fire fighting and its infrastructure, resulting in greater fire suppression and its attendant negative effects on ecosystem health. Unless this cycle is broken, the National Fire Plan is likely only to exacerbate the problem of fuel buildup and poor forest health, rather than solve it. While suppression's effects are not always obvious to people, the pervasiveness of its influence represents one of the greatest threats to the sustainability of wild lands nationwide.

In addition to threats posed by more suppression, fear of fire has led to some radical proposals to "fire-proof" forests by logging out the fuels. While it is necessary in some cases to treat fuels in order to restore a healthy, fire-sustaining forest structure, some have extended the logic to argue that if enough trees are removed, fire can be eliminated as a threat. The fault in this logic is twofold. First, fire cannot be eliminated from the forest. As fire historian Stephen Pyne has noted, "As long as [America] retains its wildlands, those wildlands will burn." Second, eliminating fire would have devastating effects on ecosystems both because of its effects on natural processes and because critical elements, such as roadless areas and old-growth forests, are likely to be lost in the "fireproofing" process.

If the National Fire Plan is going to result in real benefits to communities and ecosystems, it must focus not on eliminating fire, but on restoring fire to fire-dependent ecosystems. The first step in this process is to protect homes so that people feel safe enough to allow fire back into the forest. There is much that homeowners and local governments can do to minimize risks, including treating fuels immediately adjacent to homes, modifying buildings to resist flames, and guiding development by educating homebuilders in the "wildland/urban interface."

Next, the National Fire Plan must fund the planning necessary to allow natural fires to burn. Until fire management plans are updated to encourage natural fires, managers by law must suppress them, thus thwarting the most effective and cost-efficient way to restore fire to ecosystems.

Where natural fires cannot be allowed to burn safely, the National Fire Plan must encourage the intentional reintroduction of fire under controlled conditions. With good communication among all parties and more resources to ensure that fire will not produce undesirable effects, these "prescribed burns" can be conducted safely. Only as a last resort should we have to cut trees far from homes.

If the National Fire Plan can stay focused on restoring fire, rather than preventing it, it has a strong chance of addressing one of the West's most vexing natural resource challenges.

TASKS

Sample answers are provided on p. 346 of the *Teacher Guide*.

1. List some of the benefits of having forests burn periodically.

_____

_____

_____

2. If fire is to be restored to our national forests, Greg Aplet, forest ecologist, says we must do three things. List them.

_____

_____

_____

Fire Risk-Ratings: An Idea Whose Time Has Come

By Bruce Babbitt

The huge fires flaring across dry Western landscapes are mounting toward the worst fire season in memory. By the time autumn brings relief, losses will likely exceed even the 7 million acres burned during the chaotic fire season of 2000. And the evidence suggests that we are now entering a prolonged fire cycle in which extreme years will be the norm rather than the exception.

These fires inevitably bring exasperated calls for more firefighters, more air power and vastly increased firefighting budgets. But more money and manpower won't help much. The fire problem is beyond effective control by traditional responses. And if we can't banish fire we are going to have to do a better job of living with it.

One problem is climate. With the onset of global warming, the West is becoming hotter and drier. The forests themselves are also changing. They are becoming denser, with more small trees and dead and downed fuel, the ironic result of the total fire-suppression policies of the century past.

And there is the matter of lifestyle. All across the West, Americans are moving out of the cities and into the mountains and forests, placing themselves and their property directly in harm's way. It is these factors that we must examine in order to coexist with the firestorms still to come.

Back in the fire season of 2000, we began working with Congress to create a National Fire Plan. The idea was to create "defensible space" in the interface between fire-prone forests and our rural communities. That plan now provides funds to states and local communities to thin the thickets of small trees that cause fires to spread with explosive force and to apply prescribed fire to keep fuel loads down.

These programs are now being implemented around the Western United States and over time they will help protect our rural communities. But even as we work to modify forest conditions on the edge of ru-

ral communities, we continue to ignore an even larger problem: the very way we live in and near forests and fire-prone landscapes.

In the summer of 1996, I inspected a fire scene near San Diego where a fire sweeping through a nearby ravine had showered burning embers down on a new subdivision. About every fourth house was reduced to a pile of smoldering ashes. The houses left standing had one common feature: red tile roofs. The fire chief explained that the burned-out residences all had wooden shake-shingle roofs.

In the wake of that visit, I asked my staff to research building codes around the West. What I learned was that in most rural areas there are no code requirements for the use of fire resistant materials in home construction. And in many rural counties, there were not even any building codes. Every summer we are putting thousands of firefighters and air-tanker pilots at risk trying to save buildings for owners who refuse to take even simple precautions to protect their property by using proper building materials and clearing firebreaks around their property.

I also learned that casualty and property insurers who write homeowner insurance are part of the problem. After seeing that burned-over subdivision, I asked California insurance companies whether they rate the homes they insure for fire risk. Risk-rating would provide lower rates for homeowners who do take fire precautions, thereby creating incentives for fire protection. The answer I got was, "No, we can't be bothered. It's easier just to figure the losses into the rates that we charge everyone." So homeowners who do take precautions are paying extra insurance premiums to cover those who don't.

Mandating building codes for fire protection and requiring property insurance risk-rating are steps that every state in the West could take right now to reduce fire damage. Rural residents may object that these ideas infringe on their right to live and build however they want—and they will be among the first to demand that firefighters risk their lives to protect them when fire inevitably does come. Most of our large cities already use risk-rating and building-code enforcement—and it is now time to extend these procedures out into the rest of the land. That is the most important and urgent lesson from the summer of 2002.

Bruce Babbitt was secretary of the Interior during the Clinton administration.

© Bruce Babbitt

NOTE: In addition to tile or metal roofs, a fire risk-rating system might also give credits for use of fire-resistant siding on buildings, thinning of small trees and the clearing of brush in the "Red Zone," clearing brush from vacant lots, wider county roads that serve as fire breaks, volunteer fire departments, and water systems that include fire hydrants.

QUESTIONS

Sample answers are provided on p. 346 of the *Teacher Guide*.

1. How does Bruce Babbitt, former Secretary of the Interior, propose providing incentive for property owners in the "Red Zone" (or forestland-urban interface) to reduce their fire danger.

_____

_____

_____

2. What corrective actions might these property owners take?

_____

_____

_____

Name_____ Date_____ Period _____

Article	Short Summary
1. A Clear-Cut Drought Solution?	
2. Thicker Forests, Hotter Fires.	
3. Adopt-a-Forest.	
4. Fire Plan Carries Opportunities, Risk.	
5. Fire Risk-Ratings: An Idea Whose Time Has Come.	

Name _____ Date _____

DISPOSING OF TOXIC WASTE

The following is a list of six strategies for disposing of toxic waste. Rank these six strategies from 1 = best to 6 = worst and then justify your ranking.

Method	Description and/or examples	Ranking (1 = Best)	Justification of Ranking
Dilution	Add H_2O until down to legal level and dispose.		
Out of Sight	• Shoot into space. • Bury it. • Dump in ocean.		
Waste Reclamation	Change waste to valuable product. Recover and sell.		
Chemical Alteration	Change waste to nontoxic substance and dispose.		
Containment	Tie up in concrete, a barrel, or special dump.		
Waste Minimization	• Only buy what you need. • Substitute nontoxic for toxic.		

Name_____ Date_____

MULTIPLE CHOICE

1. _____ Which one of the following devices is used to control the use of property (land)?
   A. zoning
   B. convenants
   C. contracts
   D. traditional controls
   E. all of these

2. _____ Which category of land use in the United States is the *smallest?*
   A. urban and recreational
   B. pasture and grazing land
   C. deserts, swamps, and other
   D. cropland
   E. forest and woodland

3. _____ Land use includes all of the following *except*
   A. parks.
   B. housing.
   C. farming.
   D. industrial.
   E. deserts.

4. _____ Which one of the following is most closely associated with land use decisions in the United States?
   A. state legislators
   B. U.S. senators
   C. state governors
   D. the president
   E. county commissioners

5. _____ Being stewards of the land means to
   A. reconstruct the land to meet our needs.
   B. do major engineering projects now and hope that science can help correct our mistakes later.
   C. study the natural forces in a region and work with nature efforts to meet human needs.
   D. conquer the forces of nature through the application of engineering techniques and the use of electrical- and gasoline-powered machinery.

6. _____ Which statement about mined land reclamation is *not* true?
   A. The soil and rock that cover a mineral deposit is called overburden.
   B. The best seed mixtures for reclamation contain a mixture of good starter grass and native vegetation.
   C. Coal strip mines can be reclaimed, but uranium mines and sand and gravel excavations cannot.
   D. The cost of reclamation adds only a few *percent* to the cost of the mineral that is mined.
   E. Careful land reclamation adds to the cost of the coal or other mineral that is mined.

7. _____ The *Mobro 4,000*
   A. was filled with manure and agricultural wastes.
   B. became a symbol of our nation's mounting waste disposal problem.
   C. sunk in 6000 feet of water.
   D. illustrated well the attitude "waste minimization."
   E. eventually docked and unloaded its cargo in the Bahamas.

8. _____ The largest category of municipal solid waste is
   A. yard wastes.   D. paper and paperboard.
   B. glass.   E. metals.
   C. food wastes.

9. _____ The law that addresses the cleanup of inactive and abandoned hazardous waste sites and is sometimes called the *Superfund* is more correctly called
   A. EPA.   D. CERCLA.
   B. RCRA.   E. ZPG.
   C. HSWA.

10. _____ Hazardous wastes are put into all of these classifications *except*
   A. flammable or explosive.   D. toxic.
   B. corrosive.   E. radioactive.
   C. biodegradable.

11. _____ The burning of municipal solid waste to reduce its volume, reclaim some valuable substances, and, in some communities, produce steam is referred to as
   A. recycling.   D. incineration.
   B. biological breakdown. E. hazardous waste isolation.
   C. sanitary landfill.

12. _____ Your textbook takes which of the following positions on the use of technology?
   A. Technology is the main cause of our environmental problems.
   B. There are no problems technology can't solve.
   C. Technology is both part of the problem and part of the solution.
   D. Individual freedoms are more important than social needs.

13. _____ A substance that dissolves in water and breaks up into ions is
   A. an electrolyte.   D. electroplating.
   B. a current.   E. an electrode.
   C. a nonelectrolyte.

14. _____ The toxic substance in the electroplating lab we did was
   A. solid copper.   D. a precipitate.
   B. silicate.   E. copper ion.
   C. cement.

15. _____ The NIMBY Syndrome refers to:
   A. The high cost of environmental impact statements.
   B. Not wanting to live near certain types of land use.
   C. Restricting the human use of wilderness to low-impact activities.
   D. The concept of highest and best use of land.
   E. The designation of "Superfund" sites.

16. _____ Why is it desirable to solidify and fix hazardous wastes?
   A. They will not explode.
   B. They occupy less space and therefore can be transported more inexpensively.
   C. They resist the action of water and other liquids and therefore can be put in landfills.
   D. They can be processed into inexpensive sources of energy.

17. _____ All of the following are problems related to the dilution solution for disposing of toxic wastes except one. Which one is *not* a problem?
   A. The toxins are released into the environment.
   B. The toxins could again become concentrated (biologically).
   C. The disposal method is very complicated and difficult to do.
   D. The disposal requires huge quantities of water.

Resource Management: Land

18. _____ Which one of the following is the *best* strategy for dealing with the waste management problem?
A. waste minimization
B. out of sight
C. containment
D. dilution
E. chemical alteration

19. _____ All of the following can be done in an area designated as wilderness *except*
A. backpacking.
B. photography of wildlife.
C. cross-country skiing.
D. snowmobiling.
E. canoeing.

20. _____ Which of the following is *not* a benefit of wetlands?
A. They produce nutrients that support sport and commercial fishing.
B. They occupy land that is often prime real estate.
C. They help control erosion along coastlines.
D. They help recharge groundwater aquifers.
E. They soak up pollutants from nearby industries and farms.

21. _____ All of the following agencies manage federal lands *except*
A. U.S. Postal Service.
B. Bureau of Land Management.
C. National Park Service.
D. Fish and Wildlife Service.
E. U.S. Forest Service.

22. _____ Environmental Impact Statements (EISs) are required by
A. Department of Justice.
B. Clean Air Act.
C. National Environmental Policy Act.
D. FBI.
E. Occupational Safety and Health Act.

23. _____ Which of the following does *not* decrease desertification?
A. xeriscaping
B. drip irrigation
C. gathering of firewood in poorer nations
D. restrictions on the use of ORVs
E. watering restrictions in arid climates

24. _____ This symbol ♻ stands for
A. detour ahead.
B. reduce, reuse, recycle.
C. three strikes and you're out.
D. do not pass go.
E. return copper ions to disposal container.

25. _____ This federal agency has been charged with regulating and enforcing the proper disposal of hazardous waste.
A. Department of Interior
B. Governor's Office
C. Secretary of State
D. EPA
E. Congress

26. _____ As a life supporting system, a city must:
   I. import material resources
   II. have ways to remove waste
   III. maintain inputs and outputs of energy

A. I only
B. I and II
C. II and III
D. I and III
E. I, II, and III

27. _____ In the United States, _____% of the population lives in urban areas.
    A. 25   D. 75
    B. 40   E. 90
    C. 60

28. _____ Which one of the following is *not* required in an Environmental Impact Statement?
    A. An analysis of the need for the project.
    B. A comparison of reasonable alternative projects.
    C. A description of the environment affected by the project.
    D. A vote of the country commissioners in the project area.
    E. A discussion of the impacts of the proposed project and those of the possible alternatives.

29. _____ In the United States, this type of land is found mostly in the eastern half
    A. deserts   D. wilderness
    B. forest land   E. federal land
    C. agricultural land

30. _____ These lands provide more biomass per square meter per year than any other lands
    A. wetlands   D. wilderness
    B. deserts   E. grasslands
    C. forest lands

SHORT ANSWER

If your local community desires to establish a nature preserve and has a choice of several parcels of land, what type of parcel should you choose?

Choose the parcel of land which is

_____

_____

_____

BLACKLINE MASTER 15.6   A CLEAR-CUT DROUGHT SOLUTION?

1. a. Cutting the trees frees up water in a water poor area.
   b. Removal of large areas of trees reduces the fire danger.
   c. Extra water would help aquatic species (fish).
2. a. Flooding and mudslides would increase because trees hold soil.
   b. Stream quality would decrease as they fill with silt and mud.
   c. Extra water, if produced at all, only is produced in the Spring (when it is not needed). To use it, new dams and reservoirs would have to be built.

BLACKLINE MASTER 15.7   THICKER FORESTS, HOTTER FIRES

1. Reintroduce fire to restore forests to a sustainable condition.
2. Use mechanical thinning to reduce biomass in the forest as a way to limit fire spread and severity.
3. Use both prescribed fire and mechanical thinning.

BLACKLINE MASTER 15.8   ADOPT-A-FOREST

1. The amount of forest land in need of thinning is so large that professional crews can't do the job in a reasonable time.
2. The Forest Service or a Department of the Interior agency would sign a contract with an organization to take care of a particular area of forest. These organizations might be local governments, non-profit organizations, or commercial enterprises.
3. Cutting down trees and hauling forest waste is dangerous work. One can imagine chain saws cutting, trees falling, trucks moving about, Boy Scouts or little children running around unsupervised, and a whole host of other possibilities. If someone gets badly hurt, who is at fault? Who pays? Enough said. (P.S. Your author was an Eagle Scout.)

BLACKLINE MASTER 15.9   FIRE PLAN CARRIES OPPORTUNITY, RISK

1. Benefits include cycling of nutrients, regeneration of seedlings, and maintenance of healthy forest conditions → fires kill diseases and molds.
2. a. Protect homes so people will let fire back into the forests.
   b. Develop plans to allow natural fires to burn.
   c. Use controlled or prescribed burns when conditions are right. It is too expensive to cut trees far from roads and homes.

BLACKLINE MASTER 15.10   FIRE RISK-RATINGS: AN IDEA WHOSE TIME HAS COME

1. Require insurance companies to assign fire risk-ratings to homes and buildings they insure. Include fire protection in local building codes.
2. They might put tile or metal roofs on buildings. Use fire-resistant siding. Thin the forests near homes and buildings and remove brush and dead branches from vacant lots. County roads can be widened

so they serve as fire-breaks. Volunteer fire departments can be formed. Water distribution systems including hydrants can be built. It all costs money, but the alternative is not pleasant.

CHAPTER 15 ASSESSMENT

1. E
2. A
3. E
4. E
5. C
6. C
7. B
8. D
9. D
10. C
11. D
12. C
13. A
14. E
15. B
16. C
17. C
18. A
19. D
20. B
21. A
22. C
23. C
24. B
25. D
26. E
27. D
28. D
29. B
30. A

SHORT ANSWER

Choose the parcel of land which is:

1. Largest in size.
2. Most compact (square or round, not drawn out).
3. Has the most varied topography.

OPTIONS FOR THE FUTURE

LEARNING OUTCOMES

The student will:

1. speculate on how a fictitious island looked 350 years ago and how it looks today by completing the activity "Pioneers and Their Island." (C,P,A)

2. interpolate and extrapolate a graph of population, agricultural production, and resource use on a fictitious island by completing the activity "Graphing the Status of the Island." (C,P)

3. list three major reasons why the growth ethic has deep origins in the United States by writing a response. (C)

4. list five factors that determine growth on our planet. (C)

5. list three characteristics these five factors have in common. (C)

6. interpret a graph of pollution damage and cleanup cost by completing the activity "Trade-offs." (C)

7. state how allowing a small amount of pollution from automobiles can lead to environmental problems in some of our larger cities. (C)

8. evaluate a group of assumptions based on two different views of the world by rank ordering statements from the activity "Do We Live in Two Different Worlds?" (A)

9. examine the process of conflict resolution and relate it to resource use by completing the activity "Resource Allocation." (C,A,P)

10. name and briefly summarize the two major economic systems. (C)

11. state the Law of Supply and Demand by writing a sentence. (C)

12. list the two major features of the market system. (C)

13. list seven problems associated with pure free market economics. (C)

14. list five functions most governments are asked to perform to remedy problems that the market system cannot solve on its own. (C)

15. identify which governmental economic function could be used in a variety of situations and explain why the action promotes the function by completing the activity "The Economic Role of the Government." (C)

16. list strategies for dealing with population growth, resource depletion, and economic inequities by completing the activity "Strategies for Building a Sustainable World." (C)

17. recognize that some values from early America regarding resources have changed and

state why they changed by completing the activity "Changes in Attitudes." (A)

18. list social forces that tend to reduce the growth of human population. (C)

19. list methods for slowing the depletion of non-renewable resources. (C)

20. list methods that are used to expand opportunities for people. (C)

21. examine the economics of recycling aluminum by completing the activity "Recycling Aluminum." (C,P)

22. make a graph that projects the ideal future for a stranded population on an island by including population, resource use, and agricultural production by completing the activity "The Island Revisited." (C)

23. draw a map showing population distribution and resource use by a stranded populace on an island by completing the activity "The Island Revisited." (C,P)

24. write a scenario of the possible future of a stranded populace on an island and explain the social process the group would go through to attain long-term survival by completing the activity "The Island Revisited." (C)

25. describe the ways one is like a passenger on a spaceship. (C)

26. write a letter, pay a visit, or analyze consumption habits by completing the activity "Taking Action on Resource/Environmental Issues." (C,A)

27. take a quiet walk and record some personal thoughts about where he or she is, how he or she relates to what is going on around, and about the balance that exists between humans and nature by completing the activity "Introspection." (A)

KEY TERMS

pluralistic	forestall	Law of Supply
interrelated	United Nations (UN)	market equilibrium
simulate	economics	competition
The Limits to Growth	market economy	equity
variables	free enterprise (market)	sustainable economics
extrapolate	price	mechanism
sustainable	demand	tax incentive
conflict resolution	Law of Demand	value
foresee	supply	

RECOMMENDED BLACKLINE MASTERS

16.1   Graphical Representation of the Island
16.2   Simplified World Model
16.3   Standard World Model
16.4   The Sustainable Society
16.5   Trade-Offs
16.6   Strategies for Building a Sustainable World
16.7   Projection of Resource Use

The Recommended Blackline Masters listed above are supplemental to the activity/reading, and can be found on the *Teacher Resource CD*.

CHAPTER 16: OPTIONS FOR THE FUTURE

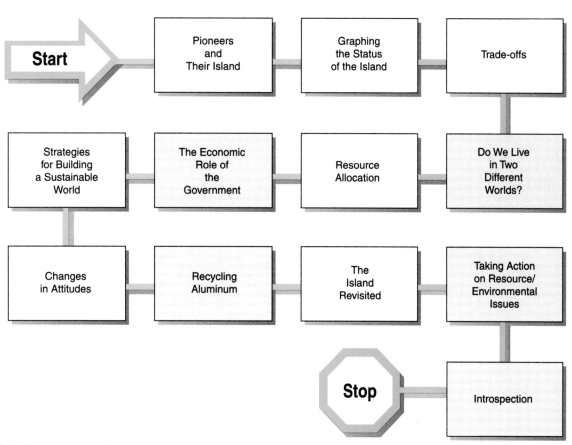

NOTE: Shaded items are lower priority.

TEACHING STRATEGIES AND ANSWERS FOR ACTIVITIES

ACTIVITY 16.1 PIONEERS AND THEIR ISLAND

See *Student Edition*, p. 674.

ADVANCE PREPARATION

Obtain one large sheet of white paper per group (butcher paper, newsprint work well). Provide each group access to six colors of magic markers: red, black, blue, green, yellow, and brown.

STRATEGIES AND PROCEDURES

Day 1

Presentation of the problem (5 min.).

Discuss what the people did for the first days and months (5 min.).

Groups speculate and draw what the island looks like today, 350 years later (30 min.). The drawings (maps) need some kind of key to indicate important features. Each group needs to plan a 5-minute presentation that involves each person in the group. They must state what the population is now and how they determined it. The first five items of the assignment must be covered.

Day 2

Island presentations and teacher-directed closure (40 min.).

Doubling time = 70/2.8 = 25 years. Number of doublings = 350/25 = 14.

Present population = 2,048,000 people. This is about half the present population of New Zealand or Colorado. It will equal those populations in only 25 years!

16.1

Transparency 16.1

ACTIVITY 16.2 Graphing the Status of the Island

See *Student Edition*, p. 675.

STRATEGIES AND PROCEDURES

Have the groups work on the assignment for the first 15–20 minutes of class. You may want to photocopy Blackline Master 16.1 for each student or for each group. Make sure they read the assignment *carefully*. Then have different groups report and state their assumptions.

RESULTS

The population grows exponentially for the first 350 years and plots as a "J." The extrapolation depends on students' assumptions. The nonrenewable resources graph is a "shrinking J." The extrapolation depends on their assumptions. The agricultural production curve most likely keeps up with the population curve. Historically, that has been the case. However, the extrapolation depends on their assumptions. *Identify the assumptions.*

This activity feeds directly into Readings 16.1–16.7 of the textbook. You will probably cover this material in a more traditional format. See the Chapter 16 Study Guide.

READING 16.1 Growth in a Finite System

See *Student Edition*, p. 676.

16.2, 16.3

Transparency 16.2

READING 16.2 The Limits to Growth Report

See *Student Edition*, p. 677.

16.4

Transparency 16.3

READING 16.3 Responding to the Prediction of Doom

See *Student Edition*, p. 679.

READING 16.4 CRITICISMS OF *THE LIMITS TO GROWTH* REPORT

See *Student Edition,* p. 680.

READING 16.5 ACCOMPLISHMENTS OF *THE LIMITS TO GROWTH* REPORT

See *Student Edition,* p. 683.

 16.4

Transparency 16.3

READING 16.6 *THE LIMITS TO GROWTH* REVISED

See *Student Edition,* p. 683.

READING 16.7 OTHER VIEWS OF THE FUTURE

See *Student Edition,* p. 684.

ACTIVITY 16.3 TRADE-OFFS

See *Student Edition,* p. 689.

 16.5

ADVANCE PREPARATION

You may wish to make a transparency of Blackline Master 16.5.

STRATEGIES AND PROCEDURES

This is primarily a graphical interpretation activity. Some of your students may have trouble understanding what the graph indicates, partly because the horizontal axis goes from 100 to 0. Point that out. The ideas presented in this activity are very important to future topics; make certain students understand them.

SAMPLE ANSWERS TO ASSIGNMENT QUESTIONS

1. Increases.
2. Increases.
3. In this case, acceptable costs are costs we are willing to pay for some pollution damages for us to continue to have or enjoy something else.
4. Decreases.
5. We are willing to accept some pollution and not pay for the damages so we can spend the money we save on other things we enjoy (desire). *Note:* We may not even be fully aware of the fact that we are paying for reduced agricultural production and/or increased hospital care (through increased insurance rates).
6. Up to a point—yes. Small amounts of sewage dumped into a river will be treated (digested) by the bacteria that live naturally in the river. A short distance downstream, the water may be "clean" and acceptable for use by someone else.

7. The ability of natural systems to cleanse themselves of pollutants has an upper limit. A small amount of pollution from each automobile may become intolerable if there are too many cars. Too many cars means that the *total* amount of pollution produced by all the cars is more than the air of a given region can handle. This condition is reached when the plants, animals, and/or humans in that region begin to suffer negative effects from the pollution—eye irritation, respiratory problems, leaf damage, and so on.

8. Grade on depth of thought.

ACTIVITY 16.4 DO WE LIVE IN TWO DIFFERENT WORLDS?

See *Student Edition*, p. 690.

This activity is designed to lead into a consideration of the sustainable world. Students need to realize that each of them views the world from a perspective that is different from everyone else.

There are no right or wrong answers to this activity. The intent is that each student obtain information about where he or she stands in relation to the two contrasting world views. Students should simply receive a grade for doing the activity and/or for the manner in which they can state where they stand in terms of the eight selected items.

Public education must not be indoctrination. Do not impose your views on your students. We do, however, have an obligation to present varying points of view on various issues. We can ask students to think about controversial issues. Further, most teachers and students are not a complete fit in one "camp" or the other.

You may choose to tie this activity to the JFK quote.

READING 16.8 LIFE IN A SUSTAINABLE WORLD

See *Student Edition*, p. 692.

ACTIVITY 16.5 RESOURCE ALLOCATION

See *Student Edition*, p. 693.

ADVANCE PREPARATION MATERIALS

tokens (such as poker chips, pennies, cardboard squares, peanuts in the shell, 10 tokens per student)
rewards can be hard candies, or something else the students value
stopwatch, wall clock, or watch that indicates minutes and seconds
CD or tape player (optional)
CD or tape of lively music (optional)
science notebook (paper/pencil)

STRATEGIES AND PROCEDURES

This activity introduces the topic of conflict resolution. It was purposely given the vague title "Resource Allocation" to not influence the outcome.

The best results are achieved when one type of competition evolves into another. This is most likely to occur if only minimal information is provided at the beginning.

Procedure (per group)

1. Seat the students in a circle (at a table or on the floor).
2. Count out, but do not distribute, 10 tokens for each student in the group. Put one-fourth of them in a separate pile.
3. At the center of each group, place the pile totaling one-fourth of all the tokens for that group. For example, if you have 10 students in a group, use 100 tokens and begin with 25 in the center.
4. Read the following rules twice to the students.

Rules

1. The tokens at the center of your table (or circle) represent valuable resources you can take and trade in for candy (or other desired item).
2. After "GO" has been signaled, you may take tokens out of the pool located near the center of your group.
3. You may trade in 10 tokens for a piece of candy (or other reward).
4. As soon as "STOP" is announced, I will double the number of tokens left in the pool at that time. The game will then continue. *Note:* There can never be more tokens in the pool than there were at the start of this activity. This is the maximum number of tokens the pool can hold.
5. You may not talk to anyone during the activity.
6. I will provide instructions on how this activity will continue.

Notes to the Teacher

Do *not* explain the significance of the tokens before playing the game. The rules are the only instructions the players get.

The players will most likely empty the pool at the start of the game. Point out that, as it's impossible to double zero, the game is over. Ask if they'd like to try again. Each student must return all of his or her tokens to the pool.

Continue to play the game for several rounds without giving the students time to communicate with one another in between.

When doubling the tokens in the pool, remember there can never be more tokens in the pool than there were at the start of the game. This is because, in any given year, only so much of a resource is available. That number is not likely to rise rapidly (from one year to the next), but it can fall quickly.

After several rounds, you may allow the students to talk so they can discuss strategies. This is a natural evolution when there is a desire to resolve a conflict or solve a problem between individuals or groups.

After five or six rounds, ask students how they feel about the way the game worked out. As a group, help students think of ways they could cooperate to allow more of them to get their 10 tokens without depleting the pool of resources. Play again using the strategies developed by the students.

1. The tokens represent resources (both renewable and nonrenewable). *Note:* Nonrenewable resources can be made available each year because they can be extracted and sold and new supplies discovered and developed.

2. It is unlikely the supply of resources will increase rapidly between rounds. This is because even if new supplies are discovered or new technologies come online, change is usually gradual. However, supplies can shrink rapidly due to increased demand, economic disruption, or natural disaster.

3. The removal of a resource from a pool, such as the cookie jar at home or "off the shelf" at the store, ultimately depletes the supply available to the group.

4. Some family members simply "watch out for themselves." Others care about the needs and feelings of other family members and learn to consider the needs/desires of others as they attempt to take care of their own needs (wants). The reward for such behavior is a more satisfying family experience.

5. Nations, like individuals, usually look after their own interests first. However, many nations have learned that a greater sense of purpose and security can be achieved by cooperating in various areas. Sometimes the cooperation is for economic advantage (OPEC, European Economic Community), other times it is for security (NATO).

6. In the early rounds, tokens are usually removed by one of the more aggressive group members. As the rounds progress, signals of dissatisfaction from other group members usually cause some restraint on aggressive behavior. Allowing some dialogue usually helps this process along. Sometimes a spirit of cooperation takes over—especially when the group begins to see that the greatest reward is achieved through cooperation.

7. Maximizing dialogue and cooperation produced the greatest gain.

8. To realize the greatest gain, individual group members had to realize that cooperation both fulfilled *their* needs plus brought gain to the *others*.

9. Maximum gain and minimum conflict is achieved when
    - there is a desire to minimize conflict and ill-feeling;
    - dialogue takes place; and
    - it is realized that all members gain by cooperating.

10. A "win-win" solution to a problem is where all parties to an agreement get something they desire. In the real world, this could be land, water, security, peace and quiet, a nature preserve, mineral wealth, and so on.

(Adapted from *People and the Planet,* an activity guide produced by Population Connection, Washington, DC., copyright 1996, 2004.)

READING 16.9 CONFLICT RESOLUTION

See *Student Edition,* p. 694.

After reading this section, you could have your students discuss this statement:

To be civilized means to choose dialogue over conflict, trust over cynicism, tolerance over ideology, and community over chaos. To function in a pluralistic society and a pluralistic world, civility is our only choice.

This statement could be related to some current event in the world.

This is a difficult exercise in that some of the answers are not clear-cut. A good class discussion should point out that the government is allowed to interfere with the economy for a variety of reasons.

1.   2   Allows other businesses to compete in the communications market.
2.   3   Prevents costly reclamation projects if deemed too damaging. The public objects to practices that tear up land and leave it worthless and ugly.
3.   1,5   Stabilizes the economy by preventing an oversupply or undersupply of money.
4.   4   Prevents monopoly of wealth by a small number of people generation after generation.
5.   5   Encourages production and consumption of domestic goods; reduces a drain on the economy.
6.   3   Increases the marketability of youth regardless of socioeconomic background.
7.   3,5   Maintains a productive labor force in times of business slumps; stabilizes production output.
8.   4,3   Gives educational opportunities to needy persons, which aids in their marketability.
9.   1,3   National security ensures business as usual.
10.   4   Encourages equal pay for equal work.
11.   1   Facilitates trade negotiations; protects consumers from being "ripped-off" in the marketplace.
12.   5   Helps prevent spiraling inflation.
13.   2   Encourages competition among fledgling companies.

14. 3   Prevents costly health expenses and cleanup projects; prevents innocent parties from having to pay for the pollution caused by others.

15. 2   Increases competition by allowing more business to be introduced into the marketplace.

READING 16.14 SUSTAINABLE ECONOMIES

See *Student Edition*, p. 703.

ACTIVITY 16.7 STRATEGIES FOR BUILDING A SUSTAINABLE WORLD

See *Student Edition*, p. 704.

MECHANISMS FOR MAINTAINING A CONSTANT POPULATION

1. New career opportunities for women.
2. Promotion of smaller families.
3. Raise the standard of living.
4. Start families at a later age.
5. Demand by women for freedom over their reproductive lives.
6. Widespread availability of birth control.
7. Remove tax incentives for children.
8. Dictatorships that mandate family size.

MECHANISMS THAT LIMIT THE RATE AT WHICH RESOURCES PASS THROUGH AN ECONOMY

1. Change consumption attitudes—education.
2. Conservation.
3. Recycling.
4. More efficient technologies.
5. Higher prices for scarce resources.
6. Rationing of scarce resources.
7. Ban advertising.
8. Auction off depletion quotas.
9. Increase use of renewables.
10. Substitute common materials for scarce materials.
11. Promote research and development by government and industry.

MECHANISMS THAT CAN EXPAND OPPORTUNITIES FOR PEOPLE

1. Welfare plans that require work or training (a "hand up" not a "handout").
2. Focus education on those less fortunate.
3. Progressive income tax for the well off.

4. Negative income tax for poorer people.
5. Job training for the underemployed.
6. Expand loans and scholarship opportunities.
7. Expand VISTA (domestic peace corps) projects.
8. Community work programs for the unemployed.

READING 16.15 MAINTAINING A STABLE POPULATION

See *Student Edition*, p. 705.

ACTIVITY 16.8 CHANGES IN ATTITUDES

See *Student Edition*, p. 706.

While some may argue that values are absolute, a good case can be made for the fact that *many* of the values of modern society differ from those of the ancients. Our world view is different from theirs.

The fact that some values have changed does not imply that all values must change. Even if some values are absolute, all values need not be absolute.

This activity implies that values mirror the needs of a society. Our needs are, in many ways, different from those of our ancestors. Thus, many of our values are different.

STRATEGIES AND PROCEDURES

1. D Reason: The forces of nature needed to be "tamed" if the
                   nation was to grow.
       Evidence: Increased environmental awareness and concern.
2. G Reason: Resources were abundant, the nation was large, the
                   tasks were big—damming rivers, building interstate
                   freeways.
       Evidence: Homes and cars, on the average, are becoming smaller
                   as waste is being reduced. (The evidence is weak.)
3. B Reason: Resources were cheap and consumption fed the
                   economy.
       Evidence: Many young Americans can't afford to match the
                   material acquisitions of their parents.
4. E Reason: Rapid production lowered the cost of an item.
       Evidence: A new appreciation of good craftsmanship and
                   greater concern for the mental well-being of laborers.
5. A Reason: The land was a gift and gifts are to be used.
       Evidence: A greater awareness of the fact that we're tied into a
                   global ecosystem.
6. I Reason: Infant mortality was high and it took many "hands" to
                   battle the forces of nature.
       Evidence: Women are reexamining their roles at home and in
                   society. The need for large families doesn't exist
                   anymore. Children cost money.

7. F Reason: Early populations were small and resources were in great abundance.

   Evidence: The prices for some resources are rising and known locations of concentrations of various resources are harder to locate.

8. C Reason: The list of problems solved by science is impressive.

   Evidence: There seems to be a realization that "solving" one problem often creates others. Example: Elimination of disease can lead to overpopulation in some areas.

9. H Reason: There seemed to be ample places to dispose of "wastes" and forget about them.

   Evidence: The concern for pollution abatement and toxic waste disposal seems to indicate a new understanding of the conservation of mass.

READING 16.16 VALUES REGARDING RESOURCE USE

See *Student Edition*, p. 707.

16.7
Transparency 16.4

READING 16.17 PROMOTING THE WISE USE OF NATURAL RESOURCES

See *Student Edition*, p. 708.

ACTIVITY 16.9 RECYCLING ALUMINUM

See *Student Edition*, p. 713.

The central focus of this activity is the recycling of the aluminum can. The recycling issue is so broad that no single activity can do justice to it. We chose the aluminum can because of its popularity as a beverage container throughout the United States, and because the significance of a recycling effort can be easily determined and personalized.

ADVANCE PREPARATION

Paper grocery sack of crushed aluminum cans. Balance to weigh the cans.

STRATEGIES AND PROCEDURES

This activity may be done as an individual assignment or as a class project. The calculations can be assigned as homework or done in class and used as the focus for class discussion. Students usually respond well in a discussion of these items.

SAMPLE ANSWERS TO DATA

1. 222 cans.
2. 7.0 pounds.
3. 0.80 kWh/can.

1. 7.0 pounds/222 = 0.0315 pounds. In 2004, it is ~ 0.030 pounds.
2. 0.40 kWh = .1 kW × t. t = 4 hours.
3. 7.0 pounds × $0.40/pound = $2.80.
4. 36 cans/7 days = 5.143 cans/day. Thus, 222 cans/5.143 cans/day = 43.2 days = 6.17 weeks ~ 1.5 months.
5. 222 cans × 0.40 kWh/can = 89 kWh.
6. 89 kWh × .95 = 85 kWh.
7. 85 kWh/15 kWk/days = 5.7 days ~ 1 week.
8. 53.8×10^9 cans/0.534 = 108×10^9 cans.
9. 53.8×10^9 cans × 0.0315 lb/can = 1.69×10^9 pounds = 8.47×10^5 tons = $1.02 billion.
10. 0.40 kWh/can × 5% = 0.02 kWh/can.
11. True.

READING 16.18 EXPANDING OPPORTUNITIES FOR ALL PEOPLE

See *Student Edition*, p. 715.

READING 16.19 MAXIMIZING STABILITY AND FREEDOM

See *Student Edition*, p. 716.

ACTIVITY 16.10 THE ISLAND REVISITED

See *Student Edition*, p. 717.

Transparency 16.4

This activity is designed to be a culmination of the entire course. It should give you a good idea about how your students synthesize all they have learned as they think about the future.

There is no one right answer to this activity. Student grades should indicate the depth of their involvement with the activity.

Although there is no one right answer, the material being considered is very important. It relates to the kind of situation we as a nation and a world are facing.

READING 16.20 POSSIBLE FUTURES FOR HUMANKIND

See *Student Edition*, p. 720.

ACTIVITY 16.11 TAKING ACTION ON RESOURCE/ENVIRONMENTAL ISSUES

See *Student Edition*, p. 722.

Citizen's action is not the type of activity normally encountered in a science class. However, if you are concerned about the effects of science on people, it is appropriate. Good science does not only involve experimentation on a small scale under carefully controlled conditions. It also attempts to determine the effects of large-scale application of a process in situations that are difficult to control. In a world where the population is large and where the time between discovery and application has rapidly diminished, we must demand that the effects of wide-scale adaptation of scientific and technical processes be determined. This is what examining issues, writing Congress, contacting industry and evaluating personal consumption is all about. You may find that through this technique, many of your students will be forced to examine an issue such as nuclear energy or power plant development to a depth much greater than is typical in the normal science class situation. It certainly is worth a try.

The addresses for the various energy/environmentally related organizations are not provided because it is part of the student's education to learn how to track down this sort of information. Students don't need to send their letters, but they need to know how to write them.

ACTIVITY 16.12 INTROSPECTION

See *Student Edition*, p. 724.

This is a rather different activity relative to the others. Some teachers choose not to do it because it is more like an English class assignment. Others reject it because there is no way to prove that a student actually did it. Some students will just jot a few things down on paper and expect to get credit.

Arguments in favor of the activity include the following. It is a chance, near the end of the course, for students to relate many of the ideas studied to themselves and their surroundings. Although the study of resource/environmental problems consists of the examination of many concepts, some very difficult and scientific, the solutions depend on the basic understanding of some fundamental relationships between humans and nature and some attitudes on how we fit into all of this. This activity gives a student a chance to think about some of these things and tie them together. Finally, some students are better at putting thoughts on paper than processing data. This activity gives them a chance to indicate what they have learned.

The following essays were put together by combining key thoughts from about 25 student papers. They aren't a typical student response, but they do summarize many of the ideas your students will express.

Introspection

I stepped out into the cold, damp air. Here I am, I thought, against my better judgment, completing another ridiculous assignment. Oh well, it won't be long until school's out and then I can do more important things—the things I want to do, the things that are relevant.

The pine smelled good and I could hear the creek rushing past the rocks. There was a slight rustling in the leaves as little breezes whisked by and a few birds chirped in anticipation of a new dawn. The moss underfoot was damp and had a spongy feel like a thick shag carpet—I like that feeling. It sure didn't seem right getting class credit for this—it isn't even painful!

As I walked along I crested a large hill. A peaceful valley lay before me. As I scanned its expanse, I realized I take so much for granted. I expected this to be beautiful; I knew it would be and yet I am awed again by the size of it all, how immense is our Earth in comparison to me.

As my eyes made several trips around the whole valley, I got an odd feeling; I felt like a stranger. I wondered if I really fit in. Clearly this could all exist without me! What a humbling thought. It's strange that although man is actually a bystander in the natural process, he thinks he is master of the universe—the pinnacle of creation, the controller of all. But if he is a master, he's a cruel master for in his quest for dominance he is destroying his natural home and in the process—himself—for although nature can exist without him, he cannot exist without nature. He cannot dominate her, but he can live in harmony with her.

Introspection

As the sun rose, I felt its warming rays against my face. It felt good. The dew began to disappear and the haze started to lift from the valley. I saw the whole valley respond to its life-giving power, its strength, its energy. It all worked so spontaneously; no gadgets, no valves, no computer—it just happened. It was so unlike the beginning of most of my days—the annoying buzz of an alarm, the frantic rush, the start of a car, the smell of exhaust, the angry looks—all to be repeated tomorrow and tomorrow and tomorrow. And then I thought—I'm part of the problem. I hadn't really planned it that way, it just sort of happened—and in a lot of ways I really don't want to give it up. After all, I've got my whole life ahead of me. But what kind of future is it? Thank heavens for a time like this to put my thoughts in order. Why does it take panoramic views, and the call of birds to make me think—maybe it's because these are the only times I really take the time.

I hope to become an engineer some day. Engineers have done so many ridiculous things. I hope I can find ways of improving our existence without degrading what's around me. There are ways. I know it can be done.

It's hard to cause change. But new ideas have to start somewhere. In the great pattern of things, other ideas got started. Why not live life to the fullest each day? Why not think new thoughts? Why not learn new things? Why not be unique? Why not be me? Why not live instead of just exist? Why not?

CHAPTER 16 SUMMARY

See *Student Edition,* p. 726.

Transparency 16.5

Name_____   Period_____

BLUE PLANET: AN IMAX SPACE FILM . . . ABOUT EARTH

Sample answers can be found on p. 369 of the *Teacher Guide*.

VIDEO NOTES

1. We placed a man on the Moon, but it was barren and _____.
2. Earth is an _____ in space.
3. Our world, unlike any other, is a world of _____.
4. Earth's _____ shields us from the radiation and harshness of outer space.
5. From space, we can see Earth as a _____.
6. Our planet's systems of water, earth, and air interact to sustain _____.
7. First humans were hunters and gatherers, then they became _____. This enabled Earth to support many more people.
8. Analysis of the record stored in ancient ice may enable us to predict future _____.
9. Satellite images (called remote sensing) help us prepare for the onslought of _____.
10. The impact of an asteroid from outerspace may have wiped out the _____.
11. At one side of a plate, new crust is forming under the ocean. At the other side of the plate, maybe a _____ miles away, plates slide under each other and plates are destroyed.
12. From space we can see that the _____ impact on the global environment is significant.
13. _____ of all the species on Earth live in the rainforests.
14. Almost _____ acre of tropical rainforest is destroyed every second.
15. There are now more than _____ billion of us spread across Earth.
16. A thin layer of _____ protects us from the ultraviolet rays of space.
17. Our world is a special place where millions of species _____. What we as humans do to our Earth will   determine how long it will support life as we know it.

We're all in it together; give Earth a chance!

Name_____ Date _____

MULTIPLE CHOICE

1. _____ The pioneers that settled and developed the United States were strong believers in the growth ethic because of all the following *except*
   A. high interest rates on Certificates of Deposit made it possible to make rapid gains on their investments.
   B. the supply of land seemed limitless.
   C. natural resources were in great abundance.
   D. it took many hands to tame the forces of nature.
   E. many of them believed the literal interpretation of "Be fruitful and multiply."

2. _____ The body of scientific evidence supports all of the following claims *except*
   A. nature is basically predictable and law abiding.
   B. there are laws that limit what we as humans are able to do.
   C. think it possible and it will become a reality.
   D. exponential growth in a finite system is not the norm in nature.

3. _____ An example of a closed system is
   A. a coal plant.
   B. Earth.
   C. a river.
   D. a continent.

4. _____ The *Limits to Growth* study claims there are five factors that determine and, in their interactions, ultimately limit growth on Earth. These factors include which of the following?
   A. population growth
   B. agricultural production
   C. pollution generation
   D. industrial output
   E. all of these

5. _____ The *Limits to Growth* study claims that the five factors tied to growth have various characteristics in common. These include all of the following *except*
   A. they are greatly influenced by economic conditions.
   B. up until recently, they have all been growing exponentially.
   C. they are all interrelated.
   D. they all appear to have some upper limit.

6. _____ According to the *Limits to Growth* study, if human behavior doesn't change (the standard world model), a worldwide collapse will occur *primarily* because (see graph)
   A. we run out of nonrenewable resources.
   B. pollution runs wild.
   C. food runs short.
   D. our industrial base collapses.
   E. insect pests destroy the ecosystem.

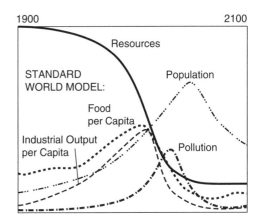

7. _____ According to the *Limits to Growth* study, the only way to stop a worldwide collapse is to
A. stop population growth.
B. stabilize industrial output.
C. both stop population growth and stabilize industrial output.
D. both stabilize industrial output and increase food production.
E. allow free-market economic forces to operate worldwide.

8. _____ According to the *Limits to Growth* study, priorities for obtaining a stable world include all of the following *except*
A. population stabilization.
B. production of sufficient food for *all* people.
C. reduction in the pollution generation per technological device.
D. greater material rewards for those that are clever and inventive.
E. a shift in preference from factory-produced material goods to nonconsumptive activities such as recreation, music, art.

9. _____ The *Limits to Growth* study can be criticized because
A. an elitist group of the wealthy are telling the rest of the world how to sacrifice.
B. it failed to consider economic factors as a means for altering human behavior.
C. skimpy evidence is extrapolated years into the future.
D. it tells us what the future should be like, but it is vague on how to obtain it.
E. all of the above are valid criticisms.

10. _____ Your textbook states that the *Limits to Growth* study can be praised for accomplishing several things. Which one of the following is *not* one of those things?
A. It forced us to look at the direction in which we seem headed.
B. It provided a clear and definite program for stopping growth around our globe.
C. It pointed to recent historical evidence that there are limits to growth.
D. It provided a glimpse of what the future might be like—if we choose the road to survival.

11. _____ *Beyond the Limits*
A. updates the *Limits to Growth* report.
B. was produced by the original authors of the *Limits to Growth*.
C. predicts a sustainable society is possible.
D. says we must control population growth and resource use.
E. all of the above.

12. _____ A sustainable economy would require three mechanisms to make it work. Which *one* of the following is *not* one of those required mechanisms?
A. Strategies for limiting the rate at which resources pass through the economy.
B. Strategies to handle banking, loans, and savings accounts.
C. Strategies for monitoring and maintaining a constant population.
D. Strategies for expanding opportunities for more people.

13. _____ If a population needs to be maintained at its present level, what strategy would work best?
A. 1 child per couple   D. no children should be born
B. 2 children per couple   E. none of the above
C. 3 children per couple

14. _____ Which one of the following does not tend to lower population growth?
A. The deduction allowed for children on our income tax forms.
B. The demand for new roles by women.
C. The choice to begin a family at a later age.
D. The demand by many women for freedom over their reproductive functions.
E. The widespread availability of birth control devices and information.

15. _____ The Law of Demand states when a product is desired and the price is
   A. high, the demand will be high.
   D. high, the supply will be low.
   B. high, the supply will be high.
   E. low, the demand will be low.
   C. low, the demand will be high.

16. _____ The condition where consumers can purchase the largest amount of a product at the cheapest price while producers can produce the most for the highest price is called
   A. shortage.
   D. scarcity.
   B. spillover.
   E. market equilibrium.
   C. surplus.

17. _____ As pollution levels are reduced, the cost of pollution control
   A. rises.
   C. stabilizes.
   B. oscillates.
   D. falls.

18. _____ The acceptance of only small amounts of pollution from various technological devices (such as automobiles) can lead to serious problems because
   A. nature can absorb and process some wastes.
   B. technological devices are available that reduce pollution levels.
   C. large numbers of devices that produce small amounts of pollution can still exceed the boundaries that exist in natural systems.
   D. the cost of pollution reduction is high.

19. _____ Under normal conditions, as the supply goes up, the market equilibrium price
   A. goes up.
   C. remains steady.
   B. goes down.
   D. is unpredictable.

20. _____ All of the following are economic functions performed by the U.S. government *except* to
   A. provide a reasonably certain legal, social, and business environment.
   B. promote and maintain competitive markets.
   C. stabilize national income, employment, and the price level.
   D. maximize human rights around the world.
   E. provide for public needs and wants.

21. _____ All of the following are problems related to the market system *except*
   A. the most important markets are dominated by a few firms so competition is minimized.
   B. the system permits some individuals to accumulate and hold vast amounts of wealth.
   C. resources and products are allocated without central direction from a governmental planning authority.
   D. the system often fails to absorb all the real costs of production of a product.
   E. free markets can be unstable.

22. _____ All of the following are advantages of the market system *except*
   A. inefficient allocation of resources is not tolerated by the system.
   B. the market causes business to provide the products desired by consumers.
   C. the full cost of an item is always represented by its price.
   D. personal freedom is maximized with the system.
   E. competition forces business to sell products as cheaply as possible.

23. _____ In terms of resource management, your textbook suggests that all of the following are positive functions of the federal government *except*
   A. reconciling conflicting interests.
   D. seizing foreign supplies.
   B. setting objectives.
   E. providing leadership.
   C. monitoring progress.

Options for the Future

24. _____ The resources of Earth are
A. finite.   C. solid.
B. infinite.   D. underground.

25. _____ A major theme of this course has been that humans are
A. masters of their natural environment.
B. partners with their natural environment.
C. independent of their natural environment.
D. able to invoke divine powers to counter natural forces.

26. _____ Which one of the following is *not* a government-imposed solution to a
resource/environmental problem?
A. gasoline rationing
B. quotas on resource extraction from federal lands
C. high taxes on materials we want to conserve
D. individual preference for products that don't pollute
E. mandatory recycling laws

27. _____ Conflicts are more likely to be resolved if
A. self-defense skills are improved.
B. people rely on defense systems.
C. conflicting groups keep talking.
D. governments become weak and people seize power.

BLUE PLANET: AN IMAX SPACE FILM . . . ABOUT EARTH

VIDEO NOTES

1. We placed a man on the Moon, but it was barren and <u>lifeless</u>.
2. Earth is an <u>oasis</u> in space.
3. Our world, unlike any other, is a world of <u>water</u>.
4. Earth's <u>air</u> shields us from the radiation and harshness of outer space.
5. From space, we can see Earth as a <u>whole</u>.
6. Our planet's systems of water, Earth, and air interact to sustain <u>life</u>.
7. First humans were hunters and gatherers, then they became <u>farmers</u>. This enabled Earth to support many more people.
8. Analysis of the record stored in ancient ice may enable us to predict future <u>climates</u>.
9. Satellite images (called remote sensing) help us prepare for the onslought of <u>hurricanes</u>.
10. The impact of an asteroid from outerspace may have wiped out the <u>dinosaurs</u>.
11. At one side of a plate, new crust is forming under the ocean. At the other side of the plate, maybe a <u>thousand</u> miles away, plates slide under each other and plates are destroyed.
12. From space we can see that the <u>human</u> impact on the global environment is significant.
13. <u>Half</u> of all the species on Earth live in the rainforests.
14. Almost <u>one</u> acre of tropical rainforest is destroyed every second.
15. There are now more than <u>five</u> billion of us spread across Earth.
16. A thin layer of <u>ozone</u> protects us from the ultraviolet rays of space.
17. Our world is a special place where millions of species <u>coexist</u>. What we as humans do to our Earth will determine how long it will support life as we know it.

We're all in it together; give Earth a chance!

CHAPTER 16 ASSESSMENT

1. A	16. E
2. C	17. A
3. B	18. C
4. E	19. B
5. A	20. D
6. A	21. C
7. C	22. C
8. D	23. D
9. E	24. A
10. B	25. B
11. E	26. D
12. B	27. C
13. B	
14. A	
15. C	

There are eight categories of content standards. The following pages summarize the correlation of the eight standards to *Global Science.*

NOTE: Content is what students should learn. Curriculum is the way content is organized and emphasized. The *Global Science* curriculum is a unique program that enables high schools to implement most of the National Science Education Content Standards while emphasizing those concepts from science that are vitally important to *all* citizens.

Key: T = Text (numbers refer to chapter and section); A = Activity (numbers refer to chapter and activity number); TG = Teacher Guide

Standard	Correlation
1. Unifying Concepts and Processes *Activities enable all students to develop an understanding of and ability to use the following concepts and processes:*	
Systems, Order, and Organization	
Systems enable us to isolate and study small portions of the natural world.	T3.5, Closed and open systems are defined and examined. A3.2, A closed system is constructed and analyzed. A3.9, A closed system is used to explain The Second Law of Thermodynamics.
The universe is orderly and law abiding.	A3.3, The Conservation of Mass. A3.6, The Conservation of Energy. A3.9 and 3.10, The Second Law of Thermodynamics.
Types and levels of organization help us arrange knowledge about the world.	Levels of organization are introduced early (Chapter 2) to clarify terms and help students see where ecology fits into the domain of science. Levels of organization of life are outlined in Chapter 6.
Evidence, Models, and Explanations	
Use evidence (data and observations) to understand interactions and predict changes.	Most activities in the textbook involve using evidence.
Models help us understand how things work.	Students construct or analyze models in about 20% of the activities.
Scientific explanation consists of internally consistent, logical statements that incorporate existing knowledge and new evidence.	Students have the opportunity to practice this standard in many experiments and investigations. A1.4 focuses on scientific explanation.
Change, Consistency, and Measurement	
Everything is becoming something else.	In an ecosystem (ecodome), the components continually change as the cycles of nature operate. (A3.2 and supporting text.)
However, some aspects of nature don't change, such as the speed of light and the total mass plus energy in the universe.	Constancy is examined in both The Conservation of Mass and The Conservation of Energy activities. (A3.3, A3.6)

continued

Standard	Correlation
◆ Evidence for change or constancy is obtained through measurement.	In *Global Science,* students measure such quantities as time, mass, temperature, heat, population, growth rate, efficiency, current, voltage, production rate, volume, pH, and concentration.
✹ Evolution and Equilibrium	
◆ The present arises from the past.	Through rapid breeding of large numbers of insects with genetic differences, immunity to pesticides and other stresses can be established quickly. (A6.4, A6.6, T6.4, T6.5, T6.6)
◆ Equilibrium is a condition where changes occur in opposite and offsetting directions.	Steady state occurs when a quantity enters a system at the same rate at which it leaves so that the total quantity present remains constant. (T3.5)
✹ Form and Function	
◆ Form and function are complementary aspects of objects, organisms, and systems.	Students explain functions by referring to form, and form by referring to function, as they examine the components of *Global Science.* Example: T6.6.

2. Science as Inquiry (A)
Inquiry-oriented activities enable all students to:

✹ Develop abilities necessary to do scientific inquiry	
◆ Formulate a testable hypothesis.	Several activities allow students to formulate and test a hypothesis. (A1.2, A1.3, A2.3, A3.7, A6.4, A13.3, A16.5)
◆ Design and conduct a scientific investigation.	Several activities allow students to design and conduct their own scientific investigation. (A1.3, A2.3, A3.7, A4.10, A6.4, A10.8, A11.2, A14.5)
◆ Use technology and mathematics to improve investigations.	Many *Global Science* activities require technical equipment and mathematical analysis.
◆ Formulate and revise scientific explanations and models.	Many *Global Science* activities involve the use and analysis of models.
◆ Recognize and analyze alternative explanations and models.	This is a common theme in *Global Science.* (A1.8, Chapter 2 Special Focus, A9.2, A10.1, A14.7, A16.10)
◆ Communicate and defend a scientific argument.	Topics such as Is the greenhouse effect something to worry about? or Is this water safe to drink? are central to *Global Science* themes. Several activities can be used to meet this standard.
✹ Understand about scientific inquiry	As students develop the abilities necessary to do scientific inquiry, they simultaneously develop understandings about scientific inquiry. Inquiry topics in *Global Science* include Can humans live in a sealed dome for long periods of time? (A3.2) Can human population growth be slowed? (A5.1) How many people can the world feed? (A7.2 extension, A7.6) What is the best way to meet our nation's energy needs? (A12.7) Is this water safe to drink? (A13.4) Can humans design a sustainable society? (A16.10)

3. Physical Science (B)
Activities enable all students to develop an understanding of:

Standard	Correlation
⚜ The structure of atoms	The activity Atoms and Molecules (A10.1) along with Chapter 10: Nuclear Energy and related exercises and activities enable students to fulfill this standard.
⚜ The structure and properties of matter	Chapter 3, Special Focus addresses states of matter. Chapter 10: Nuclear Energy summarizes atomic structure and the periodic table.
⚜ Chemical reactions	Chemical reactions are analyzed in such activities as Atoms & Molecules (A10.1), The Energy Content of a Fuel (A8.3), and the acid rain labs (A14.3, A14.4, A14.5). Additional activities can be introduced to emphasize other chemical concepts such as Activity 12.3 on fuel cells.
⚜ Motion and forces	Concepts of inertia and force are developed in The Meaning of Mass (A3.3) and at the beginning of Chapter 3. Electric charge is studied in the Electrostatic Precipitator lab (A14.6). Additional activities would be required for further development of force and motion concepts.
⚜ Conservation of energy	Activity 3.6 (Energy Transformations) and related material in Chapter 3 fulfill this standard. Energy flow in ecosystems is emphasized. (A3.1, A3.2, A3.7, A3.10)
⚜ The increase in disorder (entropy)	The Second Law of Thermodynamics is the focus of two lab activities (A3.9, A3.10) and material in Chapter 3. The connection between the tendency toward disorder and efficiency is made. Efficiency and system efficiency are emphasized.
⚜ Interactions of energy and matter	Electromagnetic waves and remote sensing are emphasized in Chapter 3. Waves are introduced and semiconductors mentioned. A teacher would have to bring in additional activities to emphasize waves, atomic spectrum, semiconductors, and superconductors.

4. Life Science (C)
Activities enable all students to develop an understanding of:

Standard	Correlation
⚜ The cell	The cell is introduced as one of the levels of Organization (Chapter 2, Special Focus). This is expanded on in Chapter 6 (Levels of Organization of Life). Reading 6.2 examines the cell as the basic unit of life. In A6.2, students examine different types of cells.
⚜ Molecular basis of heredity	Reading 6.1 and Activity 6.1 examine the nature of life. Levels of organization of life are summarized in the Chapter 6 Special Focus. Chromosomes are mentioned in Biological Effects of Radiation (T10.9). The *Global Science* Explorer CD—Lesson 2 examines the molecular basis of life.

continued

🌱 Biological evolution

Biological evolution is covered in Chapter 6 in T6.5, T6.6, T6.7, and T6.8. Topics include evolution, natural selection, extinction, why save endangered species (A6.8), and pests as they relate to the food supply. The material on seed banks and insectaries adds another dimension to this standard. A6.6 and T6.5 help clarify concepts.

🌱 Interdependence of organisms

Ecosystems are the focus of Chapters 2 and 3. Activities that illustrate interdependence include A2.2, A2.3, A2.4, A3.1, and A3.2. The concepts of carrying capacity (A7.7 and T7.6) and the human impact on the global environment are other major themes in *Global Science*.

🌱 Matter, energy, and organization in living systems

This standard primarily centers on ecosystems, energy flow in nature, and food. These topics are central to Chapters 2, 3, 6, and 7 and their related lab activities.

🌱 Behavior of organisms

Nervous systems, responses to stimuli, and behavioral biology in general are not emphasized in *Global Science*. To fulfill this standard, teachers must supplement using selected outside material.

5. Earth and Space Science (D)
Activities enable all students to develop an understanding of:

🌱 Energy in the earth system

  ◆ The earth has internal and external sources of energy.

The sun is the major external source of energy. (T2.2) Radioactive decay and gravity are the internal sources. (T3.8)

  ◆ Internal circulation propels the Earth's plates.

Students examine a convection cell model for plate movement (A11.1).

  ◆ The sun powers convection currents in the atmosphere causing wind.

Students examine the origin of wind (T11.12) and the potential of wind power. (T11.12 and A11.8)

  ◆ Global climate is driven by the sun.

The text reinforces this concept in a variety of ways.

🌱 Geochemical cycles

  ◆ The minerals in the Earth move through cycles.

Students examine the cycling of minerals in the biosphere (A3.2) and in the Earth. (T3.2, T4.7, T4.8, T4.9)

  ◆ The carbon cycle illustrates the movement of matter.

The carbon cycle ties the living and the nonliving together. (T3.2)

🌱 Origin and evolution of the Earth system

  ◆ The solar system formed from a cloud of dust.

  ◆ Geologic timeline.

The solar system is examined briefly. (A2.1) *Global Science* Explorer CD—Lesson 4.

Covered in the *Global Science* Explorer CD—Lesson 4.

  ◆ The Earth is continually changing.

The interplay between land, oceans, and atmosphere is emphasized in many ways in *Global Science.*

  ◆ Evidence for life extends over 3.5 billion years.

Covered in the *Global Science* Explorer CD—Lesson 3.

✦ Origin and evolution of the universe

◆ The origin of the universe is an interesting question.

The question of how it all began is interesting and complex. Summarized on the *Global Science* Explorer CD—Lesson 4.

◆ The universe contains billions of galaxies.

The *Global Science* Explorer CD—Lesson 4 covers this standard.

◆ Stars primarily fuse hydrogen to produce energy.

Fusion is examined as an energy source. (T10.14)

6. Science and Technology (E)
Activities enable all students to develop:

✦ Abilities of technical design

◆ Identify a problem or design an opportunity.

◆ Propose designs and choose between alternative solutions.

◆ Implement a proposed solution.

◆ Evaluate the solution and its consequence.

◆ Communicate the problem, process, and solution.

Many opportunities exist that teachers can choose from. These include:
1. Design a home that exists in harmony with its surroundings, uses the forces of nature to perform its functions, and uses the natural forms of energy that are continually available to us. (A11.2)
2. Build and use a solar oven. (A11.4)
3. Develop a landscape plan for a home that is both attractive and resource (water, energy, mineral) efficient. (A15.2)
4. Design a model wind generator. (A11.8)
5. Design a meal to meet nutritional criteria. (A7.3)
6. Design a container to transport nuclear waste. (A10.8)
7. Design the sustainable planet. (A16.10)

✦ Understanding about science and technology

◆ Many scientific investigations involve more than one scientific discipline and include engineers.

◆ Scientific advances often tie to advances in technology.

◆ Creativity, imagination, and knowledge are essential to the work of science and engineering.

◆ Science is driven by the desire to know. Technology is driven by the need to meet human needs.

◆ Technological knowledge is often not made public because of patents and financial potential. Scientific knowledge is made public at professional meetings and in publications.

Understanding about science and technology are best managed by individual classroom teachers as they guide students through the course. Much of this standard is already built into the entire *Global Science* curriculum. Individual teachers can add the emphasis. (See Chapter 15 for the section titled Technology: Friend or Foe?)

7. Science in Personal and Social Perspectives (F)
Activities enable all students to develop an understanding of:

✦ Personal and community health

◆ Hazards exist in nature.

◆ We make personal choices concerning health.

◆ Choice of foods and eating habits determine nutrition.

◆ Choices regarding sexual behavior are important.

Global Science provides a framework in which teachers can help students build respect for the environment, others, and themselves. These attitudes are the beginning of responsible behavior in society and improved individual and community health. Students can plan a diet based on nutritional criteria. (A7.3) Students examine the case for total abstinence (T5.9) and the responsibility of becoming a parent. (A5.6 and A5.7)

continued

❧ Population growth

♦ Populations can grow, decline, or stabilize.

The lab Modeling Exponential Growth (A5.1) illustrates this standard.

♦ Demographic factors tie in to population change.

The activity A Demographic Survey (A5.4) focuses on this standard.

♦ Carrying capacity is an important concept.

Carrying capacity is the topic of A7.7 and T7.6.

❧ Natural resources

♦ Humans use resources to maintain and better their life.

The entire *Global Science* curriculum focuses on this standard.

♦ Nonrenewable resources can be depleted.

See the labs on resource depletion (A9.1, A9.2) and Chapter 9: Nonrenewable Resource Depletion.

♦ Natural systems can provide resources, but they have limits.

This is a central theme in the *Global Science* curriculum.

❧ Environmental Quality

♦ Natural ecosystems are self-regulating.

♦ Humans are impacting the environment.

♦ Many factors influence environmental quality.

This standard is central to the *Global Science* curriculum. Students first focus on ecosystems and how they work. They then examine population growth. This information is then applied to the issues of food, energy, air, water, and land. Sustainability is examined.

❧ Natural and human-induced hazards

♦ Hazards exist in nature, but human activity can increase potential for hazards.

The impact of humans on the global environment receives emphasis in *Global Science*.

♦ Reducing hazards involves trade-offs.

The activity Trade-offs (A16.3) emphasizes this standard.

❧ Science and technology in local, national, and global challenges

♦ Humans decide how to use science and technology.

♦ Individuals and societies determine how science and technology are used.

Global Science emphasizes this standard throughout the curriculum. For specific examples, see T1.6, A2.5, Chapter 3 Special Focus on Remote Sensing, A3.12, T3.16, T4.14, T4.16, T6.9, T10.15, T12.10, A12.7, Solving Water Problems, T14.9, T15.18, and Chapter 16.

8. History and Nature of Science
Activities enable all students to develop an understanding of:

❧ Science as a human endeavor

♦ Individuals and teams contribute to the scientific enterprise.

This is modeled as students work alone, with a partner, or in a cooperative learning team.

♦ Scientists have ethical traditions.

The ethical traditions of science are best taught by practicing them in all phases of course work—truthful reporting of methods, data, and outcomes; making public the results of work; and peer reviews. (See A1.6 Scientific Habits of Mind.)

♦ Science is not separate from society. It is part of it.

Science is influenced by the world view of working scientists. (See A1.8)

❋ The nature of scientific knowledge

◆ Science is different from other ways of knowing.

Science gets its information by measuring things and interpreting those measurements. This is what we do in the lab. (See Activities 1.7–1.10.)

◆ Scientific explanation must be consistent with data, predictions, and logic.

Science is bound by reason. Personal belief systems, superstitions, or outside authority have nothing to do with the process. (See T1.3.)

◆ Scientific knowledge is subject to change or revision.

New information can change what scientists believe. For example, the theory of plate tectonics is relatively new. (See all of Chapter 1.) Scientific explanations change over time (Special Focus: Chapter 2).

❋ Historical perspectives

◆ Many cultures have contributed to the development of science.

◆ Change in science is usually small and gradual.

◆ A few advances in science were bold and revolutionary.

◆ Science almost always builds on earlier knowledge.

Global Science does not take a historical approach. Instead, the nature of science is emphasized by what the students do and how they gather, process, and interpret information. However, teachers wishing to emphasize a historical perspective can have students do A1.11: Environmental Science: Its History and Those Who Built It.

Global Science Explorer CD Table of Contents and Correlation

The following chart summarizes key topics on the *Global Science* Explorer CD and shows the readings and activities the topics correlate to in the student textbook. A few of the topics do not tie directly to the textbook but are tied to the science content standards of most states.

Lesson	Topics	Correlation
1. The Whole Earth System	Axis rotation, orbits the sun, seasons	A2.1
	Weathering processes	A1.3
	Tectonic plate movement	A4.6, A4.7
	Biomes-including a virtual field trip	A2.4
2. Earth Is Special	Solar system	A2.1
	Solar radiation	R2.2
	Molecules of life	A7.4
	Water is special	A2.1
3. Life on Earth	Catastrophic events	A2.2
	Carbon cycle	A3.1, R3.2
	Photosynthesis	R2.2
	Plants-structure/function	A3.7
	Plant adaptations	A2.4
	Animal adaptations	A2.4
	Human body systems	SSS
	Nutrition	R7.3, R7.4
4. Astronomy and Planet Earth	Origin of universe/Earth	SSS
	Stellar evolution	SSS
	Observing the sky	SSS
	What we know about what we see	SSS
	History and philosophy of science	A1.11
	Telescopes and spectroscopes	SSS
	Measuring distances in astronomy	SSS
	The solar system	A2.1
	Matter and energy	R3.3
	Gravity and orbits	SSS
	Motion and forces	A3.3
	Weight, mass, volume, and density	A1.9, A3.3
	Age of the Earth	SSS
	Motions of the Earth	SSS
	Earth's structure (layers)	A4.5
	Geologic time scale	SSS
5. Continental Drift	Continental drift—evidence	A4.6
6. Plate Tectonics	Plate motion, explanation, applications	R4.7, A4.7

Lesson	Topics	Correlation
7. Rocks, Minerals, and Soils	Rock cycle	R4.5
	Types of rocks	A4.4
	Minerals—defined/structure	R4.3–4.4, A4.2
	Importance of minerals	A4.11
	Soils—weathering/erosion	A1.3
	Soil formation	R7.2, A7.1
	Soil conservation	Ch.7: Special Focus
8. Hydrology	Hydrologic cycle	R3.2
	Landforms	SSS
	Watersheds	Ch13: Spec. Focus-1
	Flood plains	R15.12
	Water tables	R13.1
	Aquifers	R8.4, R13.5
	Saltwater intrusion	R13.5
	Glaciers	R13.7, R14.8
9. Oceanography	Ocean provinces	A4.6
	Ocean surface motion	SSS
	Convection in the ocean	A11.1
	Ocean layers	R11.13
	Estuaries	R2.4
	Wetlands	R15.12
	Primary production	R13.1
	Aquatic food chains	A2.4, A3.1, R3.1
	Oceans and climate	A2.1
10. Meteorology	Hurricanes	SSS
	Tornadoes	SSS
	Atmospheric layers	A14.1
	Solar radiation budget	R2.2
	Water cycle	R3.2
	Global climate zones	R2.3
	Coriolis effect	SSS
	Global weather patterns/wind	R11.12
11. Climate	Climate defined	R14.8–14.11
	The greenhouse effect	A14.7, A14.8
12. Weather Forecasting	Weather maps and symbols	SSS
	Making weather observations	SSS
	Weather fronts	SSS
	Cloud types	SSS
	Backyard weather station	SSS
13. Satellite Remote Sensing Technologies	Remote sensing defined	
	Short history of mapping	Chapter 3:
	Fundamentals of remote sensing	Special Focus-1
	Bits and bytes of data	
14. Satellite Remote Sensing Applications	Practical uses of remote sensing	Chapter 3: Special Focus-1

KEY: R = Reading; A = Activity; L = Lesson Number on the CD; SSS = State science standard

KEY: R = Reading; A = Activity

For technical support with the *Global Science Explorer*™ CD, contact support@eoascientific.com.

Week	Topic	Monday	Tuesday	Wednesday	Thursday	Friday
1	Chapter 1: Orientation to Course & Scientific Processes	Orientation to Course & Themes. Expectations.	*Activity 1.1:* Brainstorm What Is Science?	*Activity 1.2:* Asking Scientific Questions	*Activity 1.3:* Modeling the Weathering Process. Design experiment.	*Activity 1.3:* Do experiment and write it up
2	Scientific Attitudes & Behaviors. Ways of Knowing.	*Activity 1.3:* Postlab: 1. Write-up 2. Graphing	*Activity 1.4:* The Nature of Scientific Explanation	*Activity 1.5:* Sorting Out the Questions (Ways of Knowing)	*Activity 1.6:* Scientific Habits of Mind. Part = homework	*Activity 1.7:* Quality and Quantity of Data. Act. 1.8 = homework
3	Collecting & Analyzing Data	*Activity 1.9:* Measuring Aluminum	Metric System	*Postlab Act 1.9 Activity 1.10:* Parts 1&2. Rest = homework	*Video:* Scientific Methods & Values (34 min.) Ch. 1 Review	Chapter 1 Assessment
4	Chapter 2: The Basic Needs of Living Organisms	*Activity 2.2:* A Voyage to Mars (Day 1)	*Activity 2.2:* A Voyage to Mars (Day 2)	Topics: 1. Basic Needs of Organisms 2. Do Humans Have Special Needs? *Assignment* Survive Antarctic Winter	*Activity 2.3:* Investigating Ecosystems. Orientation.	*Activity 2.3:* Investigating Ecosystems. Finalize experimental design.
5	The Ecosystem Concept	*Activity 2.3:* Investigating Ecosystems. Set up experiment.	*Activity 2.3:* Investigating Ecosystems. Make/record observations.	(observations) *Activity 2.4:* Ecosystem Experts. Plan poster.	(observations) *Activity 2.4:* Ecosystem Experts. Make poster. *Assignment* Do Activity 2.5.	*Video:* The Web of Life (16 min.) Posters presented. Finalize Activity 2.3.
6	Chapter 3: Energy & Matter: The Big Picture	*Activity 3.2:* Designing Your Ecodome (Day 1)	*Activity 3.2:* Designing Your Ecodome (Day 2)	*Activity 3.2:* Designing Your Ecodome. Domes presented.	*Video:* Scientific American Explores Bios. 2.	*Activity 3.3:* Exploring the Meaning of Mass
7	Matter & Energy: A Closer Look	*Activity 3.4:* Conservation of Mass	*Activity 3.5:* Forms of Energy Experts. Preparation of report.	*Activity 3.5:* Student reports	*Activity 3.6:* Energy Transformations	*Activity 3.8:* Conversion Factors
8	Strategies for Resource Users	*Activity 3.9:* Examining the Second Law *Activity 3.10:* It's a One Way Street	Summary of The Second Law *Video:* Toast (13 min.)	*Activity 3.11:* Let's Have Tea!	*Topic:* Strategies for Resource Users	Chapter 3 Assessment
9	Chapter 4: Minerals, Rocks, Earth's Structure	*Activity 4.1:* What Is Your MAQ? *Activity 4.2:* Grow Your Own (Set up lab)	*Activity 4.3:* What Mineral Is It?	Summary of Minerals. *Video:* The Rock Cycle (18 min.)	*Activity 4.5:* What's Inside Earth?	*Activity 4.6:* Matching Continents

continued

Week	Topic	Monday	Tuesday	Wednesday	Thursday	Friday
10	Plate Tectonics	*Activity 4.7:* Map Evidence for Plate Tectonics	*Video:* Plate tectonics (18 min.)	*Activity 4.8:* Concentrate on Your Minerals	Complete/ postlab Activity 4.8	*Activity 4.9:* Good as Gold
11	The Importance of Minerals	*Activity 4.10:* Milling Lab (Day 1)	*Activity 4.10:* Milling Lab (Day 2)	*Activity 4.11:* Importance of Minerals Revisited	*Activity 4.13:* Mineral Issues (Day 1)	*Activity 4.13:* Mineral Issues (Day 2)
12	Chapter 5: The Mathematics of Growth	*Activity 5.1:* Modeling Exponential Growth (Part 1)	*Activity 5.1:* Modeling Exponential Growth (Part II)	*Activity 5.1:* Modeling Exponential Growth (Part III) plus graphing	*Activity 5.3:* Picturing Population Growth (Day 1)	*Activity 5.3:* Picturing Population Growth (Day 2). Fill out Activity 5.4 survey.
13	Growth Issues	Postlab *Activity 5.1.* *Video:* World Population Growth Rate Problems.	*Activity 5.4:* Demographic Survey. Discuss class results.	*Activity 5.5:* Analyze the Demographic Transition	*Activity 5.7:* Am I Ready for This Responsibility?	Chapter 5 Assessment
14	Chapter 6: Seeds of Life	*Activity 6.3:* Characteristics of Seeds -or- *Activity 6.5:* If You've Seen One Tomato ... Reading 6.3.	*Activity 6.6:* Competing to Survive, Surviving to Compete	Postlab of *Activity 6.6* & Reading 6.5.	Study Guide for Readings 6.6–6.9. *Activity 6.8:* Why Preserve Bio. Diversity	*Video:* Seeds (28. min.) Chapter Review.
15	Chapter 7: Agriculture and Nutrition	*Activity 7.1:* What's in That Dirt? (Day 1)	*Activity 7.1:* What's in That Dirt? (Day 2)	*Activity 7.2:* How Much Food Do I Need? (Day 1)	*Activity 7.2:* How Much Food Do I Get? (Day 2)	*Activity 7.4:* Connecting Seeds and Human Nutrition
16	Chapter 7: Feeding the Planet	Postlabs of *Activities 7.2 and 7.4*	*Activity 7.5:* Seeds for the Future	*Activity 7.6:* The Politics of Hunger (Day 1)	*Activity 7.6:* The Politics of Hunger (Day 2). Chapters 6 and 7 Review.	Chapters 6 and 7 Exam/Evaluation
17	Chapter 8: Demand for Energy	*Activity 8.1:* Where Do We Get Our Energy?	*Activity 8.2:* Energy History of the U.S.	*Activity 8.3:* The Energy Content of a Fuel	*Activity 8.4:* Unquenchable Energy Thirst	*Activity 8.5:* Simulating Oil Refining
18	Today's Energy Sources	*Video:* Fossil Fuels (19 min.)	*Activity 8.6:* Coal	*Activity 8.7:* How Electricity Is Generated	Chapter 8 Summary	Chapter 8 Assessment

Week	Topic	Monday	Tuesday	Wednesday	Thursday	Friday
19	Chapter 9: Nonrenewable Resource Depletion	*Activity 9.1:* Resource Depletion. Blacklines 9.1 and 9.2	Write up lab. (Optional: Plotting graphs using computer programs.)	*Activity 9.2:* Applying a Model to a Real World Situation	Postlabs Blacklines 9.3 and 9.4	Resources & Reserves. Blackline 9.5 *Activity 9.3:* Estimating Size of a Resource
20	How Much Do We Have? Lifetimes.	*Activity 9.4:* Comparing Nonrenewable Reserves (Making the graph)	*Activity 9.5:* Calculating Resource Lifetimes	Postlabs on Activities 9.3 and 9.4	Chapter 9 Review Blackline 9.6	Chapter 9 Assessment
21	Chapter 10: Atoms & Radioactivity	*Activity 10.1:* Atoms and Molecules (Day 1)	*Activity 10.1:* Atoms and Molecules (Day 2)	*Activity 10.2:* Working with Atomic Symbols	*Activity 10.4:* Writing Nuclear Equations	*Activity 10.5:* Half-Life Investigation
22	Using Nuclear Fuels	*Activity 10.7:* Nuclear Fuel Cycle	*Video:* Radioactive Waste Disposal: The 10,000-year Test (50 min.)	*Activity 10.9:* Calculate Your Personal Radiation Dose	Chapter 10 Summary	Chapter 10 Assessment
23	Chapter 11: Solar Heating and Cooling of Buildings	*Activity 11.2:* Design an Environmental Home (Due in one week.)	*Activity 11.5:* Analysis of a Solar Collector	*Activity 11.6:* Solar Water Heating	*Activity 11.7:* Solar Cells (Day 1)	*Activity 11.7* Solar Cells (Day 2)
24	Solar Electricity. Fuels from the Sun.	Presentation of Environmental Homes (Day 1)	Presentation of Environmental Homes (Day 2)	*Video:* Alternative Energy (26 min.)	Chapter 11 Summary	Chapter 11 Assessment
25	Chapter 12: Conservation. Energy Conversion and Storage.	*Activity 12.1:* Home Energy Plan (Due in one week.)	*Video:* Energy for Tomorrow (33 min.)	*Activity 12.2:* Fuel Efficiency *vs.* Weight	*Activity 12.3:* Operate and Analyze a Fuel Cell (Day 1)	*Activity 12.3:* Analyze a Fuel Cell (Day 2)
26	Appropriate Technology. Energy Policy.	*Activity 12.4:* Appropriate Technology	*Activity 12.6:* Summarize Your Options (Day 1)	*Activity 12.6:* (Day 2) Student reports	*Activity 12.6:* (Day 3) Student reports	Chapter 12 Assessment, which could be *Activity 12.7:* Sorting Out Your Options
27	Chapter 13: Water Supply. Water Management.	*Activity 13.1:* Water, Water Everywhere	*Activity 13.2:* How Much Water Do You Use?	*Activity 13.3:* Your Improved Water Use	*Activity 13.4:* How Clean Is Your Water? (Day 1)	*Activity 13.4:* How Clean Is Your Water? (Day 2)
28	Water Pollution. Water Treatment.	*Activity 13.5:* Effects of Pollutants on Pond Water (Day 1)	*Activity 13.5:* Effects of Pollutants on Pond Water (Day 2)	Field trip (optional) or class analysis. Wastewater Treatment.	Chapter 13 Summary	Chapter 13 Assessment

continued

Week	Topic	Monday	Tuesday	Wednesday	Thursday	Friday
29	Chapter 14: Air Pollution	*Activity 14.2:* Driving Our Atmosphere Crazy	*Activity 14.3:* Testing pH at Home (or in the lab)	*Activity 14.4:* Acid Rain—Just the Facts	*Video:* Acid Rain: The Invisible Threat (20 min.)	*Activity 14.6:* Chart It! For Cleaner Air
30	Global Climate Issues	*Activity 14.7:* A Greenhouse Effect Model	*Video:* Greenhouse Effect (17 min.) Class discusses models.	*Activity 14.8:* CO_2 and Climate Trends: You Decide	Chapter 14 Summary	Chapter 14 Assessment
31	Chapter 15: Land Use	Intro. to Land Use. *Activity 15.1:* Land Use Decision.	*Activity 15.2:* Environmental Landscaping. CD: Water Wise Gardening.	*Activity 15.2:* Environmental Landscaping. Finalize your plan. (Day 2)	Public Lands. *Activity 15.3:* Mined Land Reclamation (Day 1)	*Activity 15.3:* Mined Land Reclamation (Day 2) & Special Focus
32	Chapter 15: Land Management	*Activity 15.4:* Land Use Analysis	*Activity 15.5:* Western Forest Management	Readings 15.8–15.13 and related questions	*Video:* The Salt Marsh (22 min.)	*Activity 15.6:* Not in My Backyard!
33	Chapter 15: Waste Management	*Activity 15.7:* Conducting Solutions	*Activity 15.8:* Copper Plating	*Activity 15.9:* Disposing of Toxic Waste	*Video:* Waste Generation . . . (45 min.)	Chapter 15 Evaluation.
34	Chapter 16: The Growth Issue	*Activity 16.1:* Pioneers and Their Island (Day 1)	*Activity 16.1:* Pioneers and Their Island (Day 2) Some group presentation	*Activity 16.2:* Graphing the Status of the Island	Pros and cons of *The Limits to Growth* Report. *Activity 16.3:* Tradeoffs	*Activity 16.5:* Resource Allocation
35	The Sustainable Planet	*Activity 16.6:* The Economic Role of the Government	*Activity 16.7:* Strategies for Building a Sustainable World	*Activity 16.8:* Changes in Attitudes	*Activity 16.10:* The Island Revisited (Day 1)	*Activity 16.10:* The Island Revisited (Day 2)
36	Introspection	*Activity 16.9:* Recycling Aluminum	*Activity 16.12:* Introspection or Class discussion of *Activity 16.10.*	*Video:* Blue Planet (42 min.)	Chapter 16 Summary	Chapter 16 Assessment

Week	Topic	Monday	Tuesday	Wednesday	Thursday	Friday
1	Chapter 1: Orientation to Course & Scientific Processes	Orientation to Course & Themes. Expectations.	Activity 1.1: Brainstorm What Is Science?	Activity 1.2: Asking Scientific Questions	Activity 1.3: Modeling the Weathering Process. Design experiment.	Activity 1.3: Do experiment and write it up
2	Scientific Attitudes & Behaviors. Ways of Knowing.	Activity 1.3: Postlab: 1. Write-up 2. Graphing	Activity 1.4: The Nature of Scientific Explanation	Activity 1.5: Sorting Out the Questions (Ways of Knowing)	Activity 1.6: Scientific Habits of Mind. Part = homework	Activity 1.7: Quality and Quantity of Data. Act. 1.8 = homework
3	Collecting & Analyzing Data	Activity 1.9: Measuring Aluminum	Metric System	Postlab Act 1.9 Activity 1.10: Parts 1&2. Rest = homework	Video: Scientific Methods & Values (34 min.) Ch. 1 Review	Chapter 1 Assessment
4	Chapter 2: Earth vs. Mars. The Basic Needs of Living Organisms.	Activity 2.1: This Place Called Earth (Stations 1–3)	Activity 2.1: This Place Called Earth (Stations 4–6)	Activity 2.2: A Voyage to Mars (Day 1)	Activity 2.2: A Voyage to Mars (Day 2)	Topics: 1. Basic Needs of Organisms 2. Do Humans Have Special Needs? Assignment Survive Antarctic Winter
5	Investigating Ecosystems	Activity 2.3: Investigating Ecosystems. Orientation.	Activity 2.3: Investigating Ecosystems. Finalize experimental design.	Activity 2.3: Investigating Ecosystems. Set up experiment.	Activity 2.3: Investigating Ecosystems. Make/record observations.	Activity 2.3: (observations) Activity 2.4: Ecosystem Experts. Plan poster.
6	Biomes & Aquatic Ecosystems	(observations) Activity 2.4: Ecosystem Experts. Make poster. Assignment Do Activity 2.5.	Video: The Web of Life (16 min.) Posters presented. Finalize Activity 2.3.	Video: Aquatic Biomes (20 min.)	Activity 2.5: Quest for the Good Life.	Chapter 2 Evaluation
7	Chapter 3: Energy Flow & Matter Cycles in the Biosphere	Activity 3.2: Designing Your Ecodome (Day 1)	Activity 3.2: Designing Your Ecodome (Day 2)	Activity 3.2: Designing Your Ecodome. Domes presented.	Video: Scientific American Explores Bios. 2.	Video: The Carbon Cycle (20 min.)
8	Standards Adjust— Astronomy	Activity 2.1: Return and Review	G.S. Explorer CD: The Planets	G.S. Explorer CD: Our Galaxy	G.S. Explorer CD: The Universe	Astronomy Assessment
9	Qtr. I Adjustment Week	This week is left blank to adjust for Quarter Exams, holidays, power outages/snow days, assemblies, etc.				

continued

Week	Topic	Monday	Tuesday	Wednesday	Thursday	Friday
10	Matter & Energy: A Closer Look	*Activity 3.3:* Exploring the Meaning of Mass	*Activity 3.4:* Conservation of Mass	*Activity 3.5:* Forms of Energy Experts. Preparation of report.	*Activity 3.5:* Student reports	*Activity 3.6:* Energy Transformations
11	The Second Law of Thermodynamics	*Activity 3.8:* Conversion Factors	*Activity 3.9:* Examining the Second Law	*Activity 3.10:* It's a One Way Street	*Activity 3.1:* What Eats What? - or - All Tied Up! (in Teacher Guide)	Reading 3.1 *Activity 3.7:* Plants as Energy Transformers (Plan Out)
12	Strategies for Resource Users	*Activity 3.7:* Plants as Energy Transformers (Set up)	Summary of The Second Law *Video:* Toast (13 min.)	*Activity 3.11:* Let's Have Tea!	Reading 3.12 and related problems	*Activity 3.12:* Match Source to End-Use. Summarize Strategies.
13	Chapter 4: Minerals & Rocks	*Activity 4.1:* What Is Your MAQ? *Activity 4.2:* Grow Your Own (Set up lab)	*Activity 4.3:* What Mineral Is It?	Summary of Minerals	*Activity 4.4:* What Rock Is It?	*Video:* Rock Cycle (18 min.)
14	Earth's Structure Plate Tectonics	*Activity 4.5:* What's Inside Earth?	*Activity 4.6:* Matching Continents	*Activity 4.7:* Map Evidence for Plate Tectonics	*Video:* Plate Tectonics (18 min.)	*Activity 4.12:* Mineral Imports
15	Mineral Concentration	*Activity 4.8:* Concentrate on Your Minerals	Complete/ postlab Activity 4.8.	*Activity 4.9:* Good as Gold	*Activity 4.10:* Milling Lab (Day 1)	*Activity 4.10:* Milling Lab (Day 2)
16	The Importance of Minerals	*Activity 4.11:* Importance of Minerals Revisited	*Activity 4.13:* Mineral Issues (Day 1)	*Activity 4.13:* Mineral Issues (Day 2)	*Video:* Common Ground (26 min.) Ch. 4 Review	Chapter 4 Assessment
17	Standards Adjustment — Motion	*Physics Activity:* Analyze Uniform Motion	*Physics Activity:* Analyze Free Fall	*Physics Activity:* Unbalanced Forces	*Physics Activity:* Newton's Second Law	Summary of the Laws of Motion
18	Semester Review/Exam	←		End of Semester I		→

NOTE: Week 17 (Motion) could follow Week #10.

Week	Topic	Monday	Tuesday	Wednesday	Thursday	Friday
19	Standards Adjustment: Introduction to Waves	*Activity* Waves on Springs	*Activity* Ripple Tanks (Day 1)	*Activity* Waves in a Ripple Tank (Day 2)	*Activity* Waves in a Ripple Tank (Day 3)	*Activity* Polarization
20	Standards Adjustment: Wave Phenomena	*Activity* Images in a Plane Mirror	*Activity* Electromagn. Spectrum	*Activity* Interesting Wave Phenomena	Wave Review	Wave Assessment
21	Chapter 5: The Mathematics of Growth	*Activity 5.1:* Modeling Exponential Growth (Part I)	*Activity 5.1:* Modeling Exponential Growth (Part II)	*Activity 5.1:* Modeling Exponential Growth (Part III) plus graphing	*Activity 5.2:* What's a Billion?	Reading 5.1 & Problems. Reading 5.2
22	Histograms & Demographics	*Activity 5.3:* Picturing Population Growth (Day 1)	*Activity 5.3:* Picturing Population Growth (Day 2). Fill out Activity 5.4 survey.	Postlab *Activity 5.1.* *Video:* World Population.	*Activity 5.4:* Demographic Survey. Discuss class results.	*Video:* Population: How Many is Enough? (32 min.)
23	Growth Issues	*Activity 5.5:* Analyze the Demographic Transition	*Activity 5.6:* Estimating the Cost of Raising a Child	*Activity 5.7:* Am I Ready for This Responsibility?	Chapter 5 Review	Chapter 5 Assessment
24	Chapter 6: The Essence of Life	*Activity 6.1:* What Is Life?	Special Focus: Levels of Organization of Life.	*Activity 6.2:* Cells — A Quick Look	*Video:* Cells: An Introduction (20 min.)	*Activity 6.3:* Characteristics of Seeds. *Video:* The Power of Seeds (15 min.).
25	Standards Adjustment— Cells	Examination of major molecules of life *Global Science Explorer* CD— Lesson 2	Modeling how polymers are built	*Model Activity:* Students in 3 groups. Start work.	*D2: Build Models:* Use household items. Show Str. & Function	*D3 Presentation:* a. prokaryote b. eukaryote c. virus
26	Standards Adjustment— Cells	*Osmosis Lab:* (with dialysis tubing)	Postlab & exam of other forms of act. & pass. trans.	How carbohydrates are made by photosynthesis	*Lab:* CO_2 Prod. *vs.* Physical Activity	*Activity:* Model the Structure of DNA
27	Qtr. III Adjustment Week	This week is left blank to adjust for Quarter Exams, holidays, power outages/snow days, assemblies, staff development, etc.				

NOTES: 1. The physics unit on waves (Weeks 19-20) is a suggested unit to meet some state standards. It is up to you to design.

2. The additional two weeks on cells (Weeks 25-26) are a suggested extension. It is up to you to design and assemble.

continued

Week	Topic	Monday	Tuesday	Wednesday	Thursday	Friday
28	Chapter 6: Seeds of Life	*Activity 6.5:* If You've Seen One Tomato . . . Reading 6.3	*Activity 6.6:* Competing to Survive, Surviving to Compete	Postlab of *Activity 6.6* & Reading 6.5.	Study Guide for Readings 6.6–6.9. *Activity 6.8:* Why Preserve Bio. Diversity	*Video:* Seeds (28. min.). Chapter Review.
29	Chapter 7: Agriculture	*Activity 7.1:* What's in That Dirt? (Day 1)	*Activity 7.1:* What's in That Dirt? (Day 2)	*Activity 7.2:* How Much Food Do I Need? (Day 1)	*Activity 7.2:* How Much Food Do I Get? (Day 2)	*Activity 7.2:* How Much Land to Grow My Food? (Day 3)
30	Standards Adjustment— Genetics	A week of genetics could be tied to seeds and agriculture ———————————————→				
31	Chapter 7: Nutrition	*Video:* The Living Soil (20 min.)	*Activity 7.3:* Nutrition	*Activity 7.4:* Connecting Seeds and Human Nutrition	*Activity 7.3:* Postlab	*Activity 7.4:* Postlab
32	Chapter 7: Feeding the Planet	*Activity 7.5:* Seeds for the Future	*Activity 7.6:* The Politics of Hunger (Day 1)	*Activity 7.6:* The Politics of Hunger (Day 2)	Chapters 6–7 Review	Chapters 6–7 Assessment
33	Chapter 8: Demand for Energy	*Activity 8.1:* Where Do We Get Our Energy?	*Activity 8.2:* Energy History of the U.S.	*Activity 8.3:* The Energy Content of a Fuel	*Activity 8.4:* Unquenchable Energy Thirst	*Activity 8.5:* Simulating Oil Refining
34	Today's Energy Sources	*Video:* Fossil Fuels (19 min.)	*Activity 8.6:* Coal	*Activity 8.7:* How Electricity Is Generated	Chapter 8 Summary	Chapter 8 Assessment
35	Standards Adjustment— Electricity	*Activity:* Ohm's Law	*Activity:* Ohm's Law Problems	*Activity:* Series & Parallel Wiring	*Activity:* Home Wiring	*Topic:* Electrical Power Distribution. Electrical Safety.
36	Semester Review/Exam	←——————————— End of Semester II ———————————→				

Week	Topic	Monday	Tuesday	Wednesday	Thursday	Friday
37	Chapter 9: Nonrenewable Resource Depletion	Activity 9.1: Resource Depletion. Blacklines 9.1 and 9.2.	Write up lab. (Optional: Plotting graphs using computer programs.)	Activity 9.2: Applying a Model to a Real World Situation	Postlabs Blacklines 9.3 and 9.4	Resources & Reserves. Blackline 9.5 Activity 9.3: Estimating Size of a Resource
38	How Much Do We Have? Lifetimes.	Activity 9.4: Comparing Nonrenewable Reserves. (Making the graph.)	Activity 9.5: Calculating Resource Lifetimes	Postlabs on Activities 9.3 and 9.4	Chapter 9 Review. Blackline 9.6	Chapter 9 Assessment
39	Chapter 10: Atoms & Radioactivity	Activity 10.1: Atoms and Molecules (Day 1)	Activity 10.1: Atoms and Molecules (Day 2)	Activity 10.2: Working with Atomic Symbols	Activity 10.3: Observations in a Cloud Chamber	Activity 10.4: Writing Nuclear Equations
40	Using Nuclear Fuels	Activity 10.5: Half-Life Investigation	Activity 10.6: Simulating a Radioactive Decay Chain	Activity 10.6: Postlab. Readings 10.3–10.5.	Activity 10.7: Nuclear Fuel Cycle	Video: Radioactive Waste Disposal: The 10,000-year Test (50 min.)
41	The Future of Nuclear Power	Activity 10.8: Transporting Nuclear Waste— Design Container	Activity 10.8: Transporting Nuclear Waste— Test Container	Activity 10.9: Calculate Your Personal Radiation Dose	Chapter 10 Summary & Study Guide	Chapter 10 Assessment
42	Standards Adjustment— Chemistry	Adjustment week to tie to state standards regarding chemical reactions, chemical equations, and chemical equilibrium.				
43	Chapter 11: Synfuels & Local Options	Readings 11.1–11.3 Synfuels	Readings 11.4–11.6 Local Options	Activity 11.1: Geothermal Convection Currents	Activity 11.2: Design an Environmental Home (Due in one week.)	Activity 11.3: Passive Solar Home
44	Solar Heating & Solar Electricity	Activity 11.5: Analysis of a Solar Collector	Activity 11.6: Solar Water Heating	Activity 11.7: Solar Cells (Day 1)	Activity 11.7 Solar Cells (Day 2)	Presentation of Environmental Homes (Day 1)
45	Qtr. V Adjustment Week	This week is left blank to adjust for Quarter Exams, holidays, power outages/snow days, assemblies, staff development, etc.				

continued

Week	Topic	Monday	Tuesday	Wednesday	Thursday	Friday
46	Summary of Energy Alternatives	Presentation of Environmental Homes (Day 2)	*Video:* Energy Alternatives (20 min.)	*Activity 11.4* -or- *Activity 11.8* -or- Readings 11.16–11.18	Chapter 11 Summary	Chapter 11 Assessment
47	Chapter 12: Conservation, Energy Conversion and Storage.	*Activity 12.1:* Home Energy Plan (Due in one week.)	*Video:* Renewable Power (28 min.)	*Activity 12.2:* Fuel Efficiency *vs.* Weight	*Activity 12.3:* Operate and Analyze a Fuel Cell (Day 1)	*Activity 12.3:* Analyze a Fuel Cell (Day 2)
48	Comparing Sources Appropriate Technology	Readings 12.6–12.7 Comparing Sources	*Activity 12.4:* Appropriate Technology	*Activity 12.5:* World Oil (Group work)	*Activity 12.5:* World Oil (class discussion)	Chapter 12 Study Guide
49	Energy Policy	*Activity 12.6:* Summarize Your Options (Day 1)	*Activity 12.6:* (Day 2) Student reports	*Activity 12.6:* (Day 3) Student reports	*Activity 12.6:* (Day 4) Student reports	Chapter 12 Assessment, which could be *Activity 12.7:* Sorting Out Your Options
50	Chapter 13: Water Supply. Water Management.	*Activity 13.1:* Water, Water Everywhere	*Activity 13.2:* How Much Water Do You Use?	*Activity 13.3:* Your Improved Water Use	*Case Study:* The Colorado River	*Video:* The Great Lakes Ecosystem (23 min.)
51	Water Pollution	*Activity 13.4:* How Clean Is Your Water? (Day 1)	*Activity 13.4:* How Clean Is Your Water? (Day 2)	*Activity 13.5:* Effects of Pollutants on Pond Water (Day 1)	*Activity 13.5:* Effects of Pollutants on Pond Water (Day 2)	Chapter 13 Study Guide
52	Wastewater Treatment	Field trip (optional) or class analysis. Wastewater Treatment	*Video:* Wastewater Treatment & Discharge (27 min.)	*Special Focus:* Invasive Species	Chapter 13 Summary	Chapter 13 Assessment
53	Standards Adjustment— Topographic Maps	*Activity E-1:* Making Topo. Maps	Postlab E-1	*Activity E-2:* Using Topo. Maps	Postlab E-2	Maps Assessment
54	Semester Review/Exam	← ———————— Semester III Review/Exam ———————— →				

NOTE: The additional week on topographic maps (Week 53) is a suggested week tied to some state standards. It is up to you to design and assemble. Science Kit sells a plastic mountain used to show how topography maps are made.

Week	Topic	Monday	Tuesday	Wednesday	Thursday	Friday
55	Field Investigation	Video: Gathering Environmental Data (58 min.)	Planning Field Investigation	Two days of outdoor field work could include topography maps.		Finalize Field Reports
56	Chapter 14: The Atmosphere	Activity 14.1: What's Up There? (Day 1)	Activity 14.1: What's Up There? (Day 2)	Activity 14.2: Driving Our Atmosphere Crazy	Video: The Search for Clean Air (57 min.)	Activity 14.3: Testing pH at Home (or in the lab)
57	Air Pollution	Activity 14.4: Acid Rain—Just the Facts	Video: Acid Rain: The Invisible Threat (20 min.)	Activity 14.6: Chart It! For Cleaner Air	Chapter 14 Study Guide	Video: Ozone: Cancer of the Sky (40 min.)
58	Global Climate Issues	Activity 14.7: A Greenhouse Effect Model	Video: Greenhouse Effect (17 min.). Class discusses models.	Activity 14.8: CO_2 and Climate Trends: You Decide	Chapter 14 Summary	Chapter 14 Assessment
59	Physiology (Week 1)	Intro/Overview: Nervous Syst. Discussion. AV.demo.	Lab: Neurobiology (Sensory)	Postlab Neuro. Intro/Overview: Endocrine System	Endocrine Lab: Example- Diabetes Lab	Intro/Overview: Digestion, Respiration, & Cellular Respiration
60	Physiology (Week 2)	Digestion or Respiration Lab	Intro/Overview Circulatory & Excretory System	Circulatory Lab: Ex. Cardiovascular Disease. Pulse Rate.	Excretory Lab: Similated urinology lab.	Activity (D1)- Review all systems. Dissect. (or sim.) Fetal Pig/Rat.
61	Physiology (Week 3)	Activity (D2): Dissection or alternative	Activity (D3): Dissection or alternative	Intro/Overview: Immune System Discussion. AV. demo.	Microbiology Lab: Ex: Handwash, mouthwash, etc.	Immune System Lab: Ex. Simulate how viruses are spread
62	Standards Adjustment— Wireless Communication	Activity Transistors	Demonstration: Electromagnetic Waves	Demonstration: Hertz Experiment	Activity Design a Radio (Day 1)	Build a Radio (Day 2)
63	Qtr. VII Adjustment Week	This week is left blank to adjust for Quarter Exams, holidays, power outages/snow days, assemblies, staff development, etc.				

NOTES: 1. Physiology (Weeks 59–61) is a suggested unit to meet some state standards. It is up to you to design.
2. The physics unit on wireless communication is a suggested unit to meet some state standards. It is up to you to design.

continued

Week	Topic	Monday	Tuesday	Wednesday	Thursday	Friday
64	Chapter 15: Land Use	Intro. to Land Use. *Activity 15.1:* Land Use Decision.	*Activity 15.2:* Environmental Landscaping. CD:Water Wise Gardening	*Activity 15.2:* Environmental Landscaping. Finalize your plan. (Day 2)	Public Lands. *Activity 15.3:* Mined Land Reclamation (Day 1)	*Activity 15.3:* Mined Land Reclamation (Day 2) & Special Focus.
65	Land Management	*Activity 15.4:* Land Use Analysis	*Activity 15.5:* Western Forest Management	Readings 15.8–15.13 and related questions	*Video:* The Salt Marsh (22 min.)	*Activity 15.6:* Not in My Backyard!
66	Waste Management	*Activity 15.7:* Conducting Solutions	*Activity 15.8:* Copper Plating	*Activity 15.9:* Disposing of Toxic Waste	*Video:* Waste Generation, . . . Disposal (45 min.)	Chapter 15 Evaluation
67	Chapter 16: The Growth Issue	*Activity 16.1:* Pioneers and Their Island (Day 1)	*Activity 16.1:* Pioneers and Their Island (Day 2). Some group presentations.	*Activity 16.2:* Graphing the Status of the Island	Pros and cons of *The Limits to Growth* Report. *Activity 16.3:* Tradeoffs	*Activity 16.4:* Do We Live in Two Different Worlds?
68	The Challenge of Sustainability	*Activity 16.5:* Resource Allocation	Readings 16.10–16.13 Chapter 16 Study Guide	*Activity 16.6:* The Economic Role of the Government	*Activity 16.7:* Strategies for Building a Sustainable World	*Activity 16.8:* Changes in Attitudes
69	Building the Sustainable Planet	*Activity 16.9:* Recycling Aluminum	*Activity 16.10:* The Island Revisited (Day 1)	*Activity 16.10:* The Island Revisited (Day 2)	Class discussion of *Activity 16.10*	*Activity 16.11:* Taking Action
70	Introspection	*Activity 16.12:* Introspection	*Video:* Blue Planet (42 min.)	*Discussion:* Think Globally, Act Locally.	Chapter 16 Summary	Chapter 16 Assessment
71	Course Review	Review of the entire 72 weeks of *Global Science*				
72	Semester IV	← Semester IV Exams →				

Theme	Core Lab(s)	Justification
Nature of Science	◆ Asking Scientific Questions	Students develop a scientific process for answering scientific questions.
	◆ Modeling the Weathering Process	Students develop their own plan of attack when faced with a scientific question.
	◆ Measuring Aluminum	Basic graphing skills are established and the power of graphing is illustrated.
Ecosystems	◆ A Voyage to Mars	Students identify the major components of an ecosystem.
	◆ Investigating Ecosystems	Students design ways to investigate how the major components interact.
	◆ Designing Your Ecodome	We all live in and depend on the ecosphere. We must understand and preserve it.
Mineral Resources	◆ Importance of Minerals	Minerals are a foundation on which modern societies are built.
Human Population	◆ Modeling Exponential Growth	The characteristics of exponential growth must be understood by all citizens.
	◆ A Demographic Survey: Questions Regarding Marriage and Children	The survey helps students understand current demographic trends and the demographic transition.
	◆ Analyzing the Demographic Transition	This activity provides students with a humane solution to the population challenge.
Agriculture	◆ Characteristics of Seeds or If You've Seen One Tomato Seed . . .	The wonder of seeds is established as well as some understanding of the kind of information that is stored in them.
	◆ Competing to Survive, . . .	The nature of natural selection is established as students engage in the process.
	◆ How Much Food Energy Do I Need?	It is useful to know how many Calories we require and use each day. The number also helps us understand Calorie data from other countries. Part C allows better students to estimate how much land it takes to raise their food each year. This number can be used to introduce carrying capacity estimates.
Energy (Today)	◆ Unquenchable Energy Thirst	Students examine energy use patterns over the years to begin understanding our present situation and begin looking to the future.
	◆ Resource Depletion	The production cycle for nonrenewable resources must be understood and applied.
	◆ Applying a Model to a Real World Situation	
Energy (Tomorrow)	◆ Designing an Environmental Home	All our students will live in some type of home. It is important they think about the energy/environmental impact of that home.
	◆ Home Energy Plan	
Water	◆ How Clean Is Your Water?	Students should have some idea of why and how we test for water quality.
	Water Delivery/Treatment System (teacher designed)	Students should know how water gets to major cities and to their home and how wastewater is treated.
Atmosphere	◆ Acid Rain—Just the Facts	Acid rain and global warming are two major environmental issues of our time.
	◆ The Greenhouse Effect Model	
Land Use	◆ Environmental Landscaping	Since most students will live in a home that has a yard, the environmental impact of yards should be examined.
Waste	◆ Not in My Backyard	This activity forces students to focus on the problem of waste disposal.
	◆ Disposing of Toxic Waste: The Decision	This activity focuses on waste disposal options. If possible, A15.7 & 15.8 should be done first.
Decision Making: The Sustainable World	◆ Pioneers and Their Island	Helps students understand the resource/environmental situation of our planet.
	◆ The Island Revisited	Island revisited gives students an opportunity to develop a sustainable world.

Title	Description	Length	Source
Scientific Methods and Values	This video can serve as both a summary and extension of Chapter 1. Part 1 gives a brief history of how scientific methods and values came to be. Part II outlines methods and values in science today.	34 minutes VHS Color	Hawkhill Associates, Inc. 125 E. Gilman Street PO Box 1029 Madison, WI 53701-1029 (800) 422-4295
Equipment and Sampling Techniques: Gathering Environmental Data	Provides step-by-step instructions on how to make four pieces of terrestrial and aquatic sampling equipment. Students demonstrate how to test the quality of water for CO, hardness, DO, pH, nitrates, and phosphates.	58 minutes VHS Color	Films for the Humanities & Sciences 2572 Brunswick Pike Lawrenceville, NJ 08648 (800) 257-5126 www.films.com
Cloning: How and Why	Cloning is one of the most controversial issues in science today. In this video students learn some of the details of how cloning is done. They are challenged to consider the implications.	31 minutes VHS Color	Hawkhill Associates, Inc. 125 E. Gilman Street PO Box 1029 Madison, WI 53701-1029 (800) 422-4295
Biomes	Explore the delicate vegetation of the tundra, the amazing ecological adaptations of desert life, and the rich biological diversity of tropical rain forests.	20 minutes VHS Color	Scott Resources PO Box 2121 Fort Collins, CO 80422 (800) 289-9299
Aquatic Biomes	Students are introduced to a variety of the world's aquatic biomes. The characteristics of saltwater and freshwater environments are clearly described.	20 minutes VHS Color	Films for the Humanities & Sciences 2572 Brunswick Pike Lawrenceville, NJ 08648 (800) 257-5126 www.films.com
The Web of Life	A good introduction or summary of the ecosystem concept. Defines ecology and summarizes conservation of energy and the second law of thermodynamics. Looks at food chains, matter recycling, biomes, and the human impact on the global environment.	16 minutes VHS Color	Hawkhill Associates, Inc. 125 E. Gilman Street PO Box 1029 Madison, WI 53701-1029 (800) 422-4295
The Hydrologic Cycle: Water in Motion	With graphics and live action, this video journeys through the water cycle to understand this precious resource.	20 minutes VHS Color	Scott Resources PO Box 2121 Fort Collins, CO 80422 (800) 289-9299
Sharing Carbon: The Carbon Cycle	Focuses on how the transfer of carbon and other elements between the biotic and abiotic parts of the global ecosystem supports life. The impact of humans on the carbon cycle is examined.	20 minutes VHS Color	Films for the Humanities & Sciences 2572 Brunswick Pike Lawrenceville, NJ 08648 (800) 257-5126 www.films.com
Scientific American Frontiers Explores Biosphere 2	Alan Alda takes you on a journey inside Biosphere 2, the world's largest controlled ecological laboratory. Inside, you meet engineers who operate the complex apparatus and scientists who explore its mysteries.	12 minutes VHS Color	Write to: The Biosphere PO Box 689 Oracle, AZ 85623
Toast	Provides an overview of our complex food production system and illustrates the concept of net energy. Our daily toast is the end product of an energy intensive process that begins with the exploration for oil, which is transported, refined, piped, and used in fertilizer production. Fertilizer is spread on fields to nurture wheat, which is harvested and ground into flour. The flour is mixed into dough, baked into bread, and marketed.	13 minutes VHS Color	Bullfrog Films Box 149 Oley, PA 19547 (800) 543-3764

Title	Description	Length	Source
The Rock Cycle	This video unravels the complex processes that create, change, and break down earth materials. Clear and concise definitions of the major rock types are illustrated using full-motion video and colorful computer graphics.	18 minutes VHS Color	Scott Resources PO Box 2121 Fort Collins, CO 80422 (800) 289-9299
Plate Tectonics: The Puzzle of the Contents	This video explores the fundamentals of the plate tectonics theory from Alfred Wegener's observations on continental drift to the latest computer analysis of movements at plate boundaries.	18 minutes VHS Color	Scott Resources PO Box 2121 Fort Collins, CO 80422 (800) 289-9299
Common Ground	The importance of minerals and mining to our standard of living are emphasized in this video. Subjects covered include history, environmental concerns, exploration, mine development, and public perceptions and involvement. Teacher Guide included.	26 minutes VHS Color $5.00 S&H	Mineral Information Institute 501 Violet Street Golden, CO 80401 (303) 277-9190
World Population	A graphic presentation of world population growth and distribution from I A.D. to the present, and projected to 2020 A.D. The most popular population film ever. A must when teaching Chapter 5.	6.5 minutes VHS Color	Population Connection 1400 16th Street, NW, Suite 320 Washington, DC 20036 (800) 767-1956
Population: How Many Is Enough?	A summary of a variety of views on this subject.	32 minutes VHS Color	Hawkhill Associates, Inc. 125 E. Gilman Street PO Box 1029 Madison, WI 53701-1029
A Journey Through the Cell: Cells— An Introduction	In this virtual journey, viewers become familiar with cells and their properties. Another segment describes the organization of cells and the formation of tissues, organs, and systems.	20 minutes VHS Color	Films for the Humanities & Sciences 2572 Brunswick Pike Lawrenceville, NJ 08648 (800) 257-5126 www.films.com
The World of Living Organisms: The Power of Seeds	This program details the structure, germination, growth, and response of seeds using greenhouse examples.	15 minutes VHS Color	Films for the Humanities & Sciences 2572 Brunswick Pike Lawrenceville, NJ 08648 (800) 257-5126 www.films.com
Seeds	Filmed in Peru, Turkey, and North America, this video documents the value of the world's genetic pool upon which all our food depends.	26 minutes VHS Color	Bullfrog Films Box 149 Oley, PA 19547 (800) 543-3764
The Living Soil: The Value of Humus	This video shows how nutrients are replenished in healthy soil through the interaction of plant roots, nitrogen-fixing bacteria, fungi, and other organisms to create humus. Human impacts on soil also are discussed.	20 minutes VHS Color	Films for the Humanities & Sciences 2572 Brunswick Pike Lawrenceville, NJ 08648 (800) 257-5126 www.films.com
Fossil Fuels	This video helps students understand the processes that lead to the formation, utilization, and environmental impact of our nonrenewable energy resources—fossil fuels.	19 minutes VHS Color	Scott Resources PO Box 2121 Fort Collins, CO 80422 (800) 289-9299

continued

Title	Description	Length	Source
Radiation and You	The nature of radiation and what it can do for people, and the risks and the benefits are summarized.	21 minutes VHS Color	Hawkhill Associates, Inc. 125 E. Gilman Street PO Box 1029 Madison, WI 53701-1029 (800) 422-4295
Radioactive Waste Disposal, the 10,000 Year Test	This program investigates current research in the middle of the Nevada desert where a nuclear dump is to be located, with scientists creating computer simulations that take into consideration rocks, weather, groundwater behavior, and human activity.	50 minutes VHS Color	Films for the Humanities & Sciences 2572 Brunswick Pike Lawrenceville, NJ 08648 (800) 257-5126 www.films.com
Alternative Energies: Fuels for the Future	Learn how solar, wind, biomass, and other alternatives work and can meet the demand for clean and renewable sources of energy.	20 minutes VHS Color	Scott Resources PO Box 2121 Fort Collins, CO 80422 (800) 289-9299
Renewable Power: Earth's Clean Energy	Renewable Power offers a vision of a world transformed by clean energy. Solar and wind are examined along with the hydrogen economy and fuel cells.	28 minutes VHS Color	The Video Project PO Box 77188 San Francisco, CA 94107 (800) 4-PLANET www.videoproject.net
The Great Lakes Ecosystem	The largest chain of fresh water lakes in the world has special ecological problems of its own. This video stresses the sea lamprey, toxic wastes in the lakes, and the arrival of the zebra mussel and ruffe.	23 minutes VHS Color	Hawkhill Associates, Inc. 125 East Gilman Street Madison, WI 53703 (800) 422-4295 www.hawkhill.com
Wastewater Treatment and Discharge	This video illustrates the physical, biological, and chemical processes used to treat industrial and residential wastewater and ways in which discharge is being put to work. New approaches and challenges also are examined.	27 minutes VHS Color	Films for the Humanities & Sciences 2572 Brunswick Pike Lawrenceville, NJ 08648 (800) 257-5126 www.films.com
The Search for Clean Air	A clear and thorough examination of the problem of air pollution: its causes; its effects on forests, streams, and human health; and the issues involved in correcting the problems.	57 minutes VHS Color	Films for the Humanities & Sciences 2572 Brunswick Pike Lawrenceville, NJ 08648 (800) 257-5126 www.films.com
Acid Rain: The Invisible Threat	Expert interviews, exciting on-location footage, and computer animation explain clearly how acid rain affects forests, lakes, and the human environment.	20 minutes VHS Color	Scott Resources PO Box 2121 Fort Collins, CO 80422 (800) 289-9299
The Greenhouse Effect	The causes and effects of global warming are explored, as well as the use of computer modeling to predict Earth's changing climate.	17 minutes VHS Color	Scott Resources PO Box 2121 Fort Collins, CO 80422 (800) 289-9299
Greenhouse Crisis: The American Response	This video explores the link between energy use and global warming. The consequences of global warming are examined, and strategies for resolving this problem are highlighted.	11 minutes VHS Color	The Video Project PO Box 77188 San Francisco, CA 94107 (800) 4-PLANET www.videoproject.net
Ozone: Cancer of the Sky	The causes and potential consequences of ozone layer depletion are examined. Strategies to reverse this threat are proposed and examined.	40 minutes VHS Color	The Video Project PO Box 77188 San Francisco, CA 94107 (800) 4-PLANET www.videoproject.net

Title	Description	Length	Source
Water Wise Gardening	This comprehensive CD contains all the information necessary for students to do a thorough job of completing Activity 15.2: Environmental Landscaping.	CD Color PCs Only No charge.	Sonoma County Water Agency Attention: Ali Davidson 2227 Capricorn Way, Suite 108 Santa Rosa, CA 95406 (707) 547-1933
The Salt Marsh: A Question of Values	A study of the ecological system of estuaries. Of special interest is the section on measuring the productivity of marsh grasses. The video emphasizes the need to conserve salt marshes.	22 minutes VHS Color	Britannica, Inc. 310 S. Michigan Avenue Chicago, IL 60664-9839 (800) 554-9862
Waste Generation, Characterization, Collection, Transfer, and Disposal	This two-part video examines the generation of municipal solid waste (MSW) in the United States and the methods of collecting, transferring, and disposing of them. The impact of RCRA is assessed.	45 minutes VHS Color	Films for the Humanities & Sciences 2572 Brunswick Pike Lawrenceville, NJ 08648 (800) 257-5126 www.films.com
Toxic Wastes	This video attempts to put the issue of toxic waste into perspective. Serious toxic waste problems from past history are examined. We are then challenged to take intelligent action as we deal with toxic waste problems today.	36 minutes VHS Color	Hawkhill Associates, Inc. 125 E. Gilman Street PO Box 1029 Madison, WI 53701-1029 (800) 422-4295
Life Cycle Assessment	This video examines the life cycle assessment technique for determining the energy/environmental impact of various products. This topic ties to Activity 16.9. Consumers need this kind of information if they desire to live in a sustainable world.	30 min. VHS Color	Films for the Humanities & Sciences 2572 Brunswick Pike Lawrenceville, NJ 08648 (800) 257-5126
Blue Planet	Filmed in IMAX by astronauts aboard five space shuttle missions, *Blue Planet* is "a stunning look at our planet as a living being—beautiful, volatile, and extremely vulnerable." *The Washington Post*	42 minutes VHS Color	Do an internet search—Blue Planet IMAX Video available from Amazon.com

Each *Global Science* student edition and teacher's guide includes a *Global Science Explorer*™ CD-ROM. This CD-ROM supplements *Global Science* with further investigations into an entire range of earth sciences (geology, oceanography, meteorology, astronomy), chemistry, physics, and life sciences.

Global Science Explorer™ is one of many fine CD-ROM products designed and developed by EOA Scientific Systems. EOA Scientific distributes hundreds of CD-ROM science educational software titles in three categories for Grades 6–8 and Grades 9–12:

- Earth and Space Sciences
- Physical and Chemical Sciences
- Life/Biology and Environmental Sciences

In addition to hundreds of individual titles, EOA Scientific also bundles sets of CD titles to allow discount pricing for network/site licenses and to maximize comprehensiveness of instructional content. Some of these bundles follow. These include virtual labs and simulations, plus extensive interactive multimedia tutorials:

EARTH/SPACE SCIENCE SERIES SET/16 CD TITLES

- Geology Edu-Tutor #1: Planet Earth
- Geology Edu-Tutor #2: Rocks, Minerals, & Resources
- Geology Edu-Tutor #3: Earth's Changing Surface
- Geology Edu-Tutor #4: Evolving Earth/Plate Tectonics
- Oceans Edu-Tutor #1: Introduction to Earth's Oceans
- Oceans Edu-Tutor #2: Waterworld
- Oceans Edu-Tutor #3: Our Living Ocean
- Oceans Edu-Tutor #4: Water: Vapor, Liquid, and Solid
- Weather Edu-Tutor #1: Weather Fundamentals
- Weather Edu-Tutor #2: Storms, Tornadoes, Floods
- Weather Edu-Tutor #3: Weather Forecasting
- Weather Edu-Tutor #4: Climate: Remote Sensing
- Astronomy Edu-Tutor #1: Our Universe
- Astronomy Edu-Tutor #2: Earth and the Inner Planets
- Astronomy Edu-Tutor #3: The Outer Planets
- Astronomy Edu-Tutor #4: Mission Climate

LIFE SCIENCE AND BIOLOGY SERIES SET/ 12 CD TITLES

- Biology Illustrations
- Blood & the Circulatory System
- Cell Processes
- Cell Structure & Function
- DNA: Molecule of Life
- Exploring w/ a Microscope
- Five Kingdom
- Genetics Simulation
- Human Anatomy Illustrations
- Mitosis & Meiosis
- Plants
- Systems of Human Body

PHYSICAL/CHEMICAL SCIENCE SERIES SET/ 13 CD TITLES

- Atoms & Elements
- Chemical Reactions
- Chemistry
- Electrical Charge/Electromagnetism
- Electricity & Magnetism
- Elements, Mixtures, & Compounds
- Force & Motion
- Heat & Energy
- Ions, Symbols, & Valency
- Light & Optics
- Periodic Table: Classification of the Elements
- Structure of Matter
- Waves & Sound

For more information, contact EOA Scientific. Make sure you mention Kendall/Hunt *Global Science.*

EOA Scientific Systems, Inc.
www.eoascientific.com
sales@eoascientific.com; info@eoascientific.com

For sales or information, call
 1-888-666-6362 or (902) 477-6336.
For technical support with the *Global Science Explorer*™, contact support@eoascientific.com

Vernier Software & Technology is the recommended software and data collection hardware/software provider for *Global Science*. They have a 24-year history of providing high-quality products at affordable prices.

Two of their offerings are of particular interest in the *Global Science* laboratory program:

1. Their Graphical Analysis software (GA-WIN or GA-MAC) allows students to process data they collect in the laboratory, display it in a professional manner, and analyze it in ways that become more sophisticated as their background and math ability grows.

2. The Vernier LabPro interface allows students to collect data using a variety of sensors. Using the LabPro, data can be collected in the field or in the classroom. The LabPro can then be interfaced with either a computer or a Texas Instruments graphing calculator. Thus, data can be viewed at the site of the experiment or collected and stored at the site and viewed later on a computer screen. The LabPro is compatible with Windows or Macintosh computers, serial or USB port, with Logger Pro software (sold separately), and with TI graphing calculators. Sensors are available for temperature, dissolved oxygen, pH, voltage, nitrate concentration, and many other variables.

The following activities tie well to the Graphical Analysis Software:

The following activities tie well to the use of the LabPro and related sensors:

For more information and current pricing, contact:

Vernier Software & Technology
13979 SW Millikan Way
Beaverton, OR 97005-2886

Phone: (503) 277-2299
Web: www.vernier.com
E-mail: info@vernier.com
Fax: (503) 277-2440

Before You Start

Student use of the Internet is a mixed blessing. The net or web contains vast resources of information. It is novel and students are initially motivated to learn. There is a wealth of information that can greatly aid in teaching students content and research skills, yet it also has some real pitfalls. The Internet is unregulated, which means that any student can gain access to websites that are totally unrelated to what you want to teach and websites with objectionable content. Furthermore, the vastness of the web can result in low student productivity. So the question to be answered is how do you get the most out of this resource?

Management and Planning

If you have a class of 30 students who all will have Internet access at the same time, your primary activity in the Internet lab will be to monitor and facilitate. You will be busy, and without a real plan and preparation, the bad stuff will happen. The following are things to do before letting the students go.

- Check with your network administrator to be certain that all machines are working and that the server has the correct Internet software. Familiarize yourself with the interface so that you are comfortable with it. It's hard to teach a student something you do not know.

- Assign computer stations (allows you to examine the web page path if improper conduct is suspected).

- Prepare an introduction to the browser (Netscape or Internet Explorer) to demonstrate all of the essential features of naviga-

Source: Dick Filson Past-President, California Science Teachers Association. E-mail: dfilson@inreach.com

tion. It is best to limit students to just one website for this introduction, and if possible, use a projected image of the web page you are working from. Things students will need to know:

- location bar for URLs (web site address)
- status bar for monitoring connections
- recognizing and clocking links
- forward and back buttons
- the use of bookmarks

- Prepare and go over an Internet-use agreement to be signed by the student and parents that explains your rules and limitations for the use of the Internet. This also might include assignment of accounts for e-mail use.

- Prepare a lesson on Internet search strategies. Include some practice topics and require students to list the steps of their search and the web address of where the desired information was found.

Internet Activities for Environmental Science

Research is the most obvious use of the Internet. However, other activities could involve collaborative investigations with other schools. Here are some ideas. Short-term assignments are easily developed using key questions you provide for each chapter that require students to find answers on the Internet. For example, what is the relationship between birthrate and poverty? Give the website that provides data to support your answer. What is the relationship between rainfall and habitat type?

Long-term assignments could be comparable to term papers. You provide the theme and the criteria. The students research the information and put together the report with appropriate citations. The availability of graphics is a real plus for these kinds of assignments. They can be downloaded easily for student use. The best approach to such papers is a preselected list of themes, 40 or more. Some examples include "Nuclear Power: The Good, the Bad, and the Ugly," "Is Sustained Growth an Ecological Oxymoron?," "Nobody Ever Dies of Overpopulation."

On-line collaborations present some of the most innovative uses of the Internet. Some ecological collaborations include:

* Project GREEN, Global Rivers Environmental Education Network
  http://www.igc.org/green/
* Project GLOBE, Global Learning and Observations to Benefit the Environment
  http://www.globe.gov

* Access Excellence, on-line collaborations on Acid Snow, Ray Day, video Biomes
  http://www.gene.com/ae/

The thing to remember about the instructional use of the Internet is to have a plan with real objectives that you can evaluate.

For in-depth help in using the Internet, consider purchasing a copy of *The Internet for Teachers* by Brad Williams, IDG Books, ISBN 1-56884-600-2.

A Student Guide to the Internet

Background

The Internet, popularly known as the "web," is a complex maze of computer networks that are connected by high-speed telephone lines. What originally began as a way for universities and government agencies to communicate inexpensively now can reach any household in the world with a telephone line and a personal computer. Today, millions of people use the Internet daily to find information, share information, and/or communicate with each other. With the commercialization of the Internet, there has been an exponential growth of services and products available on-line. The value of the Internet to you as a student is that you can gather information, chat with another student or a scientist thousands of miles away, or you can become involved in collaborative scientific studies on a global scale.

Getting Started

You are likely already familiar with the basic operation of your computer. If your school has a computer network, there will be a designated "network administrator" who is responsible for the operation of the system. This person should be your resource for internal problems. There are two main ways you can use the Internet: browsing the web, that is, going from website to website for information of interest; and the use of e-mail, electronic mail that communicates with specific individuals just as you might send a letter through the U.S. mail. This guide will concentrate on browsing the web.

To browse the web, you will need a personal computer that is connected to the Internet. School networks are usually connected through the network's server. Stand-alone computers re-quire a modem (small box) between the computer and the phone connection. Internet software should already be installed. Two popular programs are Netscape and Internet Explorer. Netscape is used more commonly. Both work about the same with some differences in their options and the location of various buttons. The main point is that both programs are mouse-driven. You just point and click.

Going On-line

To reach a website, start your Internet software and type in the website address (URL, universal resource locator) into the space where your cursor is blinking (location bar). Most URLs look something like this: **http://www.gene.com/ ae/.** (This is a real web site for biology.) All web addresses start with "http://" and often include www. Http stands for hyper text transfer protocol, which is the language used in transmitting web pages through the system. Www stands for World Wide Web. Once the web address is typed into the location bar, press RETURN and a message will go out to the website. At the bottom of your browser window, you will see messages like "connect," "transferring data," etc. As the data arrive, the web page begins to appear. Once the web page is complete, you can scroll through it and look for useful information.

Recognizing and Using Links

On nearly every website, you will find additional links to other web pages within the site or to other websites. You can easily recognize these links since they are always underlined and have a contrasting color such as blue as opposed to black. Clicking on these links will take you to these sites. If you want to go back, you can go up to your tool bar at the top of your page, click the back button (arrow) or just hold down your

SOURCE: Dick Filson, Past-President, California Science Teachers Association. E-mail: dfilson@inreach.com

mouse button until the options menu appears, and select BACK. You can go forward again in the same way. Notice that previously visited links have changed color, which helps you know where you have been. If you want to go several steps back, you go to the menu bar to GO and select what you want. An important and useful feature is bookmarks.

Using Bookmarks and Navigating

If you find a great site that you will want to revisit again, you can record its web address by using the bookmark menu. The website addresses provided with this guide were selected according to the theme of each chapter. Websites are something like a tree, so if you enter it at an extra branch, your choices are limited. But there is a way to maximize your choices. For example, the guide provides a site address for water data: *http://h2o.usgs.gov/public/wid/html/WD.html*. Notice the single slashes in the address. These are branches within the website. So going to *http://h2o.usgs.gov* will take you to the "home page" of the USGS water resources division. From there you have the broadest choice of destinations.

Search Engines

One of the most powerful tools for web browsing is the search engine. A search engine is a feature that uses key words to search websites and web pages for the words or titles you are seeking. A broad search can yield a list of thousands while a narrow search may yield only a few. A good starting point for a search engine is *http://www.yahoo.com*. In addition to a guide and tips for searches, you will find access to other search engines such as Alta Vista and Infoseek. Advanced

websites often have their own search engines. The trick in any search is to use "key words," which will be found in the desired document and not found in undesired documents. For example, the word *world* would yield thousands of responses, whereas, *world biome maps* would yield a much more limited and useful list.

Reliability of Data

The Internet is an unregulated domain, which means that anyone can publish anything on the net. So as a seeker and consumer of information, you must beware. Just because you found something on the Internet does not mean that the information is correct and without bias. You must consider the source. Here is a guideline. Scientific data and reports on university sites usually involve peer review. This means that someone who cares about the reputation of the university or field of science has examined the work before it was published. Government websites also contain information for which individuals are held accountable. Both types of sites are generally reliable, although data can always contain some errors. Commercial sites are obviously offering a product. Noninstitutional sites usually have a point of view or philosophy they wish to advance. These may have information that is slanted and may not be subject to review by others. Many noninstitutional environmental websites may have a bias you can detect. This is all right as long as you remember that there may be differing points of view on the same subject. The important thing is that you must be objective and form your own point of view through critical thinking. If you use any Internet data in writing, it would be proper and wise to cite the source in your report. Citation is a common practice to give credit where credit is due.

General Information

Contact Kendall/Hunt
Publishing Company
at 1-800-228-0810

Activity 1.3

Modeling the
 Weathering Process
Stopwatch or wall clock
Safety goggles
1—Thermometer (F/C)
4—Antacid tablets
3—Beakers (or plastic cups)
Waste container
Ice cubes (or cold water)
Hot and room temperature
 water
Graph paper

Activity 1.9

Measuring Aluminum
5—Aluminum samples,
 different
Set of graduated cylinders
 (100 mL, 250 mL, 500 mL,
 1000 mL)
1—Metric ruler
Handbook of Chemistry &
 Physics
Balance (to mass in grams)
Supply of water and beakers
Medicine dropper
Graph paper

Activity 2.2

A Voyage to Mars
Equipment/lab group:
 Lab handout, including
 Mars
 Information Sheet
Some teachers place the
 above in brown legal-size
 envelopes labeled
 Confidential.

Activity 2.3

Investigating Ecosystems
10—Test tubes with corks
 (or culture tubes)
Masking tape for labeling
2—Test-tube racks
4—Pieces of *Elodea*
4—Small snails
Bromthymol blue solution
 in dropper bottle
Roll of parafilm
Pond (or aquarium) water
Light source
Box to keep one set of tubes
 in the dark

Activity 3.4

The Conservation of Mass
2—100 mL beakers
0.1 M Na_2CO_3 solution
0.1 M $Ca(CH_3COO)_2$ solution
2—50 or 100 mL graduated
 cylinders
Lab balance and set of
 masses

Activity 3.11

Let's Have Tea!
1—Thermometer
 ($-10°$ to $110°C$)
1—Styrofoam cup
1—Graduated cylinder
 (100 mL or 250 mL)
1—Immersion heater
1—Watch (or stopwatch)
1—Tea bag (optional)

Activities 4.3 and 4.4

What Mineral Is It?
What Rock Is It?
Collections of mineral and
 rock samples
Hand lens
1—Steel nail
1—Dropper bottle of dil. HCl

Activity 4.8

Concentrate on Your Minerals
25 mL 0.3 M $CuSO_4$ solution
2—50 mL beakers
2—Iron nails
1—100 mL graduated cylinder
2—Test tubes and stoppers
4—10 mL graduated cylinder
1—Bottle cooking oil
1—Small bottle $KMnO_4$ crystals
2—Test-tube racks
1—250 mL Erlenmeyer flask of
 conc. NaCl solution
1—Petri dish
1—Ring stand
2—Utility clamps
1—Glass column

1—500 mL beaker
Mineral deposit #1
1—Bunsen burner or electric
 heater
3—150 mL beakers
Pair of gloves
1—Gauze pad and tape
1—Funnel
1—250 mL Erlenmeyer flask
 of supersaturated epsom
 solution
Safety goggles
1—Fine screen
Mineral deposit #2

Activity 4.10

Milling Lab
1—Vial of ore
1—Electric heater (hot plate)
4—100 mL beakers
5—50 mL beakers
1—Tongs (to lift beakers)
1—Magnet
1—Distilled water
1—Magnifying glass
1—Safety goggles and lab
 apron
1—Stirring rod
1—Dropper bottle of dil. HCl
1—Tweezers
1—Wire screen filter
1—Filter paper, funnel, ring
 stand, and ring

Activity 5.1

Modeling Exponential
 Growth
200 to 300 dice or marked
 cubes
2—Large containers
2—Sheets graph paper
1—Sheet of semi-log paper
 (2 cycle)

Activity 6.6

Competing to Survive,
Surving to Compete.
Materials/lab group:
1—Cup of assorted food
 units (mix of dried black-
 eyed peas and small, dried
 elbow macaroni)
4—Empty plastic cups
Plastic knife, fork, and
 spoon (1 each)
1—Calculator
1—Watch (clock) that
 indicates seconds

Activity 7.4

Connecting Seeds and
 Human Nutrition
Assorted seeds (soaked
 overnight) or edible seeds
Boiling apparatus
Starch-detecting stain
Protein-detecting stain
Sugar-detecting stain
Lipid-detecting stain
Scalpel or single-edge razor
 blade
Petri dishes
Medicine dropper
Plastic rod with flat end
 test tubes (4)
Graduated cylinders (10 mL)
Safety goggles
Turkey, honey, butter, potato
2—250 mL beaker

Activity 8.3

Counting Calories . . . The
 Energy Content of a Fuel
1—Ring stand and ring
1—Carboard frozen juice
 can
1—Book of matches
1—Glass stirring rod
1—Large tin can chimney
1—Candle
1—Thermometer ($-10°$ to
 $110°C$)
1—Double-pan balance
1—Set of standard masses
Safety goggles
1—Graduated cylinder

Activity 8.5

Simulating Oil Refining—
 The Distillation Process
Simulated crude oil, 50 mL
 or Cherry Coke
Erlenmeyer flash, 250 mL
Rubber stopper (No. 7) with
 glass connector
Clear plastic tubing
Test tube (25 × 150)
Beaker, 500 mL
Crushed ice
Safety goggles
Ring stand
Utility clamp
Metal ring
Wire gauze
Bunsen burner
Graduated cylinder, 50 mL

404

Activity 8.6
Coal
Samples of:
   Peat
   Lignite
   Bituminous
   Anthracite

Activity 8.7
How Electricity Is Generated
1.5 V Size D battery
Flashlight bulb
Jumbo paper clip
Magnetic compass
Coil of Insulated wire
Air core solenoid
Bar magnet
Milliammeter
Hand-crank generator

Activity 9.1
Resource Depletion
4—Plastic cups
1—Earth Box (containing
   dried corn and 800 plastic
   beads)
2—Sheets graph paper
1—Timing device

Activity 10.1
Atoms and Molecules
Demineralized water
$CuSO_4$ crystals
$CuSO_4$ soln. (0.2 M)
2—Iron nails
2—50 mL beakers
Steel wool

Activity 10.3
Observations in a Cloud
   Chamber
1—Diffusion cloud chamber
1—Styrofoam base
1—Radioactive ore sample
1—Dry ice chunks
1—Canvas sack, gloves
1—Hammer
1—Flashlight
Alcohol (methyl)

Activity 10.5
Half-Life Investigation
Plastic container
200 dice
Sheet of ordinary graph
   paper
Sheet of semi-log paper

Activity 10.6
Simulating a Radioactive
   Decay Chain
150—Dice
50—Icosahedrons
120—Marbles
—or—
Decay Chain Kit
Graph paper

Activity 11.2
Designing an Environmental
   Home
Students build their own
   models.

Activity 11.3
Passive Solar Home
1—Passive solar home kit
1—Clamp lamp with
   reflector.
1—Stand to mount the sun
   simulator on
1—Clock or stopwatch
1—Sheet of ordinary graph
   paper

Activity 11.4
Build and Use a Solar Oven
Students design and build
   their own solar ovens
—or—
You can purchase a
   SunSpot Solar Oven

Activity 11.5
Analysis of a Solar Collector
1—Solar collector
1—2000 mL container
1—Siphon
1—Styrofoam cooler
2—Thermometers
   (Fahrenheit)
1—Meter stick, gloves
   (English/metric)
1—1000 mL graduated
   cylinder

Activity 11.7
Solar Cells
Equipment/lab group:
1—Solar Cell Kit

Activity 11.8
Build a Model Wind
   Generator
Students design and build
   their own wind generators
   and/or use a commercial
   wind generator.

Activity 12.3
Operate and Analyze a Fuel
   Cell
Safety goggles
This activity is designed
   around the hydro-Genius™
   Solar Hydrogen
   Technology Science Kit.

Activity 13.1
Water, Water Everywhere
   (demonstration)
1—Salt shaker
1—Graduated cylinder,
   1000 mL
1—Beaker, 1000 mL
3—Beakers, 50 mL
1—Medicine dropper

Activity 13.4
How Clean Is Your Water?
The Green Water
   Monitoring Kit (Classroom
   Set) contains all the
   materials necessary for
   doing this activity. Sargent-
   Welch Cat. No. WL 9767

Activity 13.5
The Effects of Pollutants on
   Pond Water
Sargent-Welch provides the
   Pollutant Effects of
   Phosphates and Nitrates
   Kit and/or make your own
   phosphate and nitrate
   solutions following
   directions in the Teacher
   Guide.

Activity 14.4
Acid Rain—Just the Facts
4—Baby jars and lids
1—50 mL graduated
   cylinder
1—Dropper bottle, BTB
1—Dropper bottle, IM acetic
   acid
1—Dropper bottle, IM
   NH_4OH
1—Dropper bottle,
   limewater
1—Straw and safety
   goggles
1—Kitchen match
1—Roll masking tape

Activity 14.6
Charge It! For Cleaner Air
2—Ringstands with crossbar
1—Wool cloth
1—Cotton cloth
1—Cat's fur
1—Hand rubber rod
2—Acetate strips
2—Vinylite strips
Collect easily charged
   objects

Activity 14.7
The Greenhouse Effect
   Model
1—Shoe box
1—Plastic wrap cover
1—Clamp lamp with
   reflector
1—150 W incandescent bulb
1—Thermometer ($-10°$ to
   $100°C$)
1—Graph paper
Colored pencils
Dark soil
Timing device

Activities 15.7 (Conducting Solutions) and **15.8** (Copper Plating)
These two activities can be done using the materials in the Copper Plating Kit sold by your
Kendall/Hunt representative. The kit provide enough materials for ten (8) lab groups (4
students/group) assuming you locally purchase and supply the 9-V batteries, salt, sugar, steel
paper clips, stirring rods, and copper chloride solution. See the Teacher Guide for directions for
preparing the copper chloride solution.

Activity 16.9
Recycling Aluminum
1—Grocery sack of smashed
   aluminum cans
1—Double-pan balance
1—Mass set

Name _____ Date _____

AFTER I FINISH SCHOOL . . . THEN WHAT?

The basic needs each of us has—food, clothing, shelter, transportation—answers, at one level, why we get a job. Beyond the necessities, our work may provide some of the "good life"—a stereo system, sports and recreation equipment, travel to a special place.

If one looks beyond these obvious reasons for "getting a job," what you do may determine where you live, who you associate with, when you have free time, and how much training beyond high school you will need. Choosing your life's work will be one of the most difficult and important jobs you will encounter. The exercises that follow are designed to help make that task easier. As you work through these forced-choice grids, you will gain some insight into your own interests and the values underlying those interests. Recognizing what your interests and values are will help you answer the important question, "What am I going to do after I finish school?"

USING A FORCED-CHOICE GRID

Suppose you had to choose, from the sports listed, one that you would either like to participate in or enjoy as a spectator. A forced-choice grid will tell you what you may know already or help you choose if you are not sure. If the list doesn't have your favorite sport, don't worry. This activity is designed to demonstrate how to use a forced-choice grid.

The sports are listed and numbered alphabetically for lack of a better scheme. Each activity is listed twice—in a row and then repeated in a column. Each block in the grid lies at the intersection of a row and a column. For each sport pair, choose the one you would most like to participate in or watch as a spectator. You do not have the luxury of saying, "I don't like either one so I won't make a choice." The *forced-choice* grid requires that you make a choice regardless of how undesirable that choice may be. Suppose, for example, you had to choose between jogging (listed in row 4) and ice skating (listed in column 3). Regardless of how undesirable they may be to you personally, make a choice between the two as if they were the *only* choices you had. In the grid block that lies at the intersection of row 4 (jogging) and column 3 (ice skating), write the identifying number (either a 3 or a 4) of the sport you like best— if those were choices you had.

By making a choice between sport pairs and entering the identifying number in the grid block that lies at the intersection of those pairs, you will be comparing each sport listed with every other sport— one at a time. If you then tally the number of times each sport identifying number appears in the grid, you will have a record of which sport or sports you like best and which you like least. Those that appear most frequently would rank high (1, 2); the least frequent listing ranks 7. There may be some ties as you rank the sports from most favorite to least. That is okay. In working through the grid and choosing between pairs of sports, you will have narrowed a list that had seven choices to one that has only one of a few choices. In the process, you will have learned a bit more about yourself and your desire to participate in or watch these activities.

MY FAVORITE SPORT AS A PARTICIPANT OR SPECTATOR

1. Basketball

2. Biking

3. Ice skating

4. Jogging

5. Skiing

6. Swimming

7. Volleyball

	Times Recorded	Rank
1. Basketball		
2. Biking		
3. Ice skating		
4. Jogging		
5. Skiing		
6. Swimming		
7. Volleyball		

Basketball	Biking	Ice skating	Jogging	Skiing	Swimming	Volleyball
1	2	3	4	5	6	7

VOCATIONAL DIRECTIONS

Values have been described as enduring beliefs that a mode of behavior or end-state of existence is personally or socially preferable to the opposite conduct or end-state (Rokeach, 1973). The six-item, forced-choice grid "Some Vocational Directions I Might Choose: Work Values" will help you sort through most of the big reasons that people work beyond the obvious—to pay the rent and buy a car. After you have completed the grid and tallied your responses, examine your rankings. What do the rankings reveal about your behavior (values) and the type of work you might choose?

Listed below are 15 occupational clusters identified (Cannastra, et al., 1982) by the U.S. Department of Education. Most jobs will fall into at least one of these clusters. What you learned by doing the vocational directions grid should be applied to a careful examination of this list. Which cluster interests you most? Why? Ask a counselor at school for more information on the occupational cluster you identified.

- Business and office
- Agribusiness and natural resources
- Health care
- Public service
- Environment
- Communications and media
- Hospitality and recreation
- Manufacturing
- Marketing and distribution
- Marine science
- Personal services
- Construction
- Transportation
- Consumer and homemaking education
- Fine arts and humanities

The cluster that interests me the most is _____.

WORK VALUES

The grid on work values will help you clarify further the type of career you want. Fill out this forced-choice grid. Then, tabulate your results using the chart on the page that follows. Examine your ranking of the 17 work values. Based on this ranking, write a short paragraph describing the kind of work you would like to do.

_____

_____

_____

_____

SOME VOCATIONAL DIRECTIONS I MIGHT CHOOSE: WORK VALUES

	Times Recorded	Rank
1. Helping people		
2. Managing people		
3. Putting talent to work		
4. Solving nature's puzzles		
5. Working *with* data *and* details		
6. Working with your hands		

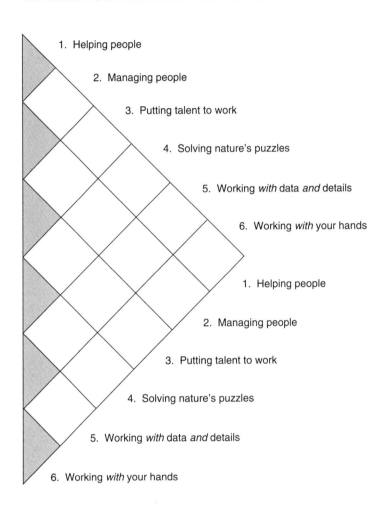

1. Helping people

2. Managing people

3. Putting talent to work

4. Solving nature's puzzles

5. Working *with* data *and* details

6. Working *with* your hands

1. Helping people

2. Managing people

3. Putting talent to work

4. Solving nature's puzzles

5. Working *with* data *and* details

6. Working *with* your hands

CLARIFYING MY WORK VALUES

1. Work alone
2. Management
3. Creativity
4. Location
5. Independence
6. Work under pressure
7. Affiliation
8. Security/stability
9. Work with others
10. Change and variety
11. Recognition/status
12. Profit/gain
13. Help/influence others
14. Competition and/or physical challenge
15. Excitement
16. Help society
17. Public contact

1. Work alone
2. Management
3. Creativity
4. Location
5. Independence
6. Work under pressure
7. Affiliation
8. Security/stability
9. Work with others
10. Change and variety
11. Recognition/status
12. Profit/gain
13. Help/influence others
14. Competition and/or physical challenge
15. Excitement
16. Help society
17. Public contact

Adapted from a list by Howard E. Figler, Director, Career Center, University of Texas at Austin.

WORK VALUES—MY SUMMARY

Work Value	Times Recorded	Rank
1. **Work alone:** Do things by myself, without much contact with others.		
2. **Management:** Have power and authority; guide and control others in their work.		
3. **Creativity:** Create new ideas, programs, drawings, organizational structures, or anything else that has not been developed by others.		
4. **Location:** Find a place to live (town, geographic area) that matches my lifestyle and allows me to do what I enjoy most.		
5. **Independence:** Decide for myself what kind of work I will do and how I will go about it; be my own boss.		
6. **Work under pressure:** Work in a situation where deadlines and high quality of work are required by my supervisors.		
7. **Affiliation:** Be recognized as a member of an organization whose type of work or status is important to me (e.g., truck driver).		
8. **Security/stability:** Be assured of keeping my job; have job duties that are largely predictable.		
9. **Work with others:** Have close working relationships with a group; work as a team toward common goals.		
10. **Change/variety:** Have job duties that often change or are done in different settings.		
11. **Recognition/status:** Be recognized for the quality of my work; be regarded as a person of intellectual achievement or an expert.		
12. **Profit/gain:** Expect to earn large amounts of money or other material possessions.		
13. **Help/influence others:** Help other people and/or be in a position to change other people's attitudes and opinions.		
14. **Competition/physical challenge:** Pit my mental or physical abilities against others or against difficult conditions.		
15. **Excitement:** Do work that is very exciting. The excitement may involve the taking of some risks.		
16. **Help society:** Contribute to the betterment of the world in which I live. Feel that my work makes the world better.		
17. **Public contact:** Have a lot of day-to-day contact with other people.		

Exploring Careers, 1979, U.S. Department of Labor.

NARROWING THE FOCUS

With a sense of vocational direction and some insight into your work values, you may explore, in greater detail, specific career clusters. Two examples, both using the forced-choice grid, are provided. Assume you have narrowed your interest to a career in geology. Seven descriptions of the kind of work a geologist might do are listed in the forced-choice grid. Work through the grid comparing each work description with every other description—one at a time. A tally of the job numbers recorded in the grid should give you a sense of what areas within the broad field of geology you might want to investigate in more detail. You will also discover areas that are of lesser interest. Please note the grid descriptions are neither complete nor exhaustive of the things geologists may do. Use the grid technique of forced choice to help you focus on areas of real interest as reflected in your work values.

A second example is provided describing some careers in the electric power industry. Whether you are interested in such a career area or not, work through the grid with a sense of how it helps you focus on what is important to you.

Can you construct your own forced-choice grid that would help you select the accessories you want in that new car? The place you would like to visit next summer? The trade school or college you would like to attend? The movie you will see next weekend? Practice making your own grids; they can be powerful tools to help you make some important choices in your life.

These career materials using forced-choice grids we developed for the *Global Science* Curriculum Project (GSCP) by David C. Ulmer, Jr., Ed.D. Dr. Ulmer is a science teacher/instructor at the University of Colorado at Colorado Springs.

Geology Careers	Times	Rank
1 Astrogeologist		
2 Engineering geologist		
3 Environmental geologist		
4 Geochemist		
5 Geochronologist		
6 Stratigraphers		
7 Volcanologist		

1. **Astrogeologist.** Uses knowledge of Earth's geology to study surface conditions on the Moon and other planets.

2. **Engineering geologist.** Understands geology and engineering principles to advise construction projects such as dams, tunnels, highways to avoid problems—landslides, foundations, soils, etc.

3. **Environmental geologist.** Solves problems with pollution, urban development; guards against hazards—flooding and erosion.

4. **Geochemist.** Investigates the nature and distribution of chemical elements in rocks and minerals.

5. **Geochronologist.** Calculates rate of decay of certain radioactive elements to determine age of certain rocks.

6. **Stratigraphers.** Investigates thickness, shape, and distribution of layered rocks in addition to mineral and fossil content.

7. **Volcanologist.** Studies geologic phenomena associated with volcanic activity.

1. **Astrogeologist.** Uses knowledge of Earth's geology to study surface conditions on the Moon and other planets.

2. **Engineering geologist.** Understands geology and engineering principles to advise construction projects such as dams, tunnels, highways to avoid problems—landslides, foundations, soils, etc.

3. **Environmental geologist.** Solves problems with pollution, urban development; guards against hazards—flooding and erosion.

4. **Geochemist.** Investigates the nature and distribution of chemical elements in rocks and minerals.

5. **Geochronologist.** Calculates rate of decay of certain radioactive elements to determine age of certain rocks.

6. **Stratigraphers.** Investigates thickness, shape, and distribution of layered rocks in addition to mineral and fossil content.

7. **Volcanologist.** Studies geologic phenomena associated with volcanic activity.

Directions adapted from *Careers in Geology,* a pamphlet distributed by the American Geological Institute and American Association of Petroleum Geologists.

1. **Accounting clerk:** Keeps records of services rendered by the company, makes up bills for customers, prepares variety of statements and statistical reports.

2. **Auxiliary equipment operator:** Checks and records readings of instruments that indicate operating condition of pumps, fans, blowers, condensors, evaporators, water conditions, compressors, and coal pulverizers.

3. **Boiler operator:** Maintains proper steam pressure needed to turn turbines. Notes and regulates fuel, air and water supply used in boilers by means of control moves, meters, and other instrumentation.

4. **Cable splicer:** Supervises installation of insulated cables on utility poles and towers, as well as those buried underground.

5. **Line installer and repairer:** Constructs and maintains network of powerlines that carries electricity from generating plants to consumers.

6. **Load dispatcher:** Operates plant equipment used to generate electricity and direct its flow throughout the area served by the utility.

7. **Meter reader:** Goes to customers premises to check meters and register amount of electricity used. Records amounts; watches for and reports any meter tampering.

8. **Switchboard operator:** Controls amount of electric power flowing from generators to outgoing powerlines by watching instrument panels and operations.

9. **Watch engineer:** Oversees workers in power plant who operate and maintain boilers, turbines, generators, transformers, switchboards, and other machinery and equipment.

Career		Times Recorded	Rank
1.	Accounting clerk		
2.	Auxiliary equipment operator		
3.	Boiler operator		
4.	Cable splicer		
5.	Line installer and repairer		
6.	Load dispatcher		
7.	Meter reader		
8.	Switchboard operator		
9.	Watch engineer		

Column headers:
1. **Accounting clerk:** Keeps records of services rendered by the company, makes up bills for customers, prepares variety of statements and statistical reports.
2. **Auxiliary equipment operator:** Checks and records readings of instruments that indicate operating condition of pumps, fans, blowers, condensors, evaporators, water conditions, compressors, and coal pulverizers.
3. **Boiler operator:** Maintains proper steam pressure needed to turn turbines. Notes and regulates fuel, air and water supply used in boilers by means of control moves, meters, and other instrumentation.
4. **Cable splicer:** Supervises installation of insulated cables on utility poles and towers, as well as those buried underground.
5. **Line installer and repairer:** Constructs and maintains network of powerlines that carries electricity from generating plants to consumers.
6. **Load dispatcher:** Operates plant equipment used to generate electricity and direct its flow throughout the area served by the utility.
7. **Meter reader:** Goes to customers premises to check meters and register amount of electricity used. Records amounts; watches for and reports any meter tampering.
8. **Switchboard operator:** Controls amount of electric power flowing from generators to outgoing powerlines by watching instrument panels and operations.
9. **Watch engineer:** Oversees workers in power plant who operate and maintain boilers, turbines, generators, transformers, switchboards, and other machinery and equipment.

Descriptions adapted from "Occupations in the Electric Power Industry," *Occupational Outlook Handbook*, 1980–81 edition, U.S. Department of Labor.